Prentice Hall
LITERATURE
Timeless Voices, Timeless Themes

Formal Assessment

COPPER LEVEL

Prentice
Hall

Upper Saddle River, New Jersey
Glenview, Illinois
Needham, Massachusetts

Grateful acknowledgment is made to the following for copyrighted material:
Atheneum
GEORGIA O'KEEFFE The "Wideness and Wonder" of Her World by Beverly Gherman. Copyright © 1986 by Beverly Gherman.

Bonanza Publishing
"The Studebaker" from CHILDREN'S STORIES, Vol. 6, TALES OF THE WILD WEST SERIES by Rick Steber. Copyright © 1989 by Rick Steber.
The Devin-Adair Publishers, Inc.
From "The Wild Duck's Nest" from THE GAME COCK AND OTHER STORIES by Michael McLaverty. Copyright © 1947 by The Devin-Adair Company, Inc.

Down East Books
From WILD FOX by Cherie Mason. Copyright © 1993 by Cherie Mason.
HarperCollins Publishers, Inc.
From THE SUMMER OF THE FALCON by Jean Craighead George. Copyright © 1962 by Jean Craighead George. From "The Fish Angel" from THE WITCH OF FOURTH ST. AND OTHER STORIES by Myron Levoy. Copyright © 1972 by Myron Levoy. From JULIE OF THE WOLVES by Jean Craighead George. Copyright © 1972 by Jean Craighead George. From MAX AND ME AND THE TIME MACHINE by Gerry Greer and Bob Ruddick. Copyright © 1983 by Gerry Greer and Bob Ruddick.

Hyperion Books for Children
From "The Bear" and from "The Moose" from FULL MOON STORIES by Eagle Walking Turtle. Copyright © 1997 by Gary McLain.
Plays, Inc.
From "The Girl Whose Fortune Sought Her" by Patricia Clapp from 30 PLAYS FROM FAVORITE STORIES edited by Sylvia E. Kamerman. Copyright © 1997 by Plays, Inc. From "Finn McCool" by May Lynch from PLAYS FROM FAVORITE FOLK TALES edited by Sylvia E. Kamerman. Copyright © 1987 by Sylvia K. Burack.

Pocket Books, a division of Simon & Schuster, Inc.
From MY LIFE WITH THE CHIMPANZEES by Jane Goodall. Copyright © 1988 by Jane Goodall.

G.P. Putnam's Sons
From BORN TO THE LAND: AN AMERICAN PORTRAIT by Brent Ashabranner. Copyright © 1989 by Brent Ashabranner.

Random House, Inc.
From "To Build a Fire" from THE CALL OF THE WILD, WHITE FANG & TO BUILD A FIRE by Jack London. Copyright © 1998 by Modern Library.

Simon & Schuster Children's Publishing
From THE WHITE MOUNTAINS by John Christopher. Copyright © 1967 by John Christopher.

Vintage International, a div. of Random House, Inc.
From PIG EARTH by John Berger. Copyright © by 1979 by John Berger.

Note: Every effort has been made to locate the copyright owner of material reprinted in this book. Omissions brought to our attention will be corrected in subsequent printings.

ISBN 0-13-058375-8

4 5 6 7 8 9 10   06 05 04 03

CONTENTS

UNIT 3: PROVING YOURSELF

UNIT 4: SEEING IT THROUGH

UNIT 8: DRAMA

UNIT 9: POETRY

UNIT 10: THE ORAL TRADITION

"The Sound of Summer Running" by Ray Bradbury

Selection Test

Critical Reading

On the line, write the letter of the one best answer.

____ 1. What motivates Douglas to offer to run errands for Mr. Sanderson?
    a. Douglas wants to earn money for a new bicycle.
    b. Douglas wants Mr. Sanderson to let him have a certain pair of sneakers for a dollar less than the usual selling price.
    c. Douglas is hoping that Mr. Sanderson will offer him a summer job once Mr. Sanderson sees what a reliable person he is.
    d. Douglas wants to make a good impression on his father.

____ 2. What catches Douglas's eye while he is walking home from a movie one night with his family?
    a. a huge ad featuring a pair of sneakers
    b. a brand new pair of sneakers that a boy who walks by is wearing
    c. a pair of sneakers in a store window
    d. a help-wanted ad posted on the door of a shoe store

____ 3. What does Douglas do in order to help convince Mr. Sanderson to accept his offer?
    a. He asks for credit for the dollar he doesn't have.
    b. He tells Mr. Sanderson to put on the sneakers.
    c. He tells Mr. Sanderson that he'll help sell shoes.
    d. He promises to run errands for him every day after school.

____ 4. Which of the following statements would Douglas's father be most likely to make to explain his reason for not buying his son a new pair of sneakers?
    a. "When I was a boy, we got along fine without wearing fancy sneakers."
    b. "We have to watch our money carefully, and we just can't afford to buy you those sneakers right now."
    c. "There is nothing wrong with the sneakers you have from last year."
    d. "This week you want Litefoot sneakers, but by next week you'll want some other kind."

____ 5. Look at each group of words below. Which group contains an item that does *not* belong with the other two, according to the images and ideas presented in the story?
    a. sneakers, summer, youth
    b. fields of wheat, tall grass, jungle heat
    c. Litefoot, running, antelopes
    d. June, magic, civilization

____ 6. How does Mr. Sanderson change during the course of the story?
    a. In the beginning, he is a person with long-established habits and attitudes; at the end, he is full of memories of what it is like to be young.
    b. In the beginning, he is unhappy because his business is doing badly; at the end, he is happy because sales have gone up.
    c. In the beginning, he is happy and optimistic; at the end, he is filled with worries.
    d. In the beginning, he is hostile to young people like Douglas; at the end, he is friendly toward them.

_____ 7. What motivates Mr. Sanderson to accept Douglas's offer?
        I. Mr. Sanderson's shop assistant had just quit, and he needed someone to help out with errands and deliveries.
       II. Mr. Sanderson admired the enthusiasm and skill with which Douglas explained his proposal.
      III. After trying on a pair of sneakers, Mr. Sanderson understood how Douglas felt.
      IV. Douglas was willing to do a great deal of work for a small amount of money.

    a. I only   c. III and IV
    b. IV only   d. II and III

_____ 8. After Douglas makes his offer to Mr. Sanderson, why does he choose to remain silent?
    a. He is trying to think of a new offer to make Mr. Sanderson.
    b. He is quiet because Mr. Sanderson is busy helping a customer.
    c. He wants the full effect of wearing the sneakers to sink in for Mr. Sanderson.
    d. He is afraid Mr. Sanderson is angry with him for talking too much.

_____ 9. In the following passage from "The Sound of Summer Running," after which words would you pause in order to read with appropriate pacing?

> The grass was still pouring in from the country, surrounding the sidewalks, stranding the houses. Any moment the town would capsize, go down and leave not a stir in the clover and weeds.

    a. after _country, sidewalks, houses, town,_ and _leave_
    b. after _grass, country, houses, town,_ and _leave_
    c. after _still, surrounding,_ and _houses,_ and before _leave_
    d. after _country, sidewalks, houses, capsize, down,_ and _stir_

_____ 10. Read the following passage from "The Sound of Summer Running." Then choose the sentence that summarizes its meaning in the context of the story.

> The grass was still pouring in from the country, surrounding the sidewalks, stranding the houses. Any moment the town would capsize, go down and leave not a stir in the clover and weeds. And here Douglas stood, trapped in the dead cement and the red-brick streets, hardly able to move.

    a. Floods were threatening the town, and there was nothing Douglas could do to help.
    b. Strange new forms of vegetation were taking over Douglas's town, and Douglas was frozen with fright.
    c. The lawns in Douglas's town needed mowing badly, but Douglas was not allowed to earn money mowing grass.
    d. Summer was in full swing, but Douglas still did not have a new pair of tennis shoes.

_____ 11. After which words in the following sentence would you pause to help you understand the sentence completely?

> It was June and long past time for buying the special shoes that were quiet as a summer rain falling on the walks.

    a. June, time, buying, shoes, quiet, rain
    b. It, past, buying, shoes, summer, falling
    c. June, past, buying, that, quiet, rain
    d. was, time, special, quiet, rain, falling

____ 12. According to "The Sound of Summer Running," Litefoot's motto and one of its ads read as follows. Why does Bradbury include these sayings in his story?

> Find friends, ditch enemies!
> Does the world run too fast? Want to catch up? Litefoot, then! Litefoot!

a. The motto and ad reflect the way Douglas feels about the sneakers.
b. Bradbury wants to show how easily Douglas is influenced by advertisements.
c. Bradbury is making fun of advertisements in general.
d. The motto and ad prove that Litefoot sneakers really are the best sneakers available.

____ 13. After Douglas asks his father for new sneakers, what does his father tell him?
a. He tells Douglas that he can't have new sneakers.
b. He tells Douglas that he'll buy him the sneakers the next day.
c. He tells Douglas to save his money.
d. He tells Douglas that they don't have enough money for new sneakers.

____ 14. During which month is the story set?
a. December   b. June   c. August   d. September

Vocabulary, Spelling, and Grammar

____ 15. Which of the following words is *not* a noun?
a. sneakers   b. fence   c. Douglas   d. capsize

____ 16. *Loam* is a type of
a. tree   b. soil   c. athletic shoe   d. soft drink

____ 17. Which of the following words in *not* spelled correctly?
a. conceited   b. height   c. recieved   d. either

____ 18. In which sentence is the noun underlined?
a. <u>She</u> ran all the way home.
b. She was looking for her <u>friend</u>.
c. The summer was just <u>starting</u> out.
d. They <u>went</u> to the movies that night.

____ 19. Which item would look and feel *alien* on a hot summer day?
a. an ice-cream sundae
b. a pair of sunglasses
c. a pair of heavy boots
d. a cloudy sky

____ 20. Which sentence contains a misspelled word?
a. It was a weird piece of information.
b. We weighed the evidence.
c. We believed our nieghbor's story.
d. We were not deceived.

Essay Questions

21. In a brief essay, describe the reading strategy that you applied while reading "The Sound of Summer Running." Explain how the strategy helped you understand the story. Provide examples from the selection to support your main points.

22. Characters' motives are the impulses, emotions, and desires that cause the characters in a story to act in a certain way. What motives drive Douglas and Mr. Sanderson in "The Sound of Summer Running"? What actions result from these motives? Answer these questions in a brief essay. Be sure to name at least one motive and one action for each character.

23. "The Sound of Summer Running" contains many lively and colorful descriptions. In a brief essay, discuss how and why these descriptions are appropriate to the story and to Douglas. Provide examples from the story to support your points.

Name _____ Date _____

"Stray" by Cynthia Rylant

Selection Test

Critical Reading

On the line, write the letter of the one best answer.

____ 1. The reason Doris's parents say she cannot keep the puppy is that
   a. they don't like dogs
   b. they can't afford to have a dog
   c. they are afraid of dogs
   d. they want to teach Doris that she can't have everything she wants

____ 2. When Mrs. Lacey smiles at her husband, her smile shows that
   a. she finds Mr. Lacey's actions funny
   b. she thinks he has behaved foolishly
   c. she knew all along that he would keep the puppy
   d. she is surprised at his unusual behavior

____ 3. Why does Doris hope that the weather will never clear?
   a. When the weather clears, her father will go back to work.
   b. When the weather clears, she will have to go back to school.
   c. She loves playing with the puppy in the snow.
   d. When the weather clears, her father will take the puppy away.

____ 4. Doris's most important reason for wanting to keep the puppy is that
   a. she knows it will grow up to be a big dog
   b. she thinks playing with the puppy will be fun
   c. she wants the love and companionship of a pet
   d. she is looking forward to training the puppy

____ 5. When Mr. Lacey says, "You'd better feed that mutt before it dies of starvation," he is letting Doris know that
   a. if she wants a dog, she has to take care of it herself
   b. giving table scraps to the dog is better than throwing them away
   c. she can keep the dog
   d. he is worried about the dog

____ 6. Doris does not give the dog a name because
   a. she hasn't found the perfect name yet
   b. she has been too upset to think about a name
   c. she thinks the dog's next owners should name it
   d. she does not want to grow too attached to the dog

____ 7. According to the ending of the story, which phrase best describes Mr. Lacey?
   a. more softhearted than he wants his family to think he is
   b. mean and insensitive toward his daughter
   c. sensitive and understanding toward his daughter
   d. less softhearted than his wife

____ 8. Why doesn't Doris want to go down to the kitchen, past the basement door?
   a. She doesn't want to be reminded of the puppy.
   b. She isn't hungry.
   c. She wants to avoid arguing with her parents.
   d. She is too upset to eat.

____ 9. Which phrase best describes Mrs. Lacey?
   a. mean and selfish
   b. practical and sensible
   c. unreasonable and stubborn
   d. generous and warm

____ 10. The author delays having Mr. Lacey reveal to Doris that he has brought the puppy home in order to
   a. let the reader know that Mr. Lacey doesn't care about Doris's feelings
   b. show that Mr. Lacey is embarrassed about changing his mind
   c. make the ending more surprising to the reader
   d. show that Mr. Lacey isn't sure he made the right decision

____ 11. In which sentence does the shade of meaning accurately express the way Mr. Lacey drinks hot coffee?
   a. Mr. Lacey tastes his coffee.
   b. Mr. Lacey sips his coffee.
   c. Mr. Lacey gulps his coffee.
   d. Mr. Lacey consumes his coffee.

____ 12. In which sentence does the shade of meaning accurately express the way Doris walked through the snow?
   a. Doris strolled through the snow.
   b. Doris trudged through the snow.
   c. Doris stepped through the snow.
   d. Doris slid through the snow.

____ 13. Which of the following statements makes you think Doris's parents will not let her keep the puppy?
   a. The puppy has been abandoned.
   b. The puppy is on its way to being a big dog.
   c. Mrs. Lacey doesn't like to waste food.
   d. Doris's parents refuse to talk to her about the dog.

____ 14. Doris doesn't argue about the puppy with her parents because
   I. She is afraid of her parents.
   II. She knows it is useless.
   III. She is, by nature, a quiet child.
   IV. She thinks if she keeps quiet, they will change their minds.

   a. I and II
   b. I and IV
   c. II and III
   d. III and IV

Vocabulary, Spelling, and Grammar

____ 15. Which of the following sentences contains a compound noun?
   a. After dinner, I loaded all the dirty plates into the dishwasher.
   b. The blue dress matched the color of the girl's eyes.
   c. It is important to have a well-rounded education.
   d. The best student in the class got a new book as a prize.

____ 16. In the sentence "The cook watched the pan on the stove closely," the word *closely* means
   a. for a long time   c. from a short distance
   b. in a careful way   d. without moving

____ 17. Which of these words is spelled incorrectly?
   a. wedge   c. courage
   b. judje   d. badge

____ 18. Which of the following sentences does *not* contain a compound noun?
   a. The best athlete received a gold medal for her race.
   b. The sandbox was full of playing children.
   c. Hoping to wake up early, we set the alarm clock.
   d. His brother-in-law is a teacher.

____ 19. In the sentence, "She did her chores cheerfully," the word *cheerfully* means
   a. in an eager way   c. in a cheerful way
   b. without thinking   d. in a bashful way

____ 20. Which of the following words is spelled *incorrectly*?
   a. large   c. fringe
   b. page   d. caje

Essay Questions

21. Although Doris's parents have much in common, they are not alike in every way. Write an essay comparing and contrasting Doris's mother and father. Show at least two ways in which they are similar, and at least one way in which they are different. Support your statements about the two characters by citing words and actions from the story as examples.

22. Early in the story, both of Doris's parents feel it is important for their daughter to learn that she cannot have everything she wants. In the end, Doris learns quite a different lesson. In an essay, write what you think Doris learns from her experience. Explain how she might use what she learns in situations that may arise later in her life.

23. All you learn directly about Doris in this story is that she very much wants to keep the puppy she has found. The author does not tell you why Doris wants the puppy, but you can make some inferences by reading "in between the lines." In an essay, analyze why it is so painful for Doris to lose her pet and why the puppy is so important to her. Use clues from the story to back up your analysis.

"Dust of Snow" by Robert Frost
"My Picture-Gallery" by Walt Whitman
"Saying Yes" by Diana Chang

Selection Test

Critical Reading

On the line, write the letter of the one best answer.

_____ 1. In "Saying Yes," to which question does the speaker answer, "No . . . not quite"?
  a. "Are you a writer?"
  b. "Are you Chinese?"
  c. "Are you American?"
  d. "*Really* Chinese?"

_____ 2. What does the speaker in "Saying Yes" mean when, at the end of the poem, she says, "I'd rather say it twice"?
  a. She would rather say that she is both Chinese and American.
  b. She would rather emphasize that she is Chinese.
  c. She would rather emphasize that she is American.
  d. She would rather tell her questioner to leave her alone.

_____ 3. In "Saying Yes," what does the questioner's repetition of the word *Really* suggest?
  a. The questioner is also Chinese American.
  b. The speaker is muttering so softly it is hard to hear her answers.
  c. The questioner is somewhat suspicious of the speaker's answers.
  d. The speaker is refusing to answer the question.

_____ 4. Reread the following lines from "Saying Yes." Then choose the statement that expresses an idea found in these lines.

   But I would rather say / yes. / Not neither-nor, / not maybe, / but both, and not only
   The homes I've had, / the ways I am
   I'd rather say it / twice, / yes.

  a. To me, there is more to being both Chinese and American than the fact that I have lived in both places.
  b. Perhaps people would think of me as being "really Chinese" if I had spent some time living in China.
  c. There is no connection between the places I've lived and who I am.
  d. I would rather not talk about the homes I've lived in.

_____ 5. In "My Picture-Gallery," to what is the speaker referring when he talks about a little round house, only a few inches from one side to another?
  a. his head
  b. a box of pictures
  c. a doll house
  d. a jar

_____ 6. Poets use images that appeal to the senses in order to
  a. convince readers of their opinions
  b. make their poems more abstract
  c. make their poems more soothing
  d. create experiences for their readers

_____ 7. What does the speaker in "My Picture-Gallery" mean when he says, "Here the tableaus of life, and there the groupings of death"?
  a. Whenever he visits an art museum, he sees pictures of famous people who are still living, as well as portraits of famous people who are no longer living.
  b. His favorite picture gallery contains both modern paintings and artifacts from cultures that no longer exist.
  c. He is frightened by death and therefore pushes thoughts about it out of his mind.
  d. In his mind, he can see many pieces of his life, and he can also bring up memories of people and things he has lost.

_____ 8. In "My Picture-Gallery," what is kept in the "little house"?
  I.   posters
  II. the speaker's imagination
  III. tools
  IV. memories

  a. I and II   c. II and IV
  b. I and III   d. IV only

_____ 9. Reread the lines from "My Picture-Gallery." Then choose the statement that best describes who or what *cicerone* is.

  Here, do you know this? This is cicerone himself,
  With finger rais'd he points to the prodigal pictures.

  a. The speaker is referring to a real *cicerone*, or guide, in an actual picture gallery.
  b. The speaker is referring to his own eyes.
  c. The speaker is referring to his father.
  d. The speaker is referring to himself.

_____ 10. In what kind of setting do the events in "A Dust of Snow" take place?
  a. a barn   c. a wooded area
  b. a seashore   d. a bustling city street

_____ 11. Which statement would the speaker in "Dust of Snow" be most likely to make?
  a. People should hide their emotions.
  b. Crows are a nuisance.
  c. Nature has the power to lift one's spirits.
  d. Winter is the most glorious season.

_____ 12. Reread the lines from "Dust of Snow." According to these lines, what was going on *before* the crow shook some snow onto the speaker?

  [The crow's action has] given my heart / A change of mood / And saved some part / Of a day I had rued.

  a. The speaker was enjoying his day.
  b. The speaker was having a bad day.
  c. The speaker was in a hurry.
  d. The speaker felt that he was in danger.

_____ 13. Which group of lines contains an image that appeals to the sense of sight?
  a. But I would rather say / yes. ("Saying Yes")
  b. In a little house keep I pictures suspended, it is not a fix'd house, / It is round, it is only a few inches from one side to the other . . . ("My Picture-Gallery")
  c. Has given my heart / A change of mood ("Dust of Snow")
  d. And saved some part / Of a day I had rued. ("Dust of Snow")

____ 14. "Dust of Snow" contains the image of a dusting of snow falling onto the speaker. To which sense or senses does this image appeal?

      I. sight
     II. sound
   III. smell
   IV. touch

  a. I only   c. I and II
  b. III and IV   d. I and IV

Vocabulary, Spelling, and Grammar

____ 15. Which of the following might you expect to find *suspended* from a wall?
  a. a large metal sculpture   c. a coat of paint
  b. a framed photograph   d. a window

____ 16. Which choice best defines a common noun?
  a. a name for something with only one possible meaning
  b. a special name for a person
  c. a general name for a person, place, thing, or idea
  d. a specific name, such as *Ms. Anderson* or *Rapid City*

____ 17. Which of the following words is *not* spelled correctly?
  a. issueing   c. rescuing
  b. arguing   d. gluing

____ 18. Which word is most nearly *opposite* in meaning to *rued*?
  a. regretted   c. pitied
  b. polite   d. celebrated

____ 19. Which word is a proper noun?
  a. hemlock   c. ocean
  b. China   d. father

____ 20. Which phrase contains a misspelled word?
  a. a truer answer   c. rescueing the dolphins
  b. the truest friend   d. rescued the swimmer

Essay Questions

21. Both "Saying Yes" and "Dust of Snow" describe experiences that many people have had. In "Saying Yes," Diana Chang describes the experience of being asked by curious acquaintances about who she is and how she sees herself. In "Dust of Snow," Robert Frost describes the experience of discovering something in his everyday world that made him feel more cheerful and optimistic. Write an essay describing an experience that you have had that is similar to the one described by either Chang or Frost. Tell which poem you identify with and why. Make your account of your experience specific but concise. Be sure to include your thoughts about what you learned from your experience.

22. Both "My Picture-Gallery" and "Dust of Snow" contain images that draw readers in. Decide which image you found most memorable in one of these works. In an essay, identify the image and explain how it added to your understanding and enjoyment of the poem.

23. "Saying Yes," "My Picture-Gallery," and "Dust of Snow" help readers see reality in new ways. Choose one of the poems, and explain in an essay how it helped you see something in a way you had never seen it before. Clearly identify the person, object, or event and be specific about what the poet did to make his or her subject surprising.

Name _____ Date _____

"Jeremiah's Song" by Walter Dean Myers

Selection Test

Critical Reading

On the line, write the letter of the one best answer.

_____ 1. Which sentence best describes how Ellie, in "Jeremiah's Song," has changed since she came home from college?
   a. She no longer cares for the people in her hometown.
   b. She thinks she knows more than everyone at home because she is a college student.
   c. She hasn't really changed very much.
   d. She appreciates her hometown more.

_____ 2. The first-person narrator of "Jeremiah's Song" is
   a. Ellie   c. a boy
   b. Macon   d. Grandpa Jeremiah

_____ 3. In "Jeremiah's Song," Grandpa Jeremiah believes that his stories are important because
   a. they teach people about history
   b. they inspire people by showing how others cope with hardship
   c. they teach that all people are linked together
   d. they provide entertainment when people need it

_____ 4. Which of the following would the first-person narrator of "Jeremiah's Song" *not* be able to know?
   a. how long Dr. Crawford thinks Grandpa Jeremiah will live
   b. that Macon cried when he heard that Grandpa Jeremiah was dying
   c. why Ellie doesn't want Grandpa Jeremiah to tell stories to Macon
   d. how Macon really feels about Ellie

_____ 5. In "Jeremiah's Song," why doesn't Ellie like Grandpa Jeremiah's stories?
   a. The stories are too old-fashioned.
   b. The stories are too scary.
   c. She has heard them so many times already.
   d. The stories are boring.

_____ 6. Which word does *not* describe Macon's attitude toward Grandpa Jeremiah?
   a. uninterested   c. concerned
   b. respectful   d. devoted

_____ 7. An important message of "Jeremiah's Song" is
   a. older people have a valuable heritage to pass on to younger generations
   b. we are responsible for taking care of older family members
   c. no one can live forever
   d. older people should be open to new ideas

_____ 8. In the following sentences from "Jeremiah's Song," which two words help you understand that the word *diagnosis* means "explanation about a person's medical condition"?

> "Are you sure of your diagnosis?" Ellie asked. . . . "Yes, I'm sure," he said. "He had tests a few weeks ago and his condition was bad then."

    a. sure; weeks   c. asked; condition
    b. bad; then   d. tests; condition

_____ 9. In "Jeremiah's Song," which sentence best reflects Grandpa Jeremiah's feelings about his stories?
    a. They reminded him of his childhood.
    b. They were suitable entertainment for his grandchildren.
    c. They helped him pass the time during his sickness.
    d. They were the stories about the past and his people.

_____ 10. Which context clue might help you to understand the use of the word *fixing* in this sentence?

> Macon was fixing to leave, so he wished Ellie good night before he walked out the door and into the front yard.

    a. wished Ellie good night
    b. to leave
    c. before he walked out the door
    d. into the front yard

_____ 11. In "Jeremiah's Song," Ellie believes that the best thing for the family's future is
    a. to expand the family's farming interests
    b. for her to marry Macon and move to Greensboro
    c. to stop living the kind of life that is rooted in the past
    d. to remember Grandpa Jeremiah's stories and pass them on to the next generation

_____ 12. Which quotation from the story best shows the perspective of the narrator?
    a. Everybody started tiptoeing around the house after that.
    b. Macon sat slant-shouldered with his guitar across his lap.
    c. "Am I going to break, Grandpa?"
    d. Grandpa wasn't getting no better, but he wasn't getting no worse, either.

_____ 13. Using context clues from the following sentence, what might you determine to be the meaning of the word *piecing* in this sentence?

> When she wasn't doing that she was piecing on a quilt she was making for some white people in Wilmington.

    a. to put together
    b. to think about
    c. to take apart
    d. to sell

Vocabulary, Spelling, and Grammar

_____ 14. Which of the following sentences contains the plural form of a personal pronoun?
    a. After Ellie went to college, she didn't want to listen to Grandpa's stories.
    b. Sister Todd and Ellie thought they knew how to help Grandpa.
    c. When Grandpa was sick, Macon visited him.
    d. Who will listen to the stories?

____ 15. Which word is spelled correctly?
   a. dissinterested
   b. disatisfied
   c. disimilar
   d. disapprove

____ 16. A person who does not share your opinion about something is said to:
   a. disagree
   b. have disrespect
   c. disappear
   d. be disinterested

____ 17. Which word below is an example of an indefinite pronoun?
   a. she
   b. I
   c. whose
   d. someone

____ 18. When someone reacts to a statement with *disbelief*, it means that he or she
   a. does not like the statement
   b. does not think the statement is funny
   c. does not think the statement is true
   d. does not understand the statement

____ 19. Which sentence contains an indefinite pronoun?
   a. During the funeral, a few of the mourners wept openly.
   b. Macon showed the mourners where to sit and which car to ride in.
   c. After she returned home, Ellie wept quietly.
   d. Macon played his guitar, but he played a different tune this time.

____ 20. Which word is spelled *incorrectly*?
   a. discourage   c. dissimilar
   b. disatisfied   d. disbelief

Essay Questions

21. In "Jeremiah's Song," Sister Todd says to Grandpa Jeremiah, "Them old ways you got ain't got nothing for these young folks." What does she mean by this? Do you think the author of the story agrees that "old ways" have no meaning for people your age? In an essay, state your opinion, and support it with examples from the story and, if possible, from your own experience.

22. The narrator in "Jeremiah's Song" is nine years old. How would the story be different if the narrator were the same age as Ellie or Macon? Write an essay explaining how the narrator's age affects the telling of the story.

23. Ellie changes during the summer of her grandfather's death. How might Ellie's life be different afterwards? How will she approach her education and friends? How will she think about music and storytelling? Write an essay predicting Ellie's life during the year following Grandpa Jeremiah's death.

"The King of Mazy May" by Jack London

Selection Test

Critical Reading

On the line, write the letter of the one best answer.

____ 1. Walt's father leaves Walt to take care of himself. This shows that the father
    a. has confidence in Walt
    b. is desperate to find gold
    c. knows the other prospectors will take care of Walt
    d. wants to test Walt's courage

____ 2. The author, Jack London, opens this story by writing, "Walt Masters is not a very large boy, but there is manliness in his make-up." Judging from Walt's actions in the story, decide which of the following combinations best describes what London means by "manliness."
    a. physical strength and athletic skill
    b. intelligence, cleverness, and creativity
    c. physical strength and persistence
    d. courage and confidence

____ 3. The claim-jumpers chase Walt because they
    a. are angry that he has been spying on them
    b. want to find out what he knows
    c. want to make sure he does not get to Dawson before they do
    d. want their dogs and sled back

____ 4. Which adjective does not describe Walt?
    a. brave
    b. honest
    c. hot-tempered
    d. quick-witted

____ 5. Walt has never seen a train or an elevator in his life because
    a. these machines have not been invented yet
    b. he prefers to stay away from cities
    c. he does not want to have anything to do with machines
    d. he lives in an area where these things have not yet come into use

____ 6. Why do you think the Klondike attracted dishonest outlaws as well as honest, hard-working prospectors?
    a. The Klondike offered the opportunity to make a new start in life.
    b. The promise of easily gained riches often attracts dishonest people.
    c. Harsh living conditions often attract dishonest people.
    d. Criminals could hide out there, without fear of being caught.

____ 7. Which is the correct signal word or phrase to fill in the blank in the following sentence?

    The men were planning to jump Loren Hall's claim, ____ Walt stopped them.

    a. since   c. on account of
    b. because   d. but

_____ 8. While being chased by the claim-jumpers, Walt sometimes runs beside the sled
        a. to lighten the load the dogs must pull
        b. to show the lead dog which way to go
        c. to warm himself up
        d. to get a better view of the trail

_____ 9. Walt does not like claim-jumpers because they
        a. think about nothing but getting rich
        b. steal what others have worked hard to get
        c. have bad tempers
        d. mistreat their dogs

_____ 10. Which two statements are true about Walt?
        I. He is unusually strong.
        II. He does not tolerate unfairness.
        III. He is very mature for his age.
        IV. He is naturally very suspicious
        a. II and III
        b. I and II
        c. II and IV
        d. I and IV

_____ 11. Each sentence has a signal word or phrase in italics. In which
sentence is the signal word or phrase _incorrect_?
        a. Walt Masters is not a very large boy, _because_ there is manliness in his makeup.
        b. _On account of_ the poor lead dog, the sled kept going off the trail.
        c. No snow had fallen for weeks, _so_ the trail was hard and icy.
        d. Walt could hear the men yelling to their dogs, _but_ he could not see them.

_____ 12. Living in the Yukon has made Walt more _____ than most boys his age.
        a. angry
        b. timid
        c. stubborn
        d. self-reliant

_____ 13. Which of the following explains why the conflict between Walt and the claim-jumpers makes the story suspenseful?
        a. Walt is outnumbered by the bigger and stronger claim-jumpers.
        b. Walt suspects the claim-jumpers' bad intentions from the beginning.
        c. The claim-jumpers are after Walt's father's claim.
        d. Walt's father has already recorded his claim.

_____ 14. The fact that Walt left the dying lead dog behind shows that he
        a. was insensitive to suffering
        b. used good judgment
        c. loved animals
        d. acted selfishly

Vocabulary, Spelling, and Grammar

_____ 15. What is the meaning of the word _liable_ in the following sentence?

    Walt was worried that Loren Hall's claim was _liable_ to be jumped.

    a. ready   c. likely
    b. easy   d. prepared

____ 16. Which sentence contains a misspelled word?
      a. The men started to broyl their meat over the fire.
      b. They planned to destroy the work others had done.
      c. Walt knew he had to spoil their plans.
      d. They would never get to enjoy Loren Hall's gold.

____ 17. Which sentence contains a pronoun that refers to the antecedent, *Walt*?
      a. Walt yelled to the lead dog, urging him to go faster.
      b. Realizing that they were gaining on him, Walt yelled to the dogs.
      c. Walt thought of Loren Hall, hoping to reach him in time.
      d. Walt has walked in moccasins all the fourteen years of his life.

____ 18. Someone who edits books or newspapers is called an
      a. editer
      b. editor
      c. edition
      d. edittor

____ 19. In which sentence would you replace a noun with a pronoun?
      a. Walt was strong, brave, and honorable.
      b The men made their plans while the men ate dinner.
      c. The dogs ran faster after Walt changed the lead dog.
      d. The trail was icy because no snow had fallen.

____ 20. In the following sentence, which word is the antecedent of the pronoun *his*?

      Many people like books by Jack London because there is a lot of action in his books.

      a. books
      b. Many people
      c. action and excitement
      d. Jack London

Essay Questions

21. "The King of Mazy May" is about a conflict between a boy and a group of men; it is also a story of conflict between good and bad. In an essay, describe Walt's good qualities and the claim-jumpers' bad qualities. Cite examples from the story to support your description.

22. Some people think that a person's character, or nature, is mainly inherited from his or her parents; others believe that a person's character is formed mainly by the experiences he or she has early in life. In an essay, analyze Walt's character and skills. Using details from the text to support your analysis, state which of his qualities are part of his nature and which might result from how and where he grew up.

23. "The King of Mazy May" is set in the Yukon territory just after 1900—a rugged wilderness with few comforts of civilization. Write an essay in which you explain the effect of this setting on the story. Begin your essay by describing the setting, using appropriate details from the text. Continue by explaining how the setting, including climate and terrain, has a significant effect on the story's events.

"The Circuit" by Francisco Jiménez
"Hard as Nails" by Russell Baker

Selection Test

Critical Reading

On the line, write the letter of the one best answer.

____ 1. In "The Circuit," how does Panchito feel about moving so often?
  a. He dislikes constantly moving from place to place.
  b. He thinks living in one place would be boring.
  c. He enjoys moving around but dislikes the work.
  d. He does not mind moving from place to place.

____ 2. In "The Circuit," the brothers hide from the school bus because
  a. they don't want to go to school
  b. they have to work instead of going to school
  c. their parents don't think education is important
  d. they think the other students will laugh at them

____ 3. The end of "The Circuit" can best be described as
  a. discouraging
  b. hopeful
  c. satisfying
  d. startling

____ 4. In "The Circuit," what does it show about Panchito's character that he asks
  Mr. Lema to help him with his English?
  a. He likes to make a good impression on people.
  b. He wants to do his best.
  c. He is too lazy to learn English by himself.
  d. He wants to appear smarter than his brother.

____ 5. "The Circuit" describes
  a. the narrator's first experience as a farm worker
  b. the narrator's worst experience as a farm worker
  c. the narrator's most memorable experience as a farm worker
  d. one of the narrator's typical experiences as a farm worker

____ 6. In "The Circuit," the narrator doesn't want to move to Fresno because
  a. he does not like the city
  b. he does not know if they will find work there
  c. he is going to be doing very hard work in very hot weather
  d. he dislikes traveling by car

____ 7. What is the key idea in the following sentence from "The Circuit"?

  I thought they were happy to see me, but when I opened the door to our shack,
  I saw that everything we owned was neatly packed in cardboard boxes.

  a. The narrator's brothers and sisters were happy to see him.
  b. The narrator opened the door to their shack.
  c. The narrator saw that the family's belongings were packed in cardboard boxes.
  d. The narrator greeted his family.

____ 8. Which word describes Panchito's work in "The Circuit"?
    a. interesting
    b. frightening
    c. satisfying
    d. exhausting

____ 9. What is the subject of the following sentence from "Hard as Nails"?

    So as soon as it was legal I went into newspaper work.

    a. it
    b. I
    c. work
    d. newspaper

____ 10. In "Hard as Nails," Russell Baker
    a. is sorry that he had to work as a young boy
    b. wishes his mother had made more money
    c. is glad that his children don't have to work
    d. thinks that his job as a paperboy taught him valuable lessons

____ 11. The virtue that "Hard as Nails" focuses on is
    a. honesty
    b. kindness
    c. determination
    d. bravery

____ 12. Which pair of words best describes Russell Baker's mother in "Hard as Nails"?
    a. tough and loving
    b. greedy and ambitious
    c. bossy and teasing
    d. careful and independent

____ 13. In "Hard as Nails," to be "hard as nails" means
    a. to be physically strong
    b. to be stubborn
    c. to be unfeeling toward other people
    d. to be tough and determined

____ 14. In "Hard as Nails," which of the following sentences best describes the narrator's feelings about Mr. Deems?
    a. He hopes to be just like Mr. Deems some day.
    b. He resents and respects Mr. Deems at the same time.
    c. He is afraid of Mr. Deems because Mr. Deems might fire him.
    d. He is suspicious of Mr. Deems because Mr. Deems cannot be trusted.

____ 15. What is the key idea of this sentence from "Hard as Nails"?

    Later, when I thought about him, I wondered if maybe he hated himself for having to make life tough for the boys.

    a. I wondered if he hated himself.
    b. I thought about him.
    c. He made life tough for the boys.
    d. He hated himself.

Vocabulary, Spelling, and Grammar

____ 16. Which sentence contains the pronoun that agrees with the antecedent *mother*?
  a. Panchito's mother helped the family by cooking delicious meals for them.
  b. Panchito's mother did all she could to keep the family happy and healthy.
  c. Panchito's mother did not work in the fields as he did.
  d. Panchito's mother worked hard and expected him to work hard, too.

____ 17. Which of the following sentences does *not* contain a compound noun?
  a. Panchito had trouble reading from the textbook.
  b. He was nervous when he walked into the classroom.
  c. Russell Baker worked for a metropolitan publisher.
  d. At the banquet, Russell did not know whether to use a tablespoon or a teaspoon.

____ 18. Which of the following sentences contains a misspelled word?
  a. Mr. Deems always wore a necktie.
  b. The draw back was having to get up very early.
  c. Russell Baker writes for a newspaper.
  d. Mrs. Russell and Mr. Deems talked on the sidewalk.

____ 19. Which sentence contains a pronoun that does not agree with its antecedent?
  a. Several of the boys thought that Mr. Deems made him work too hard.
  b. Mrs. Baker needed Russell to work selling newspapers because she didn't have much money.
  c. A few months after he took the boys down to see the city room, Mr. Deems quit.
  d. Russell knew that he was doing the best job possible selling newspapers.

____ 20. Which of the following words has a meaning that is different from that of the others?
  a. buzz
  b. hum
  c. drone
  d. drowse

Essay Questions

21. The central idea of "The Circuit" is the harshness of a young migrant farm worker's life. In an essay, analyze the ways in which the author of "The Circuit" makes the harshness of Panchito's life especially vivid. In your essay, mention sensory images, descriptions of the narrator's emotions, and any other details that effectively convey an impression of the bracero's difficult day-to-day existence.

22. The central characters in "The Circuit" and "Hard as Nails" are both boys who must go to work while still quite young. In an essay, compare and contrast Panchito and Russell, citing similarities and differences between them. Include comparison and contrast of their families, their ambitions, and their attitudes toward their work.

23. "The Circuit" and "Hard as Nails" focus on similar subjects—boys who began working early in life. However, the selections are quite different in tone. Write an essay contrasting Jiménez's tone with Baker's. First decide on a word you would use to describe each writer's tone. Then look for examples in the selection to support the words you've chosen.

Unit 1: Growing and Changing

Unit Test

Critical Reading

On the line, write the letter of the one best answer.

____ 1. In "The Sound of Summer Running," Mr. Sanderson believes that Douglas will succeed at whatever he tries because
    a. Douglas is polite
    b. Douglas is persuasive and energetic
    c. Douglas knows the value of money
    d. Douglas does not ask for credit

____ 2. In "The Sound of Summer Running," Douglas wants new tennis sneakers because
    a. new sneakers will give him energy that is right for summer activities
    b. the new sneakers look more stylish
    c. his old sneakers are worn out
    d. the new sneakers are better made than his old ones

____ 3. After which words in the following passage from "The Sound of Summer Running" would you pause in order to read with appropriate pacing?

> Lights out, with Tom asleep, Douglas lay watching his feet, far away down there at the end of the bed in the moonlight, free of the heavy iron shoes, the big chunks of winter fallen away from them.

    a. after *out, asleep, feet, moonlight,* and *shoes*
    b. after *asleep, feet, bed,* and *winter*
    c. after *with, far, free,* and *the*
    d. after *Tom* and *Douglas*

____ 4. In "Stray," Mrs. Lacey is surprised that her husband decides to keep the puppy because
    a. he has never liked dogs
    b. she worries that he is spoiling Doris
    c. he had said repeatedly that he would not keep it
    d. she thought that the puppy was a nuisance

____ 5. In "Stray," Doris tries not to cry when her father prepares to take away the puppy because
    a. she does not want to look like a baby
    b. she realizes that her parents are being sensible
    c. she does not want to make her father angry
    d. she hopes that he will change his mind

____ 6. In "Stray," which two details make readers think that the Laceys will not keep the dog?
    I. The Laceys do not make much money.
    II. Mrs. Lacey does not like to waste food.
    III. Doris is sure that her parents are determined to take the puppy to the pound.
    IV. Mr. and Mrs. Lacey insist that the puppy be kept in the basement.

    a. I and II   b. I and IV   c. III and IV   d. I and IV

_____ 7. Which sentence is closest in meaning to this line from "My Picture-Gallery"?

Yet behold, it has room for all the shows of the world, all memories!

    a. The world is like an enormous art museum.
    b. A person's mind can retain an unlimited number of memories.
    c. Memories take up very little space.
    d. The world is like a wonderful show.

_____ 8. In "My Picture-Gallery," who can see the pictures?
    a. only the speaker   c. the reader
    b. everyone   d. the person whom the speaker addresses

_____ 9. Which of these passages from "Saying Yes," "My Picture-Gallery," and "Dust of Snow" contains an image that appeals to the sense of touch?
    a. In a little house I keep pictures suspended . . .
    b. It is round, it is only a few inches from one side to the other . . .
    c. The homes I've had / the ways I am . . .
    d. The way a crow / Shook down on me / The dust of snow / From a hemlock tree . . .

_____ 10. In "Jeremiah's Song," Macon respects Jeremiah because
    a. Jeremiah has much to teach him
    b. Jeremiah is old
    c. Jeremiah treats him well
    d. Jeremiah has had a lot of formal education

_____ 11. Which of the passages from "Jeremiah's Song" demonstrates the first-person narration used in the story?
    a. Grandpa Jeremiah raised Ellie after her folks died and they used to be real close.
    b. She wiped at where a trickle of sweat made a little path through the white dusting powder she put on her chest to keep cool.
    c. Sometimes I would think about asking him to tell me one of them stories he used to tell but they was too scary now that I didn't have nobody to sleep with but myself.
    d. It was right after Ellie went back to school that Grandpa Jeremiah had him a stroke and Macon started coming around.

_____ 12. "The King of Mazy May" shows that
    a. everyone should fight like Walter
    b. the other men eventually respected Walter for his efforts
    c. life in the wilderness is better than other places
    d. young people used to be stronger than they are now

_____ 13. Which of the following sentences has a signal word or phrase that shows a relationship between ideas?
    a. Walt looked back to see how far behind him the claim-jumpers were.
    b. Walt wanted to rest, but he knew the men would catch up to him if he did.
    c. Loren Hall was unable to move very fast over the icy terrain.
    d. Walt's lead dog was too inexperienced to know how to stay on the trail.

_____ 14. In "The King of Mazy May," Walt's father shows that he has confidence in Walt by
    a. leaving him to take care of himself
    b. letting him drive the dogsled
    c. letting him watch Loren Hall's claim
    d. bringing him to the Yukon

_____ 15. In "The King of Mazy May," while Walt is being chased by the claim-jumpers, he sometimes warms himself up by
    a. quickly building a fire   c. rubbing his hands together
    b. putting on more clothing   d. running alongside the sled

____ 16. Which is the best way to break down this long sentence from "The Circuit"?

> She went through a white gate, past a row of rose bushes, up the stairs to the front door.

    a. Pause after adjectives such as *white, rose,* and *front.*
    b. Pause after verbs and stop at the period that ends the sentence.
    c. Pause after commas and stop at the period that ends the sentence.
    d. Pause after the prepositions *through, past, up,* and *front.*

____ 17. Where should the reader pause to break down this long sentence from "Hard as Nails"?

> My mother was talking to him on the sidewalk in front of the Union Square Methodist Church and I was standing as tall as I could, just out of earshot.

    a. after *mother, sidewalk, Union Square Methodist Church,* and *earshot.*
    b. after commas and periods
    c. after the prepositions *to, on, in, as,* and *out of*
    d. after *sidewalk, Church, standing,* and *could*

____ 18. What is the central idea, or theme, of "The Circuit"?
    a. If you work hard, eventually you will be successful.
    b. It can be difficult to escape from a life of poverty.
    c. Families have to stick together.
    d. Farm workers perform a valuable service to society.

____ 19. The ending of "The Circuit" shows that Panchito's desire to do well at school
    a. will enable him to achieve success
    b. is admired by his family
    c. has been destroyed
    d. has not helped him to escape from the life of a migrant worker

Vocabulary, Spelling, and Grammar

____ 20. Which sentence does *not* contain a personal pronoun?
    a. Her sister made her a card for her birthday.
    b. Russell Baker has had a long and successful career as a writer.
    c. We were looking forward to our class picnic, but it rained that day.
    d. My best friend and I have known each other since kindergarten.

____ 21. Which sentence contains a misspelled word?
    a. I siezed the ball and threw it as far as I could.
    b. Our new neighbors own a dog and a cat.
    c. After hours in the hot sun, we were relieved to jump into the pool.
    d. The Wright brothers conceived the idea of a machine that could fly.

____ 22. Which of the following words is a compound noun?
    a. elevator   b. sandwich   c. automobile   d. cardboard

____ 23. Which of the following is capitalized correctly?
    a. Hudson river   c. Mount Everest
    b. the State of California   d. new England

____ 24. If someone is described as *exhausted,* that person is
    a. unhappy   b. tired   c. puzzled   d. angry

____ 25. In the following sentence, what is the antecedent for the italicized pronoun?

> In spite of the rain, the umpires decided not to stop the game, and most of the fans stayed where *they* were.

    a. umpires   b. rain   c. fans   d. game

____ 26. Which of the following words is *not* misspelled?
   a. boil   b. enjois   c. spoyl   d. annoi

____ 27. Which of the following is *not* a pronoun?
   a. who   b. they   c. us   d. is

____ 28. Which of the following might be described as *crimson*?
   a. a tomato   b. a banana   c. grass   d. a zebra

____ 29. Which of the following compound words is spelled correctly?
   a. necktye   b. newspaper   c. erthworms   d. businesman

____ 30. In which sentence is the italicized word *not* an interrogative pronoun?
   a. I would like to know *who* wrote this poem.   c. *Who* rang the doorbell?
   b. *Why* should we listen to you?   d. *When* is she going to do her
                                                    homework?

Essay Questions

31. The stories in this unit have central characters who grow and change. Some change more than others. Write an essay about two of the following characters: Russell Baker in "Hard as Nails," Douglas in "The Sound of Summer Running," Panchito in "The Circuit," and Macon in "Jeremiah's Song." In your essay, discuss the extent to which the characters change in the course of the stories, the ways in which they change, and why the changes take place. If one of the two characters undergoes a greater change than the other, explain why. Support your conclusions with details from the stories.

32. Consider the narrator or point of view of the selections in this unit. Some are told by a first-person narrator, and others are told by a third-person narrator. Choose one of the selections, and write an essay describing how the point of view affects the selection. Support your points with examples from the selection.

33. Sometimes, poets write to inspire their readers to think or act in a certain way. At other times, their goal may be to describe or explain their own thoughts and feelings. In an essay, explain the author's purpose in one of the following poems: "Saying Yes," "Dust of Snow," or "My Picture-Gallery." Begin your essay by giving your opinion on whether the poet seeks to move the reader to a certain course of action or to provide a look into the poet's state of mind. Give specific information about what the poet wishes to achieve, using quotes from the poem to illustrate your conclusions.

34. Writers of prose and poetry use sensory images—images that appeal to the reader's sense of sight, hearing, taste, touch, or smell—to make their writing more effective and vivid. In an essay, analyze the authors' use of imagery in two of the following selections: "The Circuit," "The King of Mazy May," and "Stray." Provide examples of the images the authors create, and explain how the images help to make the authors' work more convincing and its effect on the reader more powerful. Tell whether either or neither poet uses imagery successfully, and why.

35. Some writers create plots that startle the reader with unexpected twists. Others gradually build suspense to keep the reader's interest. Still others make effective use of plots that use neither surprise nor suspense. Choose two stories that demonstrate contrasting approaches to plot mechanics: "Stray," "The King of Mazy May," and "The Circuit," and, in an essay, analyze the effect of each author's choice of plot development. Support your conclusions with details from each story.

Unit 1: Growing and Changing

Unit Test

The two passages below are followed by questions based on their content and on the relationship between the two passages.

Passage 1

"The Studebaker" by Rick Steber

It used to be every Saturday homesteaders, farmers, and ranchers from near and far brought their families to town. If they were lucky they rode in a Studebaker wagon.

The Studebaker company made one model of wagon. It was popular out west and easily recognizable with red or yellow running gear and green paint with fancy scrollwork on the wagon box. Over the years the paint weathered and peeled, leaving bare wood that was never repainted.

Many Studebaker wagons were brought over the Oregon Trail and afterward used around the homestead as an all purpose wagon. When the wagon was not employed as transportation it was used to carry a variety of rural necessities from water barrels to barbed wire, salt, grain, hay, and lumber.

Homesteaders and farmers in that era were given to fits of wanderlust. After a few years in one location a man might decide to have a look at "new country" and then the Studebaker would be loaded to overflowing with his family's belongings and the team of faithful horses would pull it to the next land of promise.

Buckaroos rode saddle horses or broncs to town for their Saturday night sprees. But when they needed to make a trip to the general store for the cook they always took the faithful Studebaker.

In 1903 Henry Ford formed the Ford Motor Company and started mass-producing automobiles. He sold 15 million Model-T Fords, and Studebaker wagons were considered obsolete. Wagons were parked behind barns or at the edge of fields. In summer the sun bleached the wood; winter snow drifted over it. Years passed and the faithful Studebaker settled slowly into the earth and turned to dust.

Passage 2

In the following passage, Frank, a farmer, is speaking with the author and a photographer while giving them a tour of his farm.

from *Born to the Land: An American Portrait* by Brent Ashabranner

"We have a hundred years of family history wrapped up in this land," Frank said.

He showed us some of his equipment. "That tractor cost $18,000 when I bought it in '77," he said, pointing to his International Harvester. "Now it's about $50,000. You can't keep up with that. I buy all my equipment secondhand. There's lots of equipment being auctioned off these days by fellows going out of business.'

Frank still has a tractor that his father bought in 1947. "You have to make your equipment last because you don't have the capital to keep renewing it," he said.

Frank admits that he keeps his father's tractor partly for sentimental reasons, but he has no such feelings about the 1971 pickup he drives. He keeps it running because it saves him the price of a new one. "I don't need the smell of new paint," he says. "I have to know how to weld, be a mechanic, an electrician, a vet—lots of different trades." On the subject of equipment again Frank said, "Years ago all the neighbors around here would throw in and help each other. One would have a thrasher, another a bean cutter. But after the war farmers became independent and went their separate ways. Now we're reverting to our old ways because we can't afford all the equipment we need. It's kind of nice."

Critical Reading

On the line, write the letter of the one best answer.

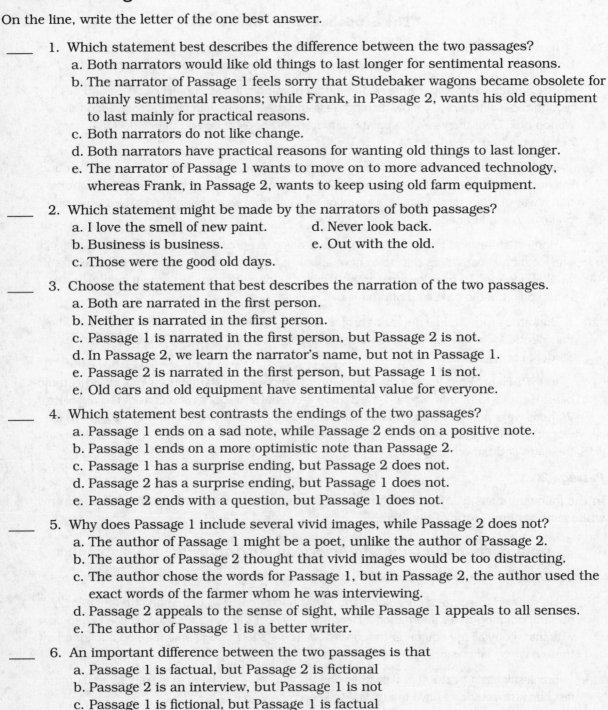

_____ 1. Which statement best describes the difference between the two passages?
   a. Both narrators would like old things to last longer for sentimental reasons.
   b. The narrator of Passage 1 feels sorry that Studebaker wagons became obsolete for mainly sentimental reasons; while Frank, in Passage 2, wants his old equipment to last mainly for practical reasons.
   c. Both narrators do not like change.
   d. Both narrators have practical reasons for wanting old things to last longer.
   e. The narrator of Passage 1 wants to move on to more advanced technology, whereas Frank, in Passage 2, wants to keep using old farm equipment.

_____ 2. Which statement might be made by the narrators of both passages?
   a. I love the smell of new paint.   d. Never look back.
   b. Business is business.   e. Out with the old.
   c. Those were the good old days.

_____ 3. Choose the statement that best describes the narration of the two passages.
   a. Both are narrated in the first person.
   b. Neither is narrated in the first person.
   c. Passage 1 is narrated in the first person, but Passage 2 is not.
   d. In Passage 2, we learn the narrator's name, but not in Passage 1.
   e. Passage 2 is narrated in the first person, but Passage 1 is not.
   e. Old cars and old equipment have sentimental value for everyone.

_____ 4. Which statement best contrasts the endings of the two passages?
   a. Passage 1 ends on a sad note, while Passage 2 ends on a positive note.
   b. Passage 1 ends on a more optimistic note than Passage 2.
   c. Passage 1 has a surprise ending, but Passage 2 does not.
   d. Passage 2 has a surprise ending, but Passage 1 does not.
   e. Passage 2 ends with a question, but Passage 1 does not.

_____ 5. Why does Passage 1 include several vivid images, while Passage 2 does not?
   a. The author of Passage 1 might be a poet, unlike the author of Passage 2.
   b. The author of Passage 2 thought that vivid images would be too distracting.
   c. The author chose the words for Passage 1, but in Passage 2, the author used the exact words of the farmer whom he was interviewing.
   d. Passage 2 appeals to the sense of sight, while Passage 1 appeals to all senses.
   e. The author of Passage 1 is a better writer.

_____ 6. An important difference between the two passages is that
   a. Passage 1 is factual, but Passage 2 is fictional
   b. Passage 2 is an interview, but Passage 1 is not
   c. Passage 1 is fictional, but Passage 1 is factual
   d. Passage 2 focuses on farmers, while Passage 1 focuses on cowboys
   e. Passage 1 praises the past, while Passage 2 praises the future

____ 7. What is the signal word in the quotation from each passage?

Passage 1: Buckaroos rode saddle horses or broncs to town for their Saturday night sprees. But when they needed to make a trip to the general store for the cook they always took the faithful Studebaker.

Passage 2: Frank admits that he keeps his father's tractor partly for sentimental reasons, but he has no such feelings about the 1971 pickup he drives.

    a. for   b. the   c. always   d. such   e. but

____ 8. Which statement best compares and contrasts the two selections?
    a. Both passages are about the West, but at different times in history.
    b. Both passages are about farmers, but at different times in history.
    c. Both passages are about the past, but Passage 1 reflects positive feelings, and Passage 2 reflects negative feelings about the past.
    d. Both passages praise new technology, but for different reasons.
    e. Both passages reflect a longing for the past, but for different reasons.

____ 9. In which important way are the two passages alike?
    a. Neither passage has a theme.
    b. The two passages share the same theme.
    c. Each passage contains more than one paragraph.
    d. Neither passage directly states the theme.
    e. Each passage directly states the theme.

____ 10. Which of the following best states the theme of Passage 1?
    a. The Studebaker wagon symbolizes a time that is no more.
    b. The Studebaker wagon was better than a Ford automobile.
    c. Change is usually for the better.
    d. The era of the Studebaker wagon was a happier one than that of the automobile.
    e. Mass production means poor quality.

____ 11. In Passage 2, Frank says it is "kind of nice" that farmers are going back to the old ways because
    a. people were more honest in the old days
    b. things weren't so expensive long ago
    c. they are beginning to share again
    d. they didn't have to work so hard before the war
    e. now farmers can grow better crops again

____ 12. In Passage 1, what is a Studebaker?
    a. an old-fashioned automobile
    b. a horse-drawn wagon
    c. an early type of self-propelled truck
    d. an old-fashioned station wagon
    e. an early type of railroad freight car

____ 13. Based on what you read in Passage 1, why were the people who brought their families to town in a Studebaker wagon "lucky"?
    a. Studebaker wagons were well-made, sturdy, and attractive.
    b. Studebaker wagons had motors.
    c. Studebaker wagons were harder to find than other wagons.
    d. Studebaker wagons were safer than other wagons.
    e. Studebaker wagons could hold a bigger and heavier load than other wagons.

____ 14. Which of the following states the theme of Passage 2?
     a. Everyone should learn how to share.
     b. Farming is a difficult job.
     c. Farmers can't succeed without up-to-date equipment.
     d. Farmers have to take good care of their equipment because new equipment is so expensive.
     e. Many generations of American farming families have cultivated the land.

____ 15. Which of the following is the best way to break down the following long sentence from Passage 2 into two meaningful sections?

> Frank admits that he keeps his father's tractor partly for sentimental reasons, but he has no such feelings about the 1971 pickup he drives.

     a. Frank admits that he keeps / his father's tractor partly for sentimental reasons, but he has no such feelings about the 1971 pickup he drives.
     b. Frank admits that he keeps his father's tractor partly for sentimental reasons, / but he has no such feelings about the 1971 pickup he drives.
     c. Frank admits / that he keeps his father's tractor partly for sentimental reasons, but he has no such feelings about the 1971 pickup he drives.
     d. Frank admits that he keeps his father's tractor partly / for sentimental reasons, but he has no such feelings about the 1971 pickup he drives.
     e. Frank admits that he keeps his father's tractor partly for sentimental reasons, but he has no such feelings / about the 1971 pickup he drives.

Essay Questions

16. The authors of Passage 1 and Passage 2 use very different writing techniques to make their subjects "come alive" for the reader. In an essay, contrast the way one author uses sensory images, while the other uses first-hand direct quotations to create a vivid impression. Use examples from both passages to support your points. Conclude your essay by explaining why each author's technique is appropriate for his subject matter.

17. In an essay, explain how the term *sentimental* applies to Passage 1 and the term *practical* applies to Passage 2. Use examples and quotations from the passages to support your explanation.

18. From reading these two passages, you can make certain inferences about the author of Passage 1 and Frank, the farmer being interviewed in Passage 2. In an essay, describe the personal qualities you can infer about each person. Back up your ideas with concrete examples from the passages.

"How to Write a Letter" by Garrison Keillor
"How to Write a Poem About the Sky" by Leslie Marmon Silko

Selection Test

Critical Reading

On the line, write the letter of the one best answer.

____ 1. An informal essay is
a. a brief, casual discussion of a topic
b. a piece of nonfiction writing explaining how to do or make something
c. a brief fictional character sketch
d. a brief autobiographical account

____ 2. According to Garrison Keillor, letters are
a. a nuisance
b. a valuable form of communication
c. an outdated form of communication
d. a way of avoiding uncomfortable face-to-face meetings

____ 3. What kind of people is Garrison Keillor writing about in the following passage?

We need to write, otherwise nobody will know who we are. They will have only a vague impression of us as A Nice Person, because, frankly, we don't shine at conversation, we lack the confidence to thrust our faces forward

a. professional writers   c. confident people
b. people who never write letters   d. shy people

____ 4. Which detail or phrase adds a humorous touch in these lines?

Such a sweet gift—a piece of hand-made writing, in an envelope that is not a bill, sitting in our friend's path when she trudges home from a long day spent among wahoos and savages, a day our words will help repair.

a. in an envelope that is not a bill
b. trudges home from a long day spent among wahoos and savages
c. a day our words will help repair
d. Such a sweet gift—

____ 5. Which of the following would the author of an informal essay be most likely to do?
a. use formal language
b. choose a tragic event from history as a main topic
c. offer personal information about himself or herself
d. sum up his or her main points in a concluding paragraph

____ 6. Which would Garrison Keillor consider to be the most important tip for someone who is writing a letter?
a. Make sure your grammar and punctuation are correct.
b. Use an attractive notecard or a good quality piece of writing paper.
c. Be natural and sincere.
d. Be funny and light-hearted.

_____ 7. What does Garrison Keillor mean here,

> The burning shame you feel when you see unanswered mail makes it harder to pick
> up a pen and makes for a cheerless letter when you finally do.

   a. It is natural to feel ashamed whenever you pick up a pen to write a letter.
   b. It is wrong to say anything negative or to share bad news in a letter.
   c. It is important for shy people to hide their lack of confidence when they write letters.
   d. It is hard to write good letters when you haven't written sooner.

_____ 8. According to Garrison Keillor, why should you keep your writing supplies in one place?
   a. so that the sight of the supplies will remind you of the letters that you owe people
   b. so that you will be ready to write whenever you feel a burst of inspiration
   c. because a neat workspace will help you think more clearly
   d. because people like you will look for any excuse not to write

_____ 9. Which word would be inappropriate in a formal essay but perfectly acceptable in an informal essay?
   a. I   b. should've   c. letter   d. therefore

_____ 10. Which item do you think Garrison Keillor would choose to put in a time capsule in order to communicate "the humanity of our times" to future generations?
   a. a newspaper
   b. a magazine article
   c. a letter in which an ordinary person describes his or her new job to a friend
   d. a map of the world

_____ 11. After which words in the following passage from "How to Write a Poem About the Sky" would you pause in order to read it with appropriate pacing?

> You see the sky now
> but the earth
> is lost in it
> and there are no horizons.
> It is all
> a single breath.

   a. after *no, it, horizons,* and *breath*
   b. after *but, is, and, It,* and *a*
   c. no pauses
   d. after *horizons* and *breath*

_____ 12. Which sentence best expresses the meaning of these lines from "How to Write a Poem About the Sky"?

> You see the sky / but the earth is called / by the same name

   a. In some languages, the words for "sky" and "earth" are the same.
   b. Tall mountains reach into the sky.
   c. The sky is reflected in a clear lake.
   d. It is impossible to see where the earth begins and the sky ends.

_____ 13. Which best summarizes what happens in "How to Write a Poem About the Sky"?
   a. On a cold, cloudy winter day, the wind starts blowing, and it begins to snow.
   b. On a cold, cloudy winter day, the sun comes out and the sky becomes clear.
   c. There is a beautiful sunset at the end of a cold, cloudy winter day.
   d. On a cold, cloudy winter day, the clouds part and some blue sky shows through.

_____ 14. To whom does the word *You* refer in "How to Write a Poem About the Sky"?
  a. the reader
  b. the poet's companion
  c. the speaker of the poem
  d. people who do not know how to write poetry

Vocabulary, Spelling, and Grammar

_____ 15. If you have *confidence*, you have
  a. a belief in your own abilities
  b. a secret that you are trying to hide
  c. a tendency to be shy
  d. artistic talent

_____ 16. In which sentence is the verb underlined?
  a. Don't feel <u>guilty</u> about not writing sooner.
  b. <u>Just</u> sit down and let the words flow naturally.
  c. <u>Share</u> whatever is on your mind with your friend.
  d. You will learn <u>something</u> along the way.

_____ 17. Which of the following letters or notes would most people consider to be *obligatory*?
  a. a postcard in which you tell your next-door neighbors about your vacation
  b. a letter asking your grandmother for her advice
  c. a note inviting people to a surprise birthday party
  d. a note to a cousin whom you've never met, thanking her for the scarf she sent

_____ 18. Which word does *not* end in the *ens* sound?
  a. confidence
  b. correspondence
  c. defense
  d. consistency

_____ 19. Which word is *not* a verb?
  a. is
  b. talk
  c. sit
  d. action

_____ 20. Which of the underlined words is misspelled?
  a. You did an excellent job designing the posters for the play; we should give you an award for artistic <u>excellence</u>.
  b. These two plates are different from each other, but I don't think that anyone will notice the <u>differance</u>.
  c. Young children like to feel independent from time to time, but it isn't wise to allow them too much <u>independence</u>.
  d. I know that you were absent; everyone noticed your <u>absence</u>.

Essay Questions

21. Discuss in an essay whether you agree with Garrison Keillor's statement that letters are a gift. In your discussion, summarize Keillor's reasons for thinking that letters are important and valuable.

22. Do you think that the informal essay is an interesting and enjoyable form of writing? In an essay describe the characteristics of an informal essay. Then explain your opinion, citing examples from "How to Write a Letter" and "How to Write a Poem About the Sky" for support.

23. In an essay, examine the humorous aspects of Garrison Keillor's writing. Point out amusing details, words, and phrases, and explain what makes each one funny. Also characterize the style of Keillor's humor. Do you find it gentle? corny? outrageous? Finally, discuss whether and how Keillor's humor adds to the overall style and message of "How to Write a Letter."

"Aaron's Gift" by Myron Levoy
"Water" by Helen Keller

Selection Test

Critical Reading

On the line, write the letter of the one best answer.

_____ 1. At the end of "Aaron's Gift," what does Aaron mean when he says his grandmother's goat "had escaped from the Cossacks at last"?
   a. Pidge's escape has helped Aaron's grandmother get over her goat's death.
   b. Aaron's grandmother finds out her goat wasn't killed after all.
   c. Aaron's grandmother imagines that her goat escaped from the Cossacks.
   d. Aaron's grandmother can now forget about the death of her goat.

_____ 2. In "Aaron's Gift," what do we learn about Aaron's character when he takes Pidge home to mend his wing?
   a. Aaron wants to be a doctor when he grows up.
   b. Aaron has always wanted a pet.
   c. Aaron is a quick thinker.
   d. Aaron is a kind, gentle person.

_____ 3. In "Aaron's Gift," Aaron's mother told him to stay away from Carl and the older boys because
   a. she thought he should play with children his own age
   b. she worried that they would keep Aaron out late at night
   c. she worried that they were involved in dangerous or violent activities
   d. she knew they didn't like animals

_____ 4. In "Aaron's Gift," why does Aaron's grandmother ask him to look in her mirror?
   a. She wants him to see his bruised face.
   b. She wants him to wash the dirt off his face.
   c. She wants him to see how beautiful he is.
   d. She wants to give him the mirror.

_____ 5. Why is it a turning point in "Aaron's Gift" when Aaron tells everyone about the pigeon?
   a. Hearing about the pigeon gives Carl and his friends ideas.
   b. Aaron's father finds out about the pigeon and gets angry.
   c. Hearing about the pigeon makes people think Aaron is strange.
   d. It ruins Aaron's grandmother's birthday surprise.

_____ 6. In "Aaron's Gift," why does calling Carl and the boys who beat him up "Cossacks" give Aaron "the strength to tear away from them"?
   a. It is the worst thing he can think of to call them.
   b. He knows the other boys don't understand the word.
   c. Thinking of the Cossacks makes him so angry, it gives him strength.
   d. Thinking about the Cossacks makes Aaron feel brave.

_____ 7. How are Carl and his friends like the Cossacks in "Aaron's Gift"?
   a. They are cruel and hateful to innocent people.
   b. They enjoy destroying people's homes.
   c. They kill people for no reason.
   d. Everyone hates them.

____ 8. After Aaron hands Pidge to Carl, in which two directions could the story go?
        a. Aaron could go to the meeting or stay home.
        b. Pidge could live or die.
        c. Pidge's wing could get better or not.
        d. Aaron's grandmother's pet goat could live or die.

____ 9. In "Water," after Helen Keller begins learning to communicate, what is the "strange, new sight" that comes to her?
        a. She is able to see.
        b. Although she is blind, she can picture things in her mind
        c. She is happy for the first time in her life.
        d. She has learned to connect words with objects.

____ 10. To Helen Keller in "Water," what is the difference between a "wordless sensation" and a "thought"?
        a. Sensations give people more pleasure than thoughts.
        b. A thought is more interesting than a sensation.
        c. A sensation can't be expressed in words.
        d. An understanding of language is necessary to have a real thought.

____ 11. Why is it a turning point when, in "Water," Helen breaks her doll?
        a. She begins to understand the meaning of the word, *doll.*
        b. She realizes, for the first time, that she loved the doll.
        c. The incident leads Miss Sullivan to take Helen out to the water pump.
        d. The incident leads Miss Sullivan to sweep up the pieces of the broken doll.

____ 12. According to the context clues in the following passage from "Aaron's Gift," what is the meaning of the word *pylon*?

> Aaron skated back and forth on the wide walkway of the park, pretending he was an aviator in an air race zooming around pylons, which were actually lampposts.

        a. lighting fixtures
        b. runway
        c. snakes
        d. upright tower

____ 13. The narrator of "Aaron's Gift" says that Aaron's grandmother's family was lucky because
        a. the Cossacks didn't burn down their house or kill any people
        b. the Cossacks didn't kill all their sheep and goats
        c. the Cossacks didn't hear the goat in the cellar
        d. The Cossacks didn't bash in any walls in their house

____ 14. According to the context clues in the following passage from "Water," what is the meaning of the word *repentance*?

> I felt my way to the hearth and picked up the pieces. I tried vainly to put them to-
> gether. Then my eyes filled with tears; for I realized what I had done, and for the
> first time I felt repentance and sorrow.

        a. feeling sorry for something done
        b. crying frequently
        c. trying to put something back together that is broken
        d. warming oneself by a fire

____ 15. In the story "Aaron's Gift," what makes Aaron's grandmother "strange"?
  a. She spends time talking to birds.
  b. She is kinder and more sensitive than most people.
  c. She is friendlier than most people.
  d. She remembers so much from her past.

Vocabulary, Spelling, and Grammar

____ 16. In "Aaron's Gift," Carl tells Aaron that Pidge will be the gang's
  a. messenger   c. carrier
  b. friend   d. mascot

____ 17. In "Water," Helen Keller writes, "the mystery of language was revealed to me." How would you add the ending s to the word mystery to make it plural?
  a. mysterys   c. mysteries
  b. mysteryies   d. mysterees

____ 18. In the following sentence from "Aaron's Gift," which group of words is a verb phrase?

  How fast the pigeon's heart was beating!

  a. heart was beating   c. the pigeon's heart
  b. was beating   d. How fast

____ 19. Which word best describes Pidge's movements as the gang members try to catch the pigeon in "Aaron's Gift"?
  a. frenzied   c. furious
  b. dangerous   d. absolute

____ 20. Which group of words is a verb phrase in the following sentence from "Water"?

  I was simply making my fingers go in monkey-like imitation.

  a. was simply making   c. was making
  b. I was   d. making my fingers go

Essay Questions

21. In "Water," an important turning point takes place at the very beginning: Miss Sullivan comes to be Helen's teacher. In an essay, explain why the arrival of Miss Sullivan is a turning point, and describe another outcome that could have occurred if Helen's parents had chosen a different teacher. Give reasons from "Water" to support your ideas.

22. The rising action in "Aaron's Gift" eventually leads to the climax of the story. In an essay give an example of three places where the action continues to rise. Then, describe the climax of the story. How is the rising action important for the reader?

23. The title of a story often expresses the most important idea in the story. In an essay, evaluate the title of "Aaron's Gift." State what you think is the main idea of the story. Then go on to show how the title does or does not express that idea.

"Zlateh the Goat"
By Isaac Bashevis Singer

Critical Reading

On the line, write the letter of the one best answer.

____ 1. Why did the warm winter mean a bad year for Reuven the furrier?
   a. No one needs a fur coat in warm weather.
   b. The peasants didn't have enough money to buy fur coats.
   c. There would be a poor harvest of winter grain that year.
   d. The peasants were saving their money for Hanukkah gifts.

____ 2. How did Zlateh help Aaron during the storm?
   a. Zlateh helped him keep warm, gave him milk, and kept him company.
   b. Zlateh gave Aaron ideas for surviving the storm.
   c. Zlateh made noise so that the peasant on the sleigh heard her.
   d. Zlateh helped Aaron find his way home.

____ 3. How does finding the haystack solve Aaron's problem in the snowstorm?
   a. The haystack is a landmark that helps Aaron find his way home.
   b. Behind the haystack, Aaron finds shelter from the wind.
   c. Inside the haystack, Aaron finds warmth and Zlateh finds food.
   d. From on top of the haystack, Aaron sees the peasant on the sleigh.

____ 4. What would have happened to Zlateh if Aaron had delivered her to Feivel the butcher?
   a. She would have been sold to another family.
   b. Feivel would have kept her as a pet.
   c. Feivel would have kept her for her milk.
   d. Feivel would have killed her and sold the meat.

____ 5. After the snowstorm, why would no one ever again think of selling Zlateh?
   a. Feivel didn't want to buy Zlateh.
   b. The family made enough money from selling Zlateh's milk.
   c. The family were thankful to Zlateh for helping save Aaron's life.
   d. Zlateh was too old to be sold.

____ 6. Which of the following best summarizes what happened inside the haystack?
   a. Zlateh and Aaron find warmth, food, and shelter from the storm.
   b. Zlateh and Aaron become best friends.
   c. Aaron decides not to sell Zlateh.
   d. Aaron dreams that it is summer.

____ 7. Zlateh trusted Aaron's family because
   a. they let her come into the kitchen
   b. they treated her like one of the family
   c. they fed her and never harmed her
   d. she knew they needed her milk

____ 8. What is the biggest problem the snowstorm causes for Aaron?
   a. Aaron can't find his way to Feivel's house in the snow.
   b. Without shelter, Aaron will freeze to death.
   c. Aaron cannot make Zlateh walk in the snow.
   d. Aaron and Zlateh are hungry and have no food to eat.

Unit 2: Reaching Out

9. Which of the following best summarizes what happens after Zlateh and Aaron return home?
   a. The family has a Hanukkah party.
   b. The family gives Zlateh a special treat to eat.
   c. Everyone is happy, and no one will ever want to sell Zlateh again.
   d. Aaron and Zlateh both go to sleep.

10. Even though Aaron loved Zlateh, he agreed to take her to Feivel the butcher because
    a. he knew it would be wrong to disobey his father
    b. he was afraid of his father
    c. he wanted the presents the money for Zlateh would buy
    d. he didn't know what would happen to Zlateh

11. What problem does the snowstorm solve for Aaron's father?
    a. The peasants will be able to grow more crops.
    b. There will be a larger supply of grain.
    c. There will be plenty of snow for Hanukkah.
    d. People will buy fur coats.

12. Which of the following best summarizes what Aaron's family does during the snowstorm?
    a. They talk about what might have happened to Aaron.
    b. They search for Aaron, Aaron's mother and sisters cry, and his father is silent and gloomy.
    c. They go out to look for Aaron and Zlateh in the storm, but finally give up the search.
    d. They anxiously await Aaron's return.

13. Which of the following best describes Aaron's actions during the storm?
    a. heroic   c. honest
    b. clever   d. loyal

Vocabulary, Spelling, and Grammar

14. Aaron stayed close to Zlateh because she *exuded* warmth. The best meaning for the word in italics is
    a. gave off   c. preserved
    b. held in   d. contained

15. Which of the following italicized words is spelled incorrectly?
    a. He made it to third *base*.
    b. Everything was in its proper *place*.
    c. She kept her rock collection in a glass *case*.
    d. The ran at a fast *pase*.

16. In which of the following sentences is the verb *hide* in the past tense?
    a. Aaron hides in the haystack until the storm is over.
    b. Aaron hid in the haystack until the storm was over.
    c. Aaron can hide in the haystack until the storm is over.
    d. Aaron will hide in the haystack until the storm is over.

17. Which of the following sentences contains the past tense of the verb *talk*?
    a. Aaron *talked* to Zlateh.
    b. Aaron will *talk* to Zlateh.
    c. Aaron can *talk* to Zlateh.
    d. Aaron *talks* to Zlateh.

____ 18. Which of the following are the four principal parts of the verb *have*?
  a. have, having, had, was having
  b. have, having, had, will have
  c. have, having, had, have had
  d. have, having, had, had had

____ 19. Zlateh comes to the conclusion that a goat should not ask questions. In other words, Zlateh
  a. predicts that a goat should not ask questions
  b. remembers that a goat should not ask questions
  c. decides that a goat should not ask questions
  d. imagines that a goat should not ask questions

____ 20. Which of the following italicized words is spelled <u>incorrectly</u>?
  a. The curtains were made of *lace.*
  b. The *fases* of the twins looked alike.
  c. It isn't *safe* to cross the street when the light is red.
  d. He came in second in the *race.*

Essay Questions

21. In an essay, write a summary of "Zlateh the Goat." Include the important details a person would need to know in order to understand the plot of the story. Do not, however, include minor details that are not necessary, even though they might make the story more interesting. Make sure you keep details in the order in which they happen in the story.

22. At the beginning of the story, we learn that Aaron never disobeys his father. Yet, at the end of the story, he brings Zlateh home instead of taking her to Feivel the butcher, as his father had told him. Explain in an essay what makes Aaron change his mind about obeying his father and taking Zlateh to the butcher.

23. Write an essay summarizing Aaron's conflict with the snowstorm. Include details about the storm itself. How does it start? How does it grow bigger and stronger? What effects does it have on Aaron and on Zlateh? What problems of survival does it pose for them? Include details about how Aaron battles the storm, solving each problem the storm presents. Conclude your essay by explaining why Aaron was able to win the battle against the storm. Which personality traits enabled him to survive?

"Door Number Four" by Charlotte Pomerantz
"Count That Day Lost" by George Eliot
"The World Is Not a Pleasant Place to Be" by Nikki Giovanni

Selection Test

Critical Reading

On the line, write the letter of the one best answer.

_____ 1. The identity of a poem's speaker is
    a. the same as the identity of the poet
    b. often different from the identity of the poet
    c. usually revealed in the first few lines of a poem
    d. usually revealed in the last line of a poem

_____ 2. When you paraphrase a difficult sentence or line from a poem, you
    a. express it in the form of a question
    b. add humor to it
    c. put it in your own words
    d. copy it down exactly as it appears in the poem

_____ 3. In "Door Number Four," what do the Indonesian words add to the poem?
    a. They help to create a puzzling and mysterious feeling.
    b. They help to create a friendly and playful feeling.
    c. They make it historically accurate.
    d. They help readers picture the items that the uncle sells in his store.

_____ 4. The speaker of "Door Number Four" is probably
    a. the poet   c. the storekeeper's wife
    b. a storekeeper   d. a child

_____ 5. In "Count That Day Lost," the speaker refers to "one word that eased the heart of him who heard." Which of the following is the best paraphrase of this idea?
    a. one word that made someone feel better
    b. one word that angered someone
    c. one word that broke someone's heart
    d. one word that saved someone's life

_____ 6. Which of the following actions would the speaker of "Count That Day Lost" consider to be part of a day that is "well spent"?
    a. You find a five-dollar bill on the sidewalk.
    b. You do all your homework as soon as you come home from school.
    c. You bring some entertaining books and magazines to a friend who is sick in bed.
    d. You watch your favorite video for the third time.

_____ 7. Which of the following phrases best describes the speaker of "Count That Day Lost"?
    a. a voice of uncertainty   c. a voice of wisdom
    b. a voice of bitterness   d. a voice of gentle humor

____ 8. Read the following lines from "The World Is Not a Pleasant Place to Be." Then choose the statement that best paraphrases the lines.

> an ocean would never laugh / if clouds weren't there / to kiss her tears

a. An ocean would be sad if she didn't have someone to hold.
b. An ocean would be sad if she didn't have the friendship of the clouds.
c. An ocean would laugh if the clouds rained down tears of sadness.
d. A river would stop its flow if only a stream were there to receive it.

____ 9. According to "The World Is Not a Pleasant Place to Be," what makes life meaningful and worthwhile?
a. having an important job
b. being able to enjoy the beauty of nature
c. traveling to distant places
d. having a friend to care about

____ 10. What is the meaning behind the following lines from "The World Is Not a Pleasant Place to Be?

> a river would stop / its flow if only / a stream were there / to receive it

a. Streams and rivers never meet.
b. A river needs a stream to flow into, just as a person needs a true friend to depend on.
c. Rivers that flow into streams are unpleasant places.
d. A river will dry up if it does not receive enough rainfall.

Vocabulary, Spelling, and Grammar

____ 11. In which of the following sentences is the verb *go* used in the present tense?
a. I went to my friend's house.
b. I go to my friend's house.
c. I will go to my friend's house.
d. I arrive at my friend's house.

____ 12. Which of the following words is most nearly opposite in meaning to *eased*?
a. upset   c. stopped
b. comforted   d. noticed

____ 13. What is the past tense of the verb *descend*?
a. descending   c. will descend
b. descends   d. descended

____ 14. Which of the following words is most nearly opposite in meaning to *pleasant*?
a. happy
b. distasteful
c. polite
d. appealing

____ 15. Which of the following words contains a *z* sound that is spelled with an *s*?
a. sensation
b. worse
c. defense
d. pause

Essay Questions

16. In an essay, describe the message about friendship and sharing that you find in "Door Number Four," "Count That Day Lost," or "The World Is Not a Pleasant Place to Be," Support your description with short quotations and paraphrases of longer passages.

17. In an essay, compare and contrast the speakers of two of the poems. Be as specific as you can in describing each speaker, and cite phrases or passages from the poem to support your description. Discuss the differences and similarities between the two speakers.

18. "Count That Day Lost" was written over a hundred years ago. In an essay, explain whether you, as a modern reader, think the poem is fresh and meaningful or quaint and old-fashioned. Support your opinion with examples from the poems.

"Old Ben" by Jesse Stuart
"Feathered Friend" by Arthur C. Clarke

Selection Test

Critical Reading

On the line, write the letter of the one best answer.

____ 1. In the following passage from "Old Ben," which word or words provide a context clue to the meaning of the word *treed*?

> He had *treed* blacksnakes, and my father had shot them down from the trees.

   a. he had
   b. blacksnakes
   c. my father
   d. shot them down from the trees

____ 2. At the beginning of "Old Ben," which of the following pairs of words best describe the father's attitude toward snakes?
   a. curiosity, admiration
   b. amusement, affection
   c. indifference, ignorance
   d. fear, dislike

____ 3. "Old Ben" suggests that the narrator's willingness to be friendly toward a snake is
   a. unusual
   b. the way most people feel
   c. foolish
   d. accepted by his family and friends

____. 4. Which event in the story first suggests that Old Ben is too trusting for his own good?
   a. He gets too close to the hogs.
   b. He lets the children pet him.
   c. He goes into the hayloft after mice.
   d. He lies down in the horse's feed box.

____ 5. In "Old Ben," the family comes to see Old Ben as a good pet because
   a. Ben has gotten rid of all the mice in the corn crib
   b. Ben has not hurt the cats
   c. Ben likes them
   d. Ben has not eaten any of the chickens or other birds

____ 6. Using context clues from the following passage, choose the best meaning for the word *sociable*.

> "Fred's never been sociable with Old Ben since he got in his box that time," Pa said. "I wonder if he could have stomped Old Ben to death."

   a. friendly
   b. unfriendly
   c. civilized
   d. dead

_____ 7. According to "Feathered Friend," which two of the following are negative aspects of life on a space station?

        I.   limited room
       II. hard work
     III. risk
     IV. bad food

a. I and III   c. I and IV
b. II and III   d. II and IV

_____ 8. In "Feathered Friend," what event first suggests that there is something wrong with the space station's air supply.
a. The narrator bangs his head against an angle beam.
b. The canary is found unconscious.
c. The narrator wakes up with a headache and has trouble undoing his bunk straps.
d. The canary revives after getting oxygen.

_____ 9. In "Feathered Friend," the crew adopts Claribel as a pet because
a. she nearly died
b. they like Sven and do not want to hurt his feelings
c. they have no way of sending the bird back to earth
d. they enjoy having the bird on board

_____ 10. In the following passage from "Feathered Friend," which words provide a context clue to the meaning of the word *leisurely*?

> . . . she did a curious kind of backward loop I'm sure no earthbound canary had ever managed, and departed with a few leisurely flicks. It was quite clear that she'd already learned how to operate in the absence of gravity, and did not believe in doing unnecessary work.

a. a curious kind of backward loop
b. she did not believe in doing unnecessary work
c. no earthbound canary
d. in the absence of gravity

_____ 11. In "Feathered Friend," small, wiry people like Sven are preferred to bigger people for space station work because
a. they fit into space suits more easily, and are quicker on their feet
b. they take up less room and add less weight to the space station
c. they are smarter and have more endurance than bigger workers
d. they are easier to train

_____ 12. In "Feathered Friend," the canary
a. saves the crew from likely death.
b. fails to alert the crew of danger.
c. eats most of their food supply.
d. divides the crew.

Vocabulary, Grammar, and Spelling

_____ 13. Which of the following sentences uses the past perfect tense?
a. He was so friendly I decided to keep him.
b. Ben had done something our nine cats couldn't.
c. Pa and I moved the corn searching for him.
d. Claribel thrived and grew fat.

____ 14. Which of these sentences has a misspelled word?
  a. I am learning how to use the diving board at the pool.
  b. The children were grateful for the gifts.
  c. We ran into each other purely by chance.
  d. Ice skateing is a popular winter sport.

____ 15. To measure something *precisely* means to measure it
  a. exactly   c. quickly
  b. repeatedly   d. willingly

____ 16. Which of the following sentences uses the future perfect tense?
  a. By the end of the year, he is going to take a course in Earth Science.
  b. By the end of the year, he will take a course in Earth Science.
  c. By the end of the year, he will have taken a course in Earth Science.
  d. By the end of the year, he has taken a course in Earth Science.

____ 17. Which word correctly completes the following sentence?

  There is a _____ that does not allow people to touch paintings at
  the museum.

  a. regulatory   c. regulate
  b. regulator   d. regulation

____ 18. Which sentence uses the present perfect tense?
  a. Sven smuggled the canary on board the space station.
  b. They have never seen a snake like Old Ben.
  c. In exchange for the toy sheep, he gave the boy a pine cone.
  d. From now on, there will always be canaries on space stations.

____ 19. Which of the following words contains a silent *e*?
  a. regulation   c. December
  b. grateful   d. winter

____ 20. What is the order of tenses in the following sentence?

  When they found the stricken bird, they knew something had gone wrong.

  a. present, past
  b. past, past perfect
  c. present perfect, past perfect
  d. past perfect, past

Essay Questions

21. In an essay, analyze the attitude of the narrator of "Old Ben," not only toward the snake, but toward animals in general. Does he consider animals to be simply useful helpers on a farm, or does he think of them as friends? Use quotes and events from the selection as examples to support your opinion.

22. The title of a story often expresses the most important idea in the story. In an essay, evaluate the title of "Feathered Friend." State what you think is the main idea of the story. Then, go on to show how the title does or does not express that idea.

23. Write an essay comparing and contrasting the roles played by the snake in "Old Ben" and Claribel the canary in "Feathered Friend." Show similarities and differences between the two animals with regard to their importance to the people around them, the way these people feel about them, and the way they react to the human beings in each story.

Unit 2: Reaching Out

Unit Test

Critical Reading

On the line, write the letter of the one best answer.

_____ 1. How would the author of "How to Write a Letter" be likely to feel about receiving personal letters?
   a. He would feel happy that someone cares enough about him to write.
   b. He would feel anxious about being obliged to write a letter in reply.
   c. He would start worrying about what to include in his reply.
   d. He would want to reply by making a telephone call to the writer.

_____ 2. What would be the most appropriate subject for an informal essay such as "How to Write a Letter"?
   a. instructions on how to use a computer
   b. an application for a job
   c. a short biography
   d. thoughts about the value of keeping a pet

_____ 3. In "How to Write a Letter," the author says that one advantage of a letter over a telephone call is that
   a. you can say less in a letter
   b. a letter can be kept for a long time
   c. it is quicker to write a letter
   d. writing a letter is cheaper

_____ 4. Which sentence best describes the attitude of the author in "How to Write a Poem About the Sky"?
   a. She wants people to write poems about nature.
   b. She thinks winter is the best season.
   c. She admires the beauty of the sun peeking through on a cold winter day.
   d. She wishes more people would visit Alaska.

_____ 5. What could be clarified by rereading the following passage from "Water"?

> Earlier in the day we had a tussle over the words "m-u-g" and "w-a-t-e-r." Miss Sullivan had tried to impress it upon me that "m-u-g" is mug and that "w-a-t-e-r" is water. But I persisted in confusing the two. In despair she had dropped the subject for the time.

   a. Helen is unable to associate words with the objects they name.
   b. Helen does not like Miss Sullivan.
   c. Helen does not know how to spell.
   d. Miss Sullivan decides that she cannot teach Helen.

_____ 6. According to the context clues in the following passage from "Water," what is the meaning of the word *tussle*?

> Earlier in the day we had had a tussle over the words "m-u-g" and "w-a-t-e-r." . . . I persisted in confounding the two. . . . I became impatient at her repeated attempts and, seizing the new doll, I dashed it upon the floor.

   a. disagreement
   b. agreement
   c. party
   d. murder

_____ 7. In "Aaron's Gift," why does Aaron want to be a member of Carl's gang?
   a. Aaron is lonely.
   b. Aaron is bored.
   c. Aaron wants to be accepted by older boys.
   d. Aaron thinks that older boys will protect him.

_____ 8. Which sentence most accurately describes the feelings of Aaron's grandmother about her childhood at the beginning of "Aaron's Gift"?
   a. She loves to remember her childhood.
   b. She has never completely recovered from the terrible experience of the pogrom.
   c. She has put the terrors of the past behind her.
   d. She wants to revisit the place where she grew up.

_____ 9. In "Aaron's Gift," Carl wants to
   a. make Pidge his own pet.   c. burn Pidge in the fire.
   b. give him to the Cossacks.   d. protect Pidge from the government officials.

_____ 10. Which sentence best summarizes the following passage from "Zlateh the Goat"?

> Sometimes Aaron felt that there could never have been a summer, that the snow had always fallen, ever since he could remember. He, Aaron, never had a father or mother or sisters. He, Aaron, was a snow child, born of the snow, and so was Zlateh.

   a. Aaron suspected that he was really an orphan.
   b. Aaron's memories of his real life began to seem unreal.
   c. Aaron lived in a very cold climate.
   d. Aaron feared that the snow was going to keep falling forever.

_____ 11. At the end of "Zlateh the Goat," Aaron's family decides never to sell Zlateh because
   a. Zlateh is still useful
   b. they would not be able to get much money for Zlateh
   c. they no longer need money
   d. Zlateh is now like a family friend

_____ 12. In "Zlateh the Goat," Aaron talks to Zlateh while they are in the haystack because
   a. he has learned to understand what Zlateh is saying
   b. he has become a bit crazy from lack of food
   c. he needs to communicate with someone and Zlateh is his only companion
   d. he feels guilty that he had been taking Zlateh to the butcher

_____ 13. Which sentence is the most accurate paraphrase of the following passage from "Door Number Four"?

> There, in lamplight,
> you will see
> a friend,
> teman,
> a friend
> who's me.

   a. The lamplight will show you a mirror.
   b. I will be there and will be your friend.
   c. Teman is the name of your new friend.
   d. The light is your friend.

_____ 14. "Count That Day Lost" is a poem in praise of
   a. honesty   c. obedience
   b. kindness   d. intelligence

_____ 15. According to the speaker of "The World Is Not a Pleasant Place to Be," which of the following things can make the world a pleasant place by itself?
   a. a library full of books   c. a group of caring friends or family
   b. a beautiful painting   d. a delicious meal

_____ 16. When the narrator of "Feathered Friend" wakes up with a headache and has trouble undoing the straps of his cot, it is a sign that
   a. there is a problem with the station's air supply
   b. the narrator has been on the space station too long
   c. something is wrong with the space station's food supply
   d. there is a contagious disease spreading around the space station

_____ 17. According to the context clues in the following passage from "Feathered Friend," what is the meaning of the word *regulation*?

   To the best of my knowledge, there's never been a regulation that forbids one to keep pets in a space station.

   a. a rule   c. a space station guidebook
   b. a standard   d. pet care instructions

_____ 18. Which of the following statements is true of the snake in "Old Ben"?
   a. He never becomes completely tame.
   b. He does not win the trust of the whole family.
   c. He becomes too trusting for his own good.
   d. He loses the ability to hunt for prey.

_____ 19. According to the context clues in the following passage from "Old Ben," what is the meaning of the word *stroked*?

   He enjoyed having his back rubbed and his neck stroked.

   a. rubbed   b. choked   c. poked   d. tickled

Vocabulary, Spelling, and Grammar

_____ 20. Which of the following sentences uses the past perfect tense?
   a. We had given our tickets to the conductor.
   b. He used to be a star athlete.
   c. The students looked through their notes.
   d. My sister was going to study medicine.

_____ 21. Which sentence contains a misspelled word?
   a. It is important to be careful while driving a car.
   b. Our meeting was purely accidental.
   c. The two brothers are always arguing with each other.
   d. The old book was extremly valuable.

_____ 22. Which family member is a *sibling*?
   a. a parent   c. a sister
   b. an aunt   d. a cousin

_____ 23. Which sentence has two verbs?
   a. Our coach taught us some useful exercises.
   b. He gave me the solution to the puzzle.
   c. The movie was full of exciting action.
   d. Yesterday at the beach, we ran and swam for hours.

_____ 24. The word closest in meaning to *consoled* is
   a. thanked   c. complimented
   b. comforted   d. helped

_____ 25. Which is the helping verb in the following sentence?

   He was running to catch the bus when he tripped and fell.

   a. was   b. running   c. tripped   d. fell

© Prentice-Hall, Inc.

____ 26. Which of the following words is spelled correctly?
   a. replyed   c. supplieing
   b. obeyed   d. copyed

____ 27. Which of the following sentences uses a linking verb?
   a. It rained heavily all afternoon.
   b. The horses stood peacefully in the meadow.
   c. The waves grew rougher the next day.
   d. Hans Christian Andersen wrote "The Little Mermaid."

____ 28. Which of the following definitions most closely fits the word *extract*?
   a. take out   c. put under
   b. place on top of   d. put into

____ 29. Which of the following words contains a *z* sound that is spelled with an *s*?
   a. horse   b. closely   c. acts   d. please

____ 30. Which is the past tense of the verb *eat*?
   a. eating   b. ate   c. eaten   d. eated

Essay Questions

31. Several selections in this unit present situations in which one or more human characters form relationships with animals that could be called friendships. Choose two of the following selections: "Old Ben," "Feathered Friend," "Zlateh the Goat," and "Aaron's Gift," and write an essay in which you analyze such relationships. Include an explanation of how the friendship happens, and of how the animal and the person (or persons) benefit from it.

32. In an essay, compare and contrast how two of the following selections demonstrate ways to show appreciation toward friends: "How to Write a Letter," "Aaron's Gift," and "Zlateh the Goat." Consider these questions: is the show of friendship in each selection a response to something the friend has done or is it made for another reason, and if so, why? Does the act of appreciation suggest a general attitude toward other people or creatures, or is it an attitude limited to the selection alone? Support your conclusions with details from the selections.

33. Write an essay in which you analyze what the authors of two of the following poems wanted to express to their readers: "How to Write a Poem About the Sky," "Door Number Four," and "Count That Day Lost." For each of the selections you choose, explain the message or the shared experience, thought, or feeling the poet describes. Compare how the poets regard their readers: as people to be taught, as friends, or in some other way. Support your opinions with details from the poems.

34. Consider the narrators of "How to Write a Letter," "Childhood and Poetry," and "Water," and the speaker of "The World Is Not a Pleasant Place," and write an essay in which you compare and contrast two of these characters with regard to how they reach out to others. Explain what difficulties, if any, stand in their way and how they overcome their difficulties, as well as why reaching out is of importance to them. Support your conclusions with details from the selections if necessary.

35. In an essay, compare the rising action and climax in two of the following stories: "Aaron's Gift," "Zlateh the Goat," and "Old Ben." Explain how the author builds the tension and then resolves it. Which author does the better job? Support your conclusion with details from the selection.

Unit 2: Reaching Out

Alternative Unit Test

The two passages below are followed by questions based on their content and on the relationship between the two passages.

Passage 1

In the following passage, Miyax, an Eskimo girl who has been living among wolves in the Alaskan tundra, awakens in the midst of the wolf pack.

from *Julie of the Wolves* by Jean Craighead George

She awoke with a start a short time later and looked about in puzzlement. The sky vaulted above her. A grass blade tickled her face, and she remembered where she was—up on the frost heave with the wolf pack! Breathing deeply to quell a sense of uneasiness, she finally relaxed, unrolled, and sat up. Kapu was curled against her leg. His feet were flipping and he yipped as if challenging some wolf badman in his dreams. Softly she stroked his fur.

"All's well," she whispered and his paws stopped moving. He sighed and dreamed on peacefully.

She glanced around. All of the wolves were asleep, although they usually went hunting when the sky was lime-green. Perhaps they knew something she didn't know. Sniffing and turning her head, she saw nothing different from any other evening. Then in the distance a thick wall of fog arose. It blotted out the horizon, the far dips and heaves, the grasses, the pond, and finally her own frost heave. The fog streamed up the wolf slope and enveloped the members of the pack one by one until only Kapu was visible. Fogs were part of the Arctic summer, rolling from the sea for only an hour or for many days, but Miyax had never given them much thought. Now she remembered that when the fog rolled over Barrow, airplanes were grounded, ships and boats had to be anchored, and even the two jeeps in town sat where they had stopped in the fog. She also remembered that people were prisoners of the fog, too. They could not see to hunt.

Passage 2

The following passage takes place in the Yukon Territory, part of a vast subarctic region in northwest Canada. Because of its northern location, the Yukon has long, cold winters with periods during which the sun does not appear at all.

from *To Build a Fire* by Jack London

Dawn had broken cold and gray, exceedingly cold and gray, when the man turned aside from the main Yukon trail and climbed the high earth-bank, where a dim and little-traveled trail led eastward through the fat spruce timberland. It was a steep bank, and he paused for breath at the top, excusing the act to himself by looking at his watch. It was nine o'clock. There was no sun nor hint of sun, through there was not a cloud in the sky. It was a clear day, and yet there seemed an intangible pall over the face of things, a subtle gloom that made the day dark, and that was due to the absence of sun. This fact did not worry the man. He was used to the lack of sun. It had been days since he had seen the sun, and he knew that a few more days must pass before that cheerful orb, due south, would just peep above the skyline and dip immediately from view.

The man flung a look back along the way he had come. The Yukon lay a mile wide and hidden under three feet of ice. On top of this ice were as many feet of snow. It was all pure white, rolling in gentle undulations where the ice jams of the freeze-up had formed. North and south, as far as his eye could see, it was unbroken white, save for a dark hairline that curved and twisted from around the spruce-covered island to the south, and that curved and twisted away into the north, where it disappeared behind another spruce-covered island. This dark hairline was the trail—the main trail—that led south five hundred miles to the Chilcoot pass, Dyea, and salt water; and that led north seventy miles to Dawson, and still on to the north a thousand miles to Nulato, and finally to St. Michael on Bering Sea, a thousand miles and half a thousand more.

Critical Reading

On the line, write the letter of the one best answer.

_____ 1. Which statement best compares and contrasts the settings of the two passages?
   a. Both passages take place in the Arctic, but Passage 1 occurs on a summer evening, while Passage 2 takes place on a winter morning.
   b. Both passages take place in the Arctic, but Passage 1 occurs in the daytime, while Passage 2 occurs at night.
   c. Both passages take place in the Arctic, but Passage 1 takes place in a warmer region than Passage 2.
   d. Passage 2 takes place in the Arctic, while Passage 1 takes place in a warmer region farther south.
   e. Passage 1 takes place in the Arctic, while Passage 2 takes place in a warmer region farther south.

_____ 2. Which statement is common to the characters in both passages?
   a. They are completely alone.
   b. They have to survive in a difficult environment.
   c. They are facing grave danger.
   d. They are afraid of darkness.
   e. They have to depend upon animals in order to survive.

_____ 3. Which of the following statements do the two passages lead you to believe?
   a. Both characters dislike the company of other humans.
   b. Both characters are lonely.
   c. Both characters are well aware of the various weather conditions of their environment.
   d. Both characters have developed keen senses of smell and hearing.
   e. Both characters wish they were in a warmer climate zone.

_____ 4. Which statement applies to only Passage 1?
   a. The sensory language appeals to the sense of sight only.
   b. The author does not use sensory language.
   c. Most of the sensory language appeals to the sense of sight.
   d. The sensory language appeals to several senses.
   e. The use of sensory language does not make the setting easier to visualize.

_____ 5. In both passages, the speaker
   a. is not a character in the story
   b. is the main character in the story
   c. is identified at the end of the passage
   d. is involved in the story
   e. is a friend of the main character's

____ 6. An important difference between the two passages is that
        a. Passage 1 is filled with exciting events, while Passage 2 is not
        b. Passage 1 describes an event, while Passage 2 describes only a setting
        c. Passage 2 is part of a narrative, while Passage 1 is not
        d. Passage 2 does not contain the climax of the story, but Passage 1 does
        e. Passage 2 describes a sequence of events, while Passage 1 does not

____ 7. Which of the following details do you envision while reading both passages?
        a. a clear day
        b. a foggy day
        c. snow and ice
        d. the sky
        e. a long trail

____ 8. One way in which Miyax, the character in Passage 1, differs from the man in Passage 2 is that
        a. Miyax, in Passage 1, seems worried and uneasy, while the man in Passage 2 seems unworried
        b. Miyax, in Passage 1, is more independent than the man in Passage 2
        c. Miyax, in Passage 1, is more intelligent than the man in Passage 2
        d. the man in Passage 2 is in a dangerous situation, while Miyax, in Passage 1, is not
        e. Miyax, in Passage 1, has less knowledge of the wilderness than does the man in Passage 2

____ 9. In both passages, sensory language is used to describe
        a. what a characters tastes and smells
        b. what a character hears in the distance
        c. what a character sees in the distance
        d. what a character wishes to see and hear
        e. what a character fears seeing in the distance

____ 10. Which detail helps you envision the trail in the following sentence from Passage 2?

> This dark hairline was the trail—the main trail—that led south five hundred miles to the Chilcoot Pass, Dyea, and salt water; and that led north seventy miles to Dawson, and still on to the north a thousand miles to Nulato, and finally to St. Michael on Bering Sea, a thousand miles and half a thousand more.

        a. ". . . the main trail . . ."
        b. ". . . that led south . . ."
        c. ". . . to the Chilcoot Pass . . ."
        d. ". . . that led north seventy miles to Dawson . . ."
        e. "This dark hairline was the trail . . ."

____ 11. Which is the best paraphrase of the following sentence from Passage 2?

> It was a clear day, and yet there seemed an intangible pall over the face of things, a subtle gloom that made the day dark, and that was due to the absence of sun.

        a. Because there was no sun, the day seemed especially cloudy.
        b. It was a clear day, but the man felt sad and depressed.
        c. Clouds and fog blotted out the sun, making the day dark and gloomy.
        d. Because there was no sun, the earth lay in total darkness.
        e. Because there was no sun, the day seemed gloomy and dark.

_____ 12. Which best describes the scene that the following sentence from Passage 2 helps you to envision?

> It was all pure white, rolling in gentle undulations where the ice jams of the freeze-up had formed.

a. a snowy landscape with beautiful ice formations
b. a pure-white landscape with snow too deep to walk in
c. a pure-white landscape with snow that looked like gentle waves on the sea
d. a pure-white landscape with snow that looked like the sand of a desert
e. a pure-white landscape covered with towering mountains of snow

_____ 13. Which of the following problems does Passage 1 make you think Miyax will have to solve?
a. If the sun does not come out, she will have to find a way to keep warm.
b. The fog will make it impossible for the wolves to hunt and bring back food.
c. The fog will make it impossible for Miyax to follow the wolves.
d. Because they are unable to hunt, the wolves are preparing to attack Miyax.
e. Something bad will happen to Kapu, and Miyax will have to rescue him.

_____ 14. Which of the following best summarizes Passage 1?
a. Miyax awakens while the wolves are still sleeping. She wonders why they are not out hunting, when a heavy fog rolls in.
b. Miyax awakens and comforts Kapu, who seems to be having a bad dream. She notices that all the wolves are still asleep.
c. After a heavy fog rolls in, Miyax remembers when she lived in Barrow. She thinks about the people she knew there.
d. Kapu is having a bad dream. Miyax comforts him, telling him, "All's well."
e. Miyax had never given much thought to fog, but now she wonders how long it will be before she will see the sun again.

_____ 15. Which of the following statements does Passage 1 lead you to believe about Miyax?
a. She has no use for the world of humans.
b. She can adapt to unfamiliar situations.
c. She is more like a wolf than a human being.
d. She is more intelligent than most humans.
e. She is easily frightened.

Essay Questions

16. Both passages use sensory language to help you envision the setting. In an essay, tell which senses the language in each passage appeals to, using quotes from the passages as examples. Then describe the setting each passage helps you to envision.

17. In an essay, briefly summarize each passage. Then explain which passage makes you more interested in reading the rest of the story. Specify the details of the narrative that capture your interest, and give your reasons for wanting to continue reading the narrative. Explain why the passage you do not choose interests you less.

18. A theme common to both passages is surviving in the Arctic. The characters in these passages must have developed personal qualities that enable them to survive harsh and difficult conditions. Write an essay in which you describe a conflict you predict each character will have with nature and explain the specific personal qualities of each character that will help him or her survive the conflict. Use details from each passage to support your points and predictions.

from *The Pigman & Me* by Paul Zindel

Selection Test

Critical Reading

On the line, write the letter of the one best answer.

____ 1. Why does John Quinn tell Paul that he had to give John his paddle?
   a. John is a bully.
   b. Paul's time to use the paddle is up.
   c. John wants to pick a fight with Paul.
   d. John thinks that Paul and Richard are finished playing paddle ball.

____ 2. The fight between Paul and John could have been avoided if
   a. John had explained the rule to Paul instead of just demanding the paddle
   b. Paul had explained to John that he was still using the paddle
   c. Paul had warned John before he hit him with the paddle
   d. Mr. Trellis hadn't showed up

____ 3. On the day of the fight between Paul and John, the kids at school learn that
   a. John really knows how to fight
   b. Paul isn't a coward
   c. fighting is not the best way to settle an argument
   d. the Zindel kids stick up for each other

____ 4. Which of the following lines from the story shows that Paul is in conflict?
   a. I was a nervous wreck.
   b. I stopped a few feet from him and put my fists up.
   c. He stopped in his tracks and the crowd froze in amazed silence.
   d. I could see my savior was my sister.

____ 5. The way Paul ends the fight shows that he is
   a. dishonest   c. clever
   b. a cheater   d. a loser

____ 6. Why does Paul turn down Jennifer's offers to help him?
   a. Paul is afraid the other kids will pick on Jennifer if she helps him.
   b. Paul has heard that John wants to call off the fight.
   c. Paul thinks that, with Nonno Frankie's help, he can win the fight.
   d. Paul doesn't want to look like a coward.

____ 7. Which of the following "borrowed" words does Nonno Frankie say that Paul should use in a curse on John Quinn?
   a. tae kwon do
   b. ziti
   c. poncho
   d. espresso

____ 8. It is clear that Jennifer is a good friend to Paul because
   a. she doesn't want Paul to fight
   b. she is completely loyal to Paul
   c. Paul thinks that she is beautiful
   d. she and Paul carved their names on the tree trunk

____ 9. Why doesn't Paul want to fight with John?
   a. Paul is afraid he will hurt John again.
   b. Paul is afraid his mother will find out and he'll get into trouble.
   c. Paul doesn't believe in fighting.
   d. Paul is afraid that John will beat him up.

____ 10. Why does Paul hit John Quinn with the paddle?
   a. Because he is a new kid at school, Paul wants to show that no one can order
      him around.
   b. Paul is so afraid that John will hit him, that he decides to hit John first.
   c. Paul is so nervous about being at a new school that he doesn't really know what
      he is doing.
   d. Paul is used to settling arguments by fighting.

____ 11. Which of the following "borrowed" words is also part of the name of a character in
   this story?
   a. frankfurter
   b. sombrero
   c. pasta
   d. kimono

____ 12. The most important things Nonno Frankie teaches Paul are
   a. how to hold his fists and how to kick
   b. that you must learn by asking questions and by reading
   c. not to be a coward and not to have negative thoughts
   d. useful facts about Alexander the Great and Genghis Khan

____ 13. Why does Paul refuse to give John the paddle?
   a. Paul doesn't know there is a rule about using the paddles.
   b. Paul wants to practice his shots.
   c. Paul doesn't want to obey the rule about using the paddles.
   d. Paul really wants to play paddle ball with John.

Vocabulary, Spelling, and Grammar

____ 14. In the following passage from the story, which two adjectives answer the question
   Which one?

   > This happened on the first Friday, during gym period, when we were allowed to
   > play games in the school yard.

   a. school, gym   c. when, school
   b. first, gym   d. first, yard

____ 15. John wanted to *exact* revenge because Paul hit him with the paddle. The best meaning for *exact* in this sentence is
   a. demand   c. repay
   b. correct   d. reform

____ 16. Which of the following italicized words is spelled correctly?
   a. Paul's conflict caused him to feel *aggravasion*.
   b. News of the fight caused a *sensasion* in school.
   c. Before the fight, you could feel the *tention* in the air.
   d. Paul wished he had never gotten himself into this *situation*.

____ 17. In the following sentence, which word is an article?

> Alexander the Great always ordered his entire army to shave their heads.

    a. always   c. army
    b. the   d. their

____ 18. Paul *groveled* on the ground, pretending to be hurt. The best meaning for the word *groveled* in this sentence is
    a. lay on his back
    b. crawled face down
    c. pounded his fists
    d. cried

____ 19. In the following sentence from the story, which question does the adjective *negative* answer?

> When he comes at you, don't underestimate the power of *negative* thinking!

    a. What kind?   c. How many?
    b. Which one?   d. How much?

____ 20. Nonno Frankie offered to help Paul by teaching him some fighting *tactics*. In other words, he offered to teach Paul some
    a. rules for fighting
    b. techniques for fighting
    c. reasons for fighting
    d. ways to avoid fighting

Essay Questions

21. Most readers would agree that Paul should not have hit John. Some, however, would say that John was also at fault for demanding the paddle from a new student without explaining the rules. In an essay, explain who you think is more at fault in the story, Paul or John, or if the two boys are equally at fault. Use specific examples from the story to support your ideas.

22. In the story, Paul gets into trouble because he doesn't know the rules in his new school. In an essay, explain the importance of learning the rules in any new situation. For example, you might explain why it would be important to know the laws in a foreign country you are visiting; to know the rules of etiquette, or good manners, when visiting a family whose culture is different from yours; or, like Paul, to learn the rules in a school where you are a new student. Back up your statements by giving examples of possible results if you are unfamiliar with laws or rules.

23. Paul thinks fighting and looking like a coward are his only choices. In an essay, explain another way in which Paul could have solved his conflict. Make clear why your ideas will allow Paul to avoid both getting beaten up and looking like a coward. Present your arguments in a logical and convincing manner.

Name _____ Date _____

Selection Test

Critical Reading

On the line, write the letter of the one best answer.

____ 1. Which of the following passages from the story creates a suspenseful atmosphere?
   a. Norman stepped down and then quickly turned to hug the butte face as the steps ended abruptly in space.
   b. The sun bathed the eastern valley in pale yellow which was spotted with dark clumps of sage.
   c. Quickly he picked up the stick and his willow cane and hurried down the hill.
   d. Matt Two Bull traced with his fingers the faint zig zag design . . .

____ 2. Norman's grandfather says the *coup* stick must be treated with respect because
   a. it is worth a lot of money
   b. it was handed down to him by his father
   c. it is an antique
   d. it is all that remains of the old life

____ 3. In which of the following pairs of words is the second word similar to the first but with a more intense shade of meaning?
   a. grinned/smiled
   b. increased/grew
   c. misgivings/fears
   d. diminutive/small

____ 4. Why does Matt Two Bull want Norman to climb the butte?
   a. There are valuable stones there.
   b. He wants him to see how the valley looks from the top or the butte.
   c. He wants him to prove his courage and seek his vision, as young men did in the old times.
   d. He has dreamed that Norman will find something important there.

____ 5. Does Norman believe that there is a message in the thunder?
   a. He firmly believes there is a message in the thunder.
   b. He does not believe there is a message in the thunder.
   c. He doesn't really believe there is a message in the thunder, but he isn't sure.
   d. He believes there is a message in the thunder, but he doesn't want to admit to being superstitious.

____ 6. Which of the following words best describes the atmosphere created by this line from the story?

   He whistled, trying to echo the meadowlarks who were greeting the day with their happy song.

   a. tense   c. exciting
   b. suspenseful   d. cheerful

_____ 7. Norman's mother doesn't want the *coup* stick in the house because
   a. she doesn't like the way it looks
   b. she doesn't want any symbols of the old ways in her home
   c. she thinks it will bring bad luck
   d. women are not allowed to touch the *coup* stick

_____ 8. How does Norman feel about the *coup* stick at the end of the story?
   a. He is proud that he found it because it is a symbol of the old ways.
   b. He is sorry that he found it because it caused a problem in his family.
   c. He thinks it will bring good luck to his family.
   d. He fears that it will bring bad luck to his family.

_____ 9. In this story, which of the following does the author use to create an atmosphere of mystery?
   a. snakes   c. darkness
   b. thunder   d. wind

_____ 10. Why does Norman obey his grandfather's command?
   a. Norman has respect for the old ways, even though he doesn't really believe in them.
   b. Norman doesn't want his grandfather to be angry with him.
   c. Norman has always wanted to climb the butte.
   d. Norman thinks his grandfather is crazy.

_____ 11. Which word best describes the atmosphere created by this line in the story?

   He began rubbing the mare down as she munched the hay in her manger.

   a. sad and pessimistic
   b. happy and optimistic
   c. safe and comfortable
   d. mysterious and uncertain

_____ 12. Which of the following words has a stronger shade of meaning than the word *difficult*?
   a. challenging
   b. hard
   c. problematic
   d. tricky

_____ 13. Norman's grandfather has commanded Norman to
   a. climb Thunder Butte
   b. bring back the *coup* stick
   c. collect agates in a salt bag
   d. learn the ways of the old ones

_____ 14. How does Norman's father feel about the old ways?
   a. He doesn't believe in them, but he respects them.
   b. He thinks they are ridiculous and superstitious.
   c. He believes that the old ways are the best.
   d. He pretends to believe in them out of respect for his father.

_____ 15. Which of the following words has a shade of meaning that suggests greater carefulness than *looked at?*
   a. viewed
   b. saw
   c. glanced at
   d. examined

Vocabulary, Spelling, and Grammar

____ 16. Which of the following words best defines the word *adamant* in this passage?

> But Sarah was *adamant* ."Take it out of the house!" she ordered, pointing to the door.

    a. confused
    b. insistent
    c. depressed
    d. mean

____ 17. Which of the following words is spelled correctly?
    a. nieghbor
    b. greif
    c. conceited
    d. apeice

____ 18. In which of the following sentences is a possessive pronoun used as an adjective?
    a. Mom will be worried because I'm late now.
    b. His boots were worn and scuffed.
    c. It belongs to you.
    d. He crossed the creek south of where Matt Two Bull's tent was pitched...

____ 19. Which is the best synonym for the word *tiny* in this sentence?

> From the top of the butte, Norman's grandfather looked tiny.

    a. diminutive
    b. variegated
    c. adamant
    d. heathen

____ 20. Which word is modified by a possessive noun in this sentence?

> Her welcoming smile turned to a frown as she saw the coup stick in Norman's hand.

    a. smile
    b. frown
    c. hand
    d. stick

Essay Questions

21. Does Norman believe in the old ways of his people? Does he think the old ways are ridiculous? Is he confused about what to believe? Write an essay explaining Norman's feelings about the old ways of his people. Use quotations and examples from the story to support your ideas.

22. Write an essay expressing your opinion on the following question: Do you believe that it is important to preserve cultural traditions from the past; or do you believe old ways hold people back and isolate them from others, and it is therefore better to forget them? Support your opinion with examples from the story and from your own knowledge and experience.

23. Norman's father wants to hang the *coup* stick on the wall. Norman's mother doesn't want the *coup* stick in the house. In an essay, explain each character's feelings about the *coup* stick. Use examples and quotations from the story to back up your points. Conclude your essay by telling which character you agree with and why.

Name _____ Date _____

"**Mowgli's Brothers**" by Rudyard Kipling

Selection Test

Critical Reading

On the line, write the letter of the one best answer.

____ 1. Why do all the animals respect and obey the Law of the Jungle?
   a. The Law of the Jungle is considered sacred.
   b. If they do not obey all the laws, they will be punished.
   c. The Law of the Jungle protects the animals from human beings.
   d. The Law of the Jungle is for the safety and good of all the animals.

____ 2. What does Akela mean when he says, "Look well, O Wolves"?
   a. The wolves must always be on their guard, in case of an attack by another pack.
   b. The wolves must always pay attention to their leader.
   c. The wolves must recognize the wolf cubs so that they will not kill any cubs from their own pack.
   d. The wolves must always follow the Law of the Jungle.

____ 3. Some of the wolves predict that Mowgli will die in the winter rains or scorch in the sun. If you agreed with that prediction, which of the following details from the story would lead you to revise that prediction?
   a. Father Wolf tells Baloo to take Mowgli away and train him "as befits one of the Free People."
   b. Mowgli does not notice when the wolves come to look him over.
   c. Bagheera says to Shere Khan, ". . . the time comes when this naked thing will make thee roar to another tune, or I know nothing of man."
   d. Mother Wolf is ready to fight to the death for Mowgli's life.

____ 4. Mother and Father Wolf like Mowgli right away because
   a. Mowgli acts bold and brave
   b. Mowgli is helpless and defenseless
   c. Mowgli is very small
   d. Mowgli is afraid of Shere Khan

____ 5. Which quote from the story reveals that Tabaqui the jackal is insincere?
   a. . . . they may never forget the hungry in this world.
   b. Ye can hear Shere Khan below in the thickets.
   c. . . . a dry bone is a good feast.
   d. How beautiful are the noble children! How large their eyes!

____ 6. What is the real reason the Law of the Jungle forbids animals to kill human beings?
   a. The animals fear humans.
   b. The animals feel sorry for humans.
   c. The animals respect humans.
   d. The animals love humans.

____ 7. None of the wolves speaks in favor of accepting Mowgli into the Pack because
   a. the Pack has too many members already
   b. at the Pack Council, Mowgli does not show enough respect for Akela
   c. the wolves are suspicious of humans
   d. the young wolves want the price Bagheera will pay for Mowgli

8. Based on the description of Baloo the bear in the story, which of the following words best describes his human characteristics?
   a. shy and nervous
   b. gentle and wise
   c. clever and cunning
   d. strict and bossy

9. Which of the following details from the story would lead you to predict that, later in *The Jungle Book*, humans will come to hunt the animals in the jungle?
   a. Shere Khan burns his feet on the woodcutter's campfire.
   b. The Law of the Jungle never orders anything without a reason.
   c. The animals think that Man is weak and defenseless.
   d. Shere Khan has been hunting Man.

10. Which of the following quotes from the story show both human and animal characteristics in Father Wolf?
    a. I have to kill for two, these days.
    b. Out and hunt with thy master.
    c. "Man!" said Father Wolf, showing all his white teeth.
    d. Shere Khan does us great honor . . .

11. If a grown wolf of the Pack kills one of the Pack's young wolf cubs, the punishment is death. According to the story, " . . . if you think for a minute you will see that this must be so." Why is this so?
    a. The punishment for breaking any law is death.
    b. If young cubs are killed, the Pack will die out.
    c. The cubs are needed to help the Pack hunt.
    d. Each wolf family wants to protect its own cubs.

12. Father Wolf says that he could easily kill Mowgli. Which of the following details in the story leads you to predict that he will not do this?
    a. Mother Wolf says, "He shall not be killed. He shall live to run with the Pack and to hunt with the Pack . . ."
    b. Shere Khan says, "Each dog barks in his own yard!"
    c. Akela says, "Look well, O Wolves!"
    d. Bagheera says, ". . . he may make better sport for you when he is grown."

13. Based on the description of Bagheera the panther in the story, which of the following words best describes his human characteristics?
    a. beautiful but selfish
    b. honest but tricky
    c. charming but dangerous
    d. cowardly but cruel

14. Which of the following details in the story leads you to predict that, later in *The Jungle Book*, Mowgli will help the Pack?
    a. Shere Khan is angry that Mowgli has not been handed over to him.
    b. Akela says, "Men and their cubs are very wise. He may be a help in time."
    c. Baloo says, "Let him run with the Pack, and be entered with the others. I myself will teach him."
    d. Mowgli will want to repay Bagheera for buying his life.

15. What reason do the animals give for the law against killing humans?
    a. They say it is wrong because humans are superior to other animals.
    b. They say it is unsportsmanlike because humans are weak and defenseless.
    c. They say it is dangerous because humans have guns.
    d. They say it is the duty of animals to protect humans.

Vocabulary, Spelling, and Grammar

____ 16. Which question is answered by the adverb *never* in this sentence from the story?

The Law of the Jungle never orders anything without a reason.

a. When?   c. Where?
b. How?   d. To what extent?

____ 17. Which of the following words is the best synonym for *fostering* in this sentence?

We will see what the pack will say to this *fostering* of man cubs.

a. taking care   c. hunting
b. killing   d. identifying

____ 18. How should you correct this sentence?

The Free People are only loyal to there own.

a. Change *there* to *they are.*
b. Change *there* to *they're.*
c. Change *there* to *their.*
d. The sentence is correct as written.

____ 19. Which word is an adverb in this sentence?

Look, he has pushed one of my babies to one side already.

a. Look   c. one
b. pushed   d. already

____ 20. Which of the following words means most nearly the opposite of *dispute*?
a. argument   c. conversation
b. agreement   d. misunderstanding

Essay Questions

21. In "Mowgli's Brothers," the author provides several details that lead readers to predict what will happen to Mowgli later on. In an essay, predict one or two events that might happen after the end of "Mowgli's Brothers." Each of your predictions must be logical and based on actual quotes or details from the story. Begin your essay by stating your predictions. Then explain the reasons for your predictions, using examples from the story to support your ideas.

22. The animal characters in "Mowgli's Brothers" have human characteristics. Write an essay in which you compare and contrast the human characteristics of one of the following pairs: Mother Wolf and Father Wolf, Bagheera the Black Panther and Baloo the Brown Bear, Shere Khan and Tabaqui. First identify the characters you are comparing and contrasting. Then explain at least one way in which they are similar and one way in which they are different. Support your analysis with examples from the story.

23. In an essay, discuss the pros and cons, or the advantages and disadvantages, of the Pack's decision to accept Mowgli. Back up your opinions with details from the story and your own logical reasoning. You may also use logical predictions about future events to back up your opinions. Be sure to support your predictions with specific details from the story. Conclude your essay by writing whether, in your view, the Pack made the right decision.

"Names/Nombres" by Julia Alvarez
"The Southpaw" by Judith Viorst
"Alone in the Nets" by Arnold Adoff

Selection Test

Critical Reading

On the line, write the letter of the one best answer.

_____ 1. According to Julia Alvarez's descriptions in "Names/Nombres," her family was
    a. divided by a long-standing feud   c. very formal and proper
    b. average and ordinary   d. large, close, and caring

_____ 2. According to the passage from "Names/Nombres," how did Julia Alvarez feel about her last name when she arrived in New York City as a young girl?

> I was too afraid we wouldn't be let in if I corrected the man's pronunciation, but I said our name to myself, opening my mouth wide for the organ blast of the *a*, trilling my tongue for the drumroll of the *r*, *All-vah-rrr-es*! How could anyone get *Elbures* out of that orchestra of sound?

    a. She felt that it was too long and foreign sounding.
    b. She was afraid that she would be confused with someone else because the name was so common.
    c. She felt that it was beautiful and rich sounding.
    d. She felt proud because her family was famous in the country that they had come from.

_____ 3. In "Names/Nombres," how does Julia react when her high school friends call her Jules, Hey Jude, and Judy Alcatraz?
    a. She feels embarrassed and ashamed. c. She feels popular and accepted.
    b. She feels proud.   d. She feels insulted.

_____ 4. Read the following passage from "Names/Nombres." Then choose the statement that best summarizes Julia's perspective at this point.

> Our first few years in the States, though, ethnicity was not yet "in." Those were the blond, blue-eyed, bobby sock years of junior high and high school before the 60's ushered in peasant blouses, hoop earring, serapes. My initial desire to be known by my correct Dominican name faded. I just wanted to be Judy and merge with the Sallys and Janes in my class.

    a. She feels uncomfortable because of all the pressure to look, talk, and act just like everyone else.
    b. She would rather fit in with a group than stand out in a crowd.
    c. She is embarrassed by the nickname Judy, because she thinks it sounds childish.
    d. She thinks that she will fit in better if she wears "ethnic" clothing.

_____ 5. In "Names/Nombres," how do Julia Alvarez's parents react to her interest in reading and writing stories and poems?
    a. They are unaware of her interest.
    b. They try to discourage her interest.
    c. They try to encourage her interest.
    d. They are puzzled by her interest.

_____ 6. In "The Southpaw," Richard and Janet disagree about
   I.   whether Richard is a good baseball player
   II. whether Janet should be allowed to play on the Mapes Street baseball team
   III. whether girls should be allowed to play on the Mapes Street baseball team
   IV. whether Janet should replace Richard as the captain of the Mapes Street base-ball team
   a. II only   b. II and III   c. I and IV   d. IV only

_____ 7. Which of the following best explains why Richard changes his mind in "The Southpaw"?
   a. He feels guilty about the fact that girls have never been allowed to play on his team.
   b. He is afraid that Janet and her friends will form a team of their own.
   c. His team experiences eight straight losses, and Janet begins to show signs of wanting to end their quarrel.
   d. His father convinces him that he has been treating Janet unfairly.

_____ 8. Which of Richard's statements in "The Southpaw" reveals the real issue behind his quarrel with Janet?
   a. Here is your stupid Disneyland sweatshirt, if that's how you're going to be.
   b. I want my comic books now—finished or not.
   c. No girl has ever played on the Mapes Street baseball team, and as long as I'm captain, no girl ever will.
   d. I hope when you go for your checkup you need a tetanus shot.

_____ 9. The title "The Southpaw" refers to
   a. Janet   c. Janet's favorite major-league baseball player
   b. Richard   d. Richard's favorite major-league baseball player

_____ 10. In "The Southpaw," what closing does Janet use in her last letter to Richard?
   a. Your friend,   b. Your enemy,   c. Your former friend,   d. Your teammate,

_____ 11. In "Alone in the Nets," which of the following events shows that the speaker does not have much confidence?
   a. She is guarding her team's net.
   b. She waits too long before falling onto the soccer ball.
   c. She avoids describing the other team, especially the lead forward.
   d. She asks many questions, ending with "Why am I here?"

_____ 12. Which sentence best describes how well the speaker's team is doing in "Alone in the Nets"?
   a. The speaker's team is playing well.
   b. The speaker's team is playing its best, but the other team is playing better.
   c. The speaker's team is playing badly.
   d. The speaker's team will probably win.

_____ 13. What is the purpose of these lines from "Alone in the Nets"?

   But Frozen Moments Can Unfreeze and I Can Stretch
   and reach for the ball flying to the corner of
                                                    our
                                                    goal.

   a. They suggest that the speaker's team is going to win the game.
   b. They show a turning point in the speaker's thoughts.
   c. They emphasize the meaning of the poem's title.
   d. They contrast with the attitude of the other team.

_____ 14. "Alone in the Nets" is told from the perspective of
  a. the defending fullback on the team that is playing badly
  b. the lead forward on the team that is playing well
  c. the coaches of the two soccer teams
  d. the goalie on the team that is playing badly

Vocabulary, Spelling, and Grammar

_____ 15. When you transport an item, you _____ it.
  a. change   c. buy
  b. lose   d. move

_____ 16. Which word means "belonging to you"?
  a. you's   c. you
  b. your   d. you're

_____ 17. Which sentence contains an adverb modifying an adjective?
  a. She sings very beautifully.   c. That song is totally unforgettable.
  b. Does she perform often?   d. There was a hushed silence throughout the
                                          concert.

_____ 18. How should you correct this sentence?

    If you want to be a good athlete, your going to have to learn teamwork.

  a. Change *your* to *you.*
  b. Change *you* to *your.*
  c. Change *your* to *you're.*
  d. The sentence is correct as written.

_____ 19. A scene that is *chaotic* is
  a. confused and disorderly   c. sad and mournful
  b. calm and soothing   d. realistic and true-to-life

_____ 20. In which sentence is the underlined word an adverb that modifies another adverb?
  a. She pitches <u>very</u> skillfully.   c. We enjoyed the game <u>immensely</u>.
  b. He is an <u>extremely</u> fast runner. d. I was so <u>sorry</u> when it ended.

Essay Questions

21. Choose either "Names/Nombres" or "The Southpaw" and explain in an essay how a character in the work chooses his or her own way of joining a group. Clearly identify the character and the nature of the group. Use details from the selection to support your description of the choice or choices that the character makes.

22. Choose one of the selections and explain in an essay how reading the work helped you consider a point of view different from your own. Summarize an important event from the selection and indicate the character or characters from whose point of view you saw the event. Discuss your own reactions to the characters' thoughts and feelings about the event.

23. In all three works, characters experience changes in their perspectives, or the ways that they see events. Choose one of the works and describe the change that occurs in the perspective of one or more of the characters involved. Also explain the reasons behind the change in perspective, using details from the selection to support your points.

"Adventures of Isabel" by Ogden Nash
"I'll Stay" by Gwendolyn Brooks
"Wilbur Wright and Orville Wright"
by Rosemary and Stephen Vincent Benét
"Dream Dust" by Langston Hughes

Selection Test

Critical Reading

On the line, write the letter of the one best answer.

____ 1. In "Adventures of Isabel," how is the doctor unlike Isabel's other enemies—the talking bear, the witch, and the giant?
   a. The doctor is nice to Isabel.   c. The doctor is the tallest.
   b. Isabel is most afraid of the doctor.   d. The doctor could be real.

____ 2. In "Adventures of Isabel," each character threatens to do something terrible to Isabel. What does the doctor threaten to do?
   a. make her swallow pills   c. send her to the hospital
   b. give her an injection   d. make her sick

____ 3. In "Adventures of Isabel," before Isabel eats up the bear, she washes her hands and straightens up her hair. Based on these examples, which pair of words below does not characterize Isabel?
   a. neat and efficient   c. determined and patient
   b. calm and confident   d. conceited and disrespectful

____ 4. In "I'll Stay," why does the speaker like the plates on the ledge of the dining room wall?
   a. The plates seem confident because they are balanced on a narrow ledge and do not fall.
   b. The plates seem efficient because they are lined up neatly and are never out of order.
   c. The speaker likes the color and design of the plates.
   d. The plates seem to have courage because they are delicately balanced on such a narrow ledge.

____ 5. What is the meaning of this stanza from "I'll Stay"?

   My name will be Up in Lights!/ I believe it! / They will know me as Nora-the-Wonderful! / It will happen! / I'll stay.

   a. The speaker hopes that she will be allowed to stay.
   b. The speaker is conceited, in addition to being confident.
   c. The speaker gives an example of how confident she is.
   d. The speaker wants to be an actor when she grows up.

____ 6. From the context, you can tell that when the speaker in "I'll Stay" talks about "shouting," she is referring to
   a. making an announcement
   b. being angry
   c. trying to get other people to listen to her
   d. expressing her happiness

_____ 7. What is the best meaning for the title "Dream Dust"?
   a. a person's hopes and dreams
   b. hopes and dreams that have come to nothing
   c. the dreams we remember when we wake up
   d. the dreams we don't remember

_____ 8. From the context, you can tell that in "Dream Dust," the "splinters" of hail are
   a. harmful weapons   b. broken hearts   c. specks of dirt   d. small pieces

_____ 9. What main message does the speaker in "Dream Dust" express to the reader?
   a. The best dreams are inspired by nature.
   b. You must work all your life to gather just a handful of dreams.
   c. Don't let go of your dreams.
   d. "Star-dust" dreams are better than any other kind of dream.

_____ 10. In "Wilbur Wright and Orville Wright," which sentence best describes the relationship between the two brothers?
   a. They enjoy competing with one another.
   b. They support and encourage one another.
   c. They help each other with constructive criticism.
   d. They enjoy traveling together.

_____ 11. Orville Wright says that the birds are "trying." Given the context, which of the following is _not_ the approximate meaning of _trying_?
   a. "bothersome"   b. "irritating"   c. "ambitious"   d. "annoying"

_____ 12. Which of the following best expresses the main idea of "Wilbur Wright and Orville Wright"?
   a. Although the Wright brothers were injured many times, they were not afraid of the dangers of flying.
   b. Although they failed many times, Wilbur and Orville Wright remained devoted to each other.
   c. Although many famous people will be forgotten, the Wright brothers will always be remembered.
   d. After many attempts, the Wright brothers finally succeeded in building an airplane that could fly.

_____ 13. In the use of stanza form, how is "Dream Dust" different from the other three poems?
   a. "Dream Dust" is only a list of words; the others are expressed in sentences.
   b. "Dream Dust" consists of only one stanza; the others have several stanzas.
   c. "Dream Dust" brings out strong emotions in the reader; the others are not emotional poems.
   d. "Dream Dust" has no rhyme scheme; the others have the same rhyme scheme.

Vocabulary, Spelling, and Grammar

_____ 14. If someone is _ravenous_, that person is feeling
   a. very angry   b. very nervous   c. very brave   d. very hungry

_____ 15. How is the italicized word in this sentence used?

   Swallow this—it will make you _well_.

   a. _Well_ is an adjective because it modifies the pronoun _you_.
   b. _Well_ is an adjective because it modifies the pronoun _it_.
   c. _Well_ is an adverb because it modifies the verb _make_.
   d. _Well_ is an adverb because it modifies the verb _swallow_.

_____ 16. In "Adventures of Isabel," Isabel showed no rage or *rancor* toward the witch. The best synonym for *rancor* is
  a. anger
  b. friendliness
  c. feelings
  d. pity

_____ 17. How is the italicized word in this sentence used?

  And so they built a glider, *first*.

  a. *First* is an adverb because it answers the question "How many?"
  b. *First* is an adverb because it answers the question "When?"
  c. *First* is an adjective because it modifies the pronoun *they*.
  d. *First* is an adjective because it modifies the noun *glider*.

_____ 18. Which sentence uses the word *grant* in the same way as it is used in these lines from "Wilbur Wright and Orville Wright"?

  A bird has feathers, it is true. / That much I freely *grant*.

  a. The millionaire gave a generous *grant* to the university.
  b. We are going to *grant* my grandmother's antique books to the library.
  c. I *grant* that your answer was correct.
  d. Will you *grant* me a favor?

_____ 19. Why is the italicized word in this line an adjective?

  They ran a *dusty* little shop

  a. The word *dusty* modifies the pronoun *they* and answers the question "Where?"
  b. The word *dusty* modifies the verb *ran* and answers the question "To what extent?"
  c. The word *dusty* modifies the noun *shop* and answers the question "What kind?"
  d. The word *dusty* modifies the verb *ran* and answers the question "How?"

_____ 20. Which of the following italicized words is not spelled correctly?
  a. The view of the lake was *gorgeous*.
  b. I think strawberries are *luscious*.
  c. Thank you for your *gracious* hospitality.
  d. Be *cautous* when you cross a busy street.

Essay Questions

21. Choose two of the following: Isabel in "Adventures of Isabel," the speaker in "I'll Stay," the speaker in "Dream Dust," or Wilbur and Orville in "Wilbur Wright and Orville Wright." Write an essay in which you compare and contrast why the characters are or will be successful. Begin by showing similar successful qualities shared by the characters in the two poems; then show their different successful qualities. Use examples from the poems to support your ideas.

22. The first three stanzas of "Adventures of Isabel" may remind you of fairy tales you have read in which the main character is threatened by an evil magical character—a talking animal, a wicked witch, or a scary giant. In an essay, choose one of these stanzas and compare and contrast what happens in the poem with what would happen in a typical fairy tale. Support your analysis with examples from the selection.

23. What is Langston Hughes's message in the poem "Dream Dust"? In an essay, explain what Hughes is saying about dreams. Support your interpretation with examples from the poem. Conclude your essay by explaining why you agree or disagree with the poet's thoughts about dreams.

Unit 3: Proving Yourself

Unit Test

Critical Reading

On the line, write the letter of the one best answer.

____ 1. In *The Pigman & Me*, what is an example of an internal conflict?
   a. Paul's refusal to give his paddle to John
   b. Moose's demand that John hit Paul some more
   c. Paul's unwillingness to fight John or look like a coward
   d. Paul's sister's fighting to protect her brother

____ 2. In *The Pigman & Me*, who is not happy when the fight ends quickly?
   a. Moose   c. Jennifer
   b. John   d. Paul

____ 3. In *The Pigman & Me*, John wants to fight Paul because
   a. John loves to fight
   b. Paul is new at the school
   c. John wants to give Paul a black eye like the one Paul gave him
   d. John feels he has to fight or look bad in front of the other kids

____ 4. Which of the following words completes this sentence with the most forceful shade of meaning?

   "Last night he had accepted his grandfather's _____ to go to the Thunder Butte without too many doubts.

   a. command   c. request
   b. words   d. instruction

____ 5. In "Thunder Butte," Norman's mother has no use for the old ways because
   a. they show no respect for women
   b. she feels that they are not appropriate for living in the modern world
   c. it embarrasses her that members of her family pay attention to them
   d. she does not like her father-in-law

____ 6. In "Thunder Butte," Norman's grandfather tells him that, in the old days, the most important factor by which a warrior was judged was
   a. the number of enemies he killed
   b. what family he came from
   c. the acts of bravery he performed
   d. his feats of strength

____ 7. In "Mowgli's Brothers," what kind of person is Shere Khan most like?
   a. a bully   c. a scholar
   b. a warrior   d. a leader

____ 8. In "Mowgli's Brothers," Mother Wolf is fiercer than Father Wolf toward Shere Khan because
   a. female wolves are always fiercer
   b. she cares more about Mowgli than her mate does
   c. she is defending her cubs
   d. she dislikes Shere Khan more than Father Wolf does

_____ 9. In "Mowgli's Brothers," the wolves make their decisions as a group because
  a. they have learned about democracy from human beings
  b. Akela has commanded them to
  c. they are the smartest animals in the jungle
  d. unlike the other animals mentioned, wolves live in packs

_____ 10. What is the main purpose of writing the title "Names/Nombres" in two languages?
  a. to ensure that both English and Spanish speakers will be able to understand it
  b. to show that the author has a Latin American heritage
  c. to show that the author can speak both Spanish and English
  d. to show that the author feels split between two cultures

_____ 11. In "Names/Nombres," Julia is reluctant to reveal that her family originally came from the Dominican Republic
  a. because of her father's involvement in politics there
  b. because she does not want to feel exotic and "different"
  c. because she actually was born in New York
  d. because she is ashamed of her heritage

_____ 12. In "The Southpaw," which line of Janet's first suggests that she is feeling less angry?
  a. I wasn't kicking exactly. I was kicking back.
  b. Nobody ever said that I was unreasonable.
  c. Congratulations on your unbroken record.
  d. Sorry about your 12-game losing streak.

_____ 13. By reading "Alone in the Nets," you can see that Arnold Adoff's main purpose is to
  a. tell a very funny story from his childhood
  b. show the wandering but inspiring thoughts of a lonely fisherman
  c. describe the conflict between opposing athletes
  d. explore the conflicting thoughts in one athlete's mind

_____ 14. How is the narrator's perspective in "Alone in the Nets" different from that of the narrator in "The Southpaw"?
  a. "Alone in the Nets" has a third-person narrator; "The Southpaw" has a first-person narrator.
  b. "Alone in the Nets" has two narrators; "The Southpaw" has only one.
  c. "Alone in the Nets" has a first-person narrator; "The Southpaw" has no narrator.
  d. "Alone in the Nets" has a first-person narrator; "The Southpaw" has two first-person narrators.

_____ 15. In the poem "Adventures of Isabel," Isabel defeats all her opponents because
  a. she is confident and self-reliant
  b. she is smarter than they are
  c. she is nicer than they are
  d. she is braver than they are

_____ 16. In the poem "I'll Stay," the speaker's mother
  a. thinks her child is overconfident
  b. gives her child encouragement
  c. worries that her child may be disappointed later in life
  d. pushes her child to be a star

_____ 17. "Dream Dust" is a poem about
  a. the empty feeling we have after awakening from a wonderful dream
  b. ways in which famous people achieved their goals long ago
  c. gathering and treasuring one's hopes and goals
  d. the sadness of seeing your dreams fail to come true

____ 18. In these lines from "Wilbur Wright and Orville Wright," how does the context help you understand the meaning of *ran*?

> They ran a dusty little shop
> For bicycle repairing,

   a. The Wrights needed to go to a bicycle shop to buy parts in order to repair their plane.
   b. Everywhere the Wrights went, they ran.
   c. The Wrights were afraid of a store that repaired bicycles.
   d. The Wrights owned a store in which they repaired bicycles.

____ 19. One message of "Wilbur Wright and Orville Wright" is "Don't let your doubts hold you back," which is most like the message of
   a. "Thunder Butte"   c. "Dream Dust"
   b. "Alone in the Nets"   d. "Mowgli and His Brothers"

Vocabulary, Spelling, and Grammar

____ 20. Which is the adverb in the sentence?

> The suitcase was too heavy for me to lift by myself.

   a. heavy   c. suitcase
   b. was   d. too

____ 21. What is the *initial* word of this question?
   a. question   b. What
   c. this   d. initial

____ 22. Which of the following words is misspelled?
   a. discussion   c. dimention
   b. rotation   d. expression

____ 23. Which sentence does not contain an article?
   a. We saw Mr. Lee feeding bread to dozens of pigeons.
   b. The ship sailed out of the harbor while she watched from the pier.
   c. Every week, our family used to go to the same restaurant for dinner.
   d. His teacher wants him to spend an hour each night studying science.

____ 24. Which word is most nearly the opposite of *boring*?
   a. unusual   c. monotonous
   b. difficult   d. interesting

____ 25. What is the function of the word *cautiously* in the following sentence?

> Norman reached cautiously for the odd-looking stick.

   a. It is an adjective that modifies the word *Norman*.
   b. It is an adverb that modifies the word *looking*.
   c. It is an adverb that modifies the word *reached*.
   d. It is an adjective that modifies the word *stick*.

____ 26. Which of the following words is spelled correctly
   a. deceitful   c. theif
   b. nieghborhood   d. cieling

____ 27. Which sentence shows an adverb modifying an adjective?
   a. Richard found Janet's note in the early afternoon.
   b. As he read her message, he became quite angry.
   c. Quickly, he wrote a heated reply.
   d. "The Southpaw" is the clever story of their war of letters.

_____ 28. Which things would a person who is *ravenous* want to do most?
    a. go to sleep   c. put on heavier clothes
    b. apologize   d. eat a big meal

_____ 29. How should you correct this sentence?

      The Wrights are working on they're airplane, and I know there going to succeed.

    a. Change *there* to *they're*.
    b. Change *they're* to *their* and *there* to *they're*.
    c. Change *they're* to *their*.
    d. Change *they're* to *there* and *there* to *their*.

_____ 30. Which word is an adverb?
    a. really   b. silly   c. friendly   d. ugly

Essay Questions

31. What does it mean to "prove yourself"? Is it a matter of proving to others that you should be accepted into their group? Or must you prove to *yourself* that you can meet a challenge? Perhaps both answers are true. Consider Paul in *The Pigman & Me*, Norman in "Thunder Butte," and Julia in "Names/Nombres." Choose *two* of these characters and write an essay explaining what each character does to prove himself or herself. Support your explanation with details from the selections.

32. As we grow older, we face new challenges. How should we meet them? In an essay, explain how two of the following poems might offer useful messages to readers preparing to face a challenge: "Alone in the Nets," "I'll Stay," "Dream Dust" and "Wilbur Wright and Orville Wright." For each poem you choose, summarize the message that a reader might find in it; then show how the reader might use it to overcome a challenge. Support your conclusions with details from the selections.

33. One important challenge many people face, both in real life and in fiction, is to be accepted into a group. In an essay, describe the groups into which two of the following characters seek acceptance: Paul in The Pigman & Me, Mowgli in "Mowgli and His Brothers," and Norman in "Thunder Butte." Compare and contrast the characters, explaining why it is important to each to be accepted, and the process by which each is judged in the story. Use details from the stories to support your conclusions.

34. Two qualities that are valuable to anyone who faces a serious challenge are self-reliance and confidence. In an essay, evaluate the extent to which two of the following characters have these qualities: Paul in *The Pigman & Me*, Mowgli in "Mowgli and His Brothers," and Janet in "The Southpaw." Finish your essay by comparing the two characters and concluding which, if either, is more self-reliant or more confident than the other. Use details from the selections to support your conclusions.

35. Authors have various ways of showing the reader how their characters regard the need to prove themselves. Consider the following selections: *The Pigman & Me*, "Thunder Butte," and "Names/Nombres." Write an essay analyzing the techniques used by two of the authors to show the difficulty of the challenges their characters face and how the characters are affected by having to meet these challenges. Consider the following questions in preparing your essay: Do the authors concentrate on the difficulties and dangers of the challenges themselves, on their effects on the characters' thoughts and feelings, or on both? Compare and contrast the ways in which the two authors deal with this problem. If you choose one selection that is a first-person narrative and one that is third-person, analyze the ways in which the two kinds of narrative affect the author's technique in demonstrating the seriousness of the challenge. Use details from the selections to support your conclusions.

Unit 3: Proving Yourself

Alternative Unit Test

The two passages below are followed by questions based on their content and on the relationship between the two passages.

Passage 1

This is an excerpt from a true story about one person's encounter with a fox.

from *Wild Fox* by Cherie Macon

I live on Deer Isle off the coast of Maine. Red foxes also live on the island, but it's not often that you get to see one. So it was a happy surprise one summer day to find a fox pup sitting in the middle of my strawberries, calmly chomping, looking right at me. I called softly, "Hi, there! And what do you think you're doing?"

The little fox continued nibbling, dipped down for another juicy berry, and trotted off. There was something about his face that stuck in my mind. Six months later, when that berry patch was buried under dazzling February snow, I happened to look out my kitchen window and was totally startled to see what looked like a broad orange crayon mark against the white. It was a lean red fox standing on his hind legs, reaching up toward a hanging birch log studded with suet for the woodpeckers.

Of course, I was delighted to see a wild animal out in the open during the daytime. But as I looked more closely, I winced. The fox's right front leg was nearly severed above the small black foot. I had seen steel-jaw leghold traps, but this was the first time I had seen their cruel work. Inch by inch, hour after hour, this poor young fox must have struggled to wrench his leg from the powerful grip of a trap.

Some chicken for our dinner lay defrosting on the kitchen counter. Quickly I grabbed a drumstick and ran outside. The fox bounded off in a three-legged hobble, so I put the food down on the ground and went back into the house to watch. After about ten minutes he cautiously returned, devoured the chicken, and limped off into the woods. Seeing his inquisitive, handsome face reminded me of the summer pup. I was pretty sure this was the same fox. I waited and watched all day for him to return, but darkness came, and no fox.

Passage 2

Fourteen-year-old June has just arrived at her family's summer home. She is determined to teach her pet falcon, Zander, to come for food when called.

from *The Summer of the Falcon* by Jean Craighead George

Late in the afternoon when the suitcases were unpacked and the fresh sheets spread on all the sun-aired beds, June stood before her falcon holding the lure. She whistled. Zander did not come. She whistled again and waited. It was almost dinner time when the hungry bird finally leaped on the air and winged to her hand to be fed.

"Now let's be faster tomorrow, Zander," she said.

The next night and the next night told the same tiresome story. He would not fly immediately, but sat and looked at the robins and bees.

During the winter June had handed Zander his food. Now she had to break him of expecting food without flying for it—and it was boring work. She would bring a pillow and sit in the yard, whistling and holding up her hand until it ached. She was taunted by voices laughing at the creek's edge and the sound of canoe paddles thumping gunnels. She wanted to run and play, but instead she tried to close her ears and concentrate on Zander.

"Come on, come on," she coaxed. "Please fly!" But the stubborn bird took his time. He would even lower his body, get ready to fly, and then straighten up and look at a moth in the air. After an hour he would answer her call, as he learned once again that the whistle meant food.

June was slowly understanding that to train a falcon was to play "come and be rewarded." A whistle is given, the bird flies. He is rewarded. This happens again and again, until the whistle is imprinted in his mind so deeply that when the bird hears it, without thinking "whistle equals food," he spreads his wings and answers the sound.

Critical Reading

On the line, write the letter of the one best answer.

_____ 1. Which of the details below proves that the atmosphere of Passage 1 is quieter and lonelier than the atmosphere of Passage 2?
  a. I waited and watched all day for him to return, but darkness came, and no fox.
  b. . . . She was taunted by voices laughing at the creek's edge . . .
  c. The next night and the next night told the same tiresome story.
  d. . . . June stood before her falcon holding the lure.
  e. "Now let's be faster tomorrow, Zander," she said.

_____ 2. For which purpose might you read both passages?
  a. information about training animals
  b. enjoyment of the author's descriptive language
  c. insight into the narrator's feelings towards animals
  d. information about animal behavior
  e. insight into a relationship between two characters

_____ 3. The statement that best compares or contrasts the perspectives of the narrators in these two passages is
  a. Both narrators present events from their own personal perspectives.
  b. The narrator of Passage 1 presents an event from her own personal perspective; the narrator of Passage 2 presents an event from a character's perspective.
  c. Both narrators present an event from the perspectives of fictional characters.
  d. The narrator of Passage 1 presents her story from the perspective of an animal, while the narrator of Passage 2 presents a story from the perspective of a person.
  e. Each narrator present an event from the perspective of an animal.

_____ 4. Knowledge about which subject would help you predict how the passages will end?
  a. the geography of the coast of Maine
  b. how birds fly
  c. hunting and trapping
  d. the physical characteristics of birds and mammals
  e. animal behavior

_____ 5. Which of the following traits are shared by the narrator in Passage 1 and June in Passage 2?
  a. fear   c. patience   e. humor
  b. anger   d. courage

_____ 6. In Passage 2, June is said to be "taunted." The context helps you know that *taunted* means "teased" or "tormented" because
   a. Jane is working with Zander while people nearby are having fun
   b. Zander is not quick about learning to come when June whistles for him
   c. Jane is having to hold up her hand for Zander and her arm aches
   d. people are watching and making jokes about her efforts
   e. June senses that Zander would rather fly free

_____ 7. Which of the following statements best describes how the relationships between the animal and the human being differ in the two passages?
   a. In Passage 1, the narrator is kind to the fox; in Passage 2, June is cruel to the falcon.
   b. In Passage 1, the fox likes the narrator; in Passage 2, the falcon dislikes its owner.
   c. In Passage 1, the narrator wants to help the fox; in Passage 2, June wants to control Zander.
   d. The falcon in Passage 2 is more stubborn than the fox in Passage 1.
   e. The fox in Passage 1 is easier to train than the falcon in Passage 2.

_____ 8. In Passage 1, which three words give different shades of meaning to the fox's eating habits?
   a. *sampled, nibbling,* and *wolfed*   d. *trotted, bounded,* and *limped*
   b. *chomping, nibbling,* and *devoured*   e. *chomping, swallowing,* and *gulping*
   c. *licked, crunched,* and *devoured*

_____ 9. Which of the following statements best explains why the animal in each passage does not behave as the human wants it to?
   a. The fox is wounded; the falcon is dangerous.
   b. The fox is wild; the falcon is tame.
   c. The fox does not understand humans; the falcon has trouble flying.
   d. The falcon needs more training; the fox doesn't trust humans.
   e. The falcon is easily distracted; the fox is hungry.

_____ 10. Which of the following details from Passage 1 shows that the narrator understands the behavior of wild animals?
   a. The fox bounded off in a three-legged hobble, so I put the food down on the ground and went back into the house to watch.
   b. There was something about his face that stuck in my mind.
   c. I live on Deer Isle off the coast of Maine.
   d. It was a lean red fox standing on his hind legs.
   e. Red foxes also live on the island, but it's not often that you get to see one.

_____ 11. Which of the following questions would it be impossible for the narrator of Passage 1 to answer?
   a. Will the fox come back?   d. What color is the fox?
   b. Is the fox hungry?   e. Is the fox afraid of humans?
   c. How did the fox hurt its leg?

_____ 12. In Passage 1, the fox pup continues eating strawberries, even when he sees and hears the narrator. Later, the same fox is afraid to take chicken from the narrator. Which sentence best explains this change in the fox's behavior?
   a. In the summer, food was more plentiful than in the winter.
   b. Being trapped and wounded has taught the fox to fear.
   c. The fox would rather eat berries than meat.
   d. The fox has been kept in a cage all winter.
   e. The fox is afraid that the narrator will shoot him.

_____ 13. When a falcon is finally trained, it no longer needs food as a lure to fly at the sound of a whistle. How is this explained in Passage 2?
  a. The falcon wants to please its owner.
  b. The falcon gets more food to eat, so it doesn't need food as a lure.
  c. The falcon gets so used to flying when it hears a whistle, it no longer needs food as a lure.
  d. The sound of a whistle sounds like the call of another falcon.
  e. The falcon finally understands that its owner is in complete control.

_____ 14. Which of the following sentences best describes June's internal conflict in Passage 2?
  a. June wants to give Zander his food, but only when the bird is hungry.
  b. June enjoys having a falcon, but doesn't like having to take care of it.
  c. June commands Zander to fly for his food, but Zander refuses to obey.
  d. June would rather be at home than at her family's summer house.
  e. June wants to have fun with the other children, but she wants to concentrate on training Zander.

_____ 15. In Passage 2, June and her family arrive at the summer house late in the afternoon. Which detail in the passage tells you how long she waits for Zander to come to her on that day?
  a. . . . the suitcases were unpacked and the fresh sheets spread.
  b. . . . June stood before her falcon holding the lure.
  c. She whistled again and waited.
  d. It was almost dinner time when the hungry bird finally leaped on the air and winged to her hand to be fed.
  e. She whistled. Zander did not come.

Essay Questions

16. Passage 1 relates how the narrator began a relationship with a wild fox. Passage 2 describes how a girl builds a relationship with a tamed falcon. Even if you've never made friends with an injured wild animal or trained a falcon, any experience you've had with animals will add to your appreciation of both passages. In an essay, describe in detail an experience you have had with an animal. If you prefer, describe such an experience you've heard about or read about. Then explain how having or hearing about this experience helped you understand how both the narrator of Passage 1 and June in Passage 2 feel about the animals in the passages.

17. Both Passage 1 and Passage 2 are about animals and the humans who relate to them. The fox in Passage 1, however, is a wild animal, while the falcon in Passage 2 is an animal that has been tamed as a pet. Each author has created an atmosphere appropriate to the animals on which the passage focuses. In an essay, explain how the author of Passage 1 creates a very natural atmosphere, while the author of Passage 2 creates a homier, more domestic atmosphere. Use specific quotations and details from the passages to support your points.

18. In many works of literature that center on animals, a broader meaning beyond the literal level can be found by applying ideas about animals to humans. Both Passage 1 and Passage 2 focus on the relationship between a human and an animal. In an essay, compare and contrast these relationships, first focusing on the literal level of meaning in each passage; then explaining what you interpret to be the broader meaning of each passage.

"Lob's Girl" by Joan Aiken
"The Tiger Who Would Be King" by James Thurber
"The Lion and the Bulls" by Aesop

Selection Test

Critical Reading

On the line, write the letter of the one best answer.

_____ 1. In "Lob's Girl," Lob is wet when he comes to the hospital to see Sandy because
    a. he has had to swim to get there
    b. it has been raining constantly
    c. he is covered with blood
    d. he was buried at sea

_____ 2. In "Lob's Girl," the character trait that Lob best represents is
    a. bravery   c. intelligence
    b. loyalty   d. gentleness

_____ 3. What does the following passage from "Lob's Girl" foreshadow?

> One evening in October all the summer visitors had left, and the little fishing town looked empty and secretive. It was a wet, windy dusk.

    a. It is going to rain.
    b. Winter will come shortly.
    c. Lob will start to miss Mr. Dodsworth.
    d. Something bad is going to take place.

_____ 4. In "Lob's Girl," the hospital officials allow Lob to be brought to Sandy because
    a. they think that she is likely to die
    b. they feel sorry for the dog
    c. they think his presence will make Sandy wake up
    d. they feel sorry for Granny Pearce

_____ 5. Which of the following details in this passage foreshadows future developments in the story?

> She picked up a bit of driftwood and threw it. Lob, whisking easily out of his master's grip, was after it like a sand-colored bullet. He came back with the stick, beaming, and gave it to Sandy. At the same time he gave himself although no one was aware of this at the time.

    a. She picked up a bit of driftwood and threw it.
    b. Lob, whisking easily out of his master's grip, was after it like a sand-colored bullet.
    c. He came back with the stick, beaming, and gave it to Sandy.
    d. At the same time he gave himself . . .

_____ 6. In "Lob's Girl," Sandy ends up in the hospital because
    a. she catches the flu after a swim in the ocean
    b. she falls down the steps to the beach and breaks her leg
    c. she is hit by a truck on the steep hill outside her house
    d. she is visiting her Aunt Rebecca

_____ 7. In "Lob's Girl," Lob wants to stay with the Pengellys because
        a. he feels an attachment to Sandy
        b. they spoil him
        c. he likes living near the sea
        d. Mr. Dodsworth is cruel to him

_____ 8. In "Lob's Girl," what two things are mentioned that might make Sandy a more appropriate owner for Lob than Mr. Dodsworth?

        I. Sandy is younger and more able to play with Lob than Mr. Dodsworth.
        II. Sandy is a nicer person than Mr. Dodsworth.
        III. Mr. Dodsworth lives in a city and Sandy lives where there is more open country.
        IV. Sandy is more experienced with dogs than Mr. Dodsworth.

        a. II and IV   c. I and III
        b. I and III   d. I and IV

_____ 9. Which statement by the tiger in "The Tiger Who Would Be King" foreshadows his failure to win a meaningful victory?
        a. When the moon rises, it will be a yellow moon with black stripes in my honor.
        b. The creatures are crying for a change.
        c. Come out and greet the king of beasts!
        d. The king is dead, long live the king!

_____ 10. In "The Tiger Who Would Be King," the tiger feels he should be king because
        a. he believes the lion is doing a poor job
        b. he has ideas on how the jungle should be run
        c. he is smarter than the lion
        d. he wants to be

_____ 11. In "The Tiger Who Would Be King," which adjective describes the tigress but not her mate?
        a. ferocious   c. boastful
        b. ambitious   d. practical

_____ 12. Another moral of "The Tiger Who Would Be King" might be that
        a. you have to fight for what you believe in
        b. even the winner of a fight may lose
        c. it is better to leave things as they are than to try to change them
        d. you should know what you are fighting for

_____ 13. In "The Lion and the Bulls," the bulls are safe as long as they
        a. are brave   c. are careful
        b. stay alert   d. stay together

_____ 14. In "The Lion and the Bulls," when we read that a plan began to form in the lion's mind, we can predict that
        a. the lion's attack on the bulls will finally succeed
        b. the lion will give up trying to attack the bulls
        c. the lion will keep attacking the bulls in the same way he has in the past
        d. the lion will make the bulls his friends

_____ 15. In contrast to the lion in "The Tiger Who Would Be King," the lion in "The Lion and the Bulls"
        a. is a coward   c. is stubborn
        b. does not want to be king of beasts   d. thinks before he acts

Vocabulary, Spelling, and Grammar

____ 16. Which is the prepositional phrase in this sentence from "The Tiger Who Would Be King"?

> He was monarch of all he surveyed, but it didn't really mean anything.

    a. really mean anything   c. of all

    b. he was monarch   d. it didn't

____ 17. Which sentence contains a misspelled word?

    a. The tiger beleived that he should be king of beasts.

    b. I received a call from my grandmother on my birthday.

    c. A bear can weigh over a thousand pounds.

    d. We found it a relief to get out of the hot sun.

____ 18. When someone makes a *slanderous* accusation, he or she

    a. makes a very serious accusation

    b. makes an accusation that is untrue and damaging

    c. makes an accusation out of anger

    d. makes an accusation that is unbelievable

____ 19. Which of the following sentences does not contain a prepositional phrase?

    a. They had a happy day before the clouds rolled in.

    b. They played ball every day.

    c. Some people choose their dogs and some dogs choose their people.

    d. The whole family was playing cards by the fire.

____ 20. If a cat *prowls*, it might be

    a. curling up for a nap   c. rolling in the grass

    b. hunting for prey   d. running from a larger animal

Essay Questions

21. In an essay, describe the character of Lob in "Lob's Girl." What kind of dog is Lob? What does he look like? What qualities does he reveal in the story? Support each character trait or quality you mention with details from the selection.

22. While the story "Lob's Girl" does not end with a moral like the fables in this selection, "Lob's Girl" focuses on an admirable trait in dogs and people: loyalty. Write an essay in which you analyze how the author demonstrates this quality in Lob, using details from the text to illustrate your ideas. You might begin your essay by defining *loyalty*. Then go on to show how Lob's actions in the story fit your definition.

23. The characters in each fable in this selection are animals but are portrayed differently. For example, the animals in "The Tiger Who Would Be King" speak like human beings, but the animals in "The Lion and the Bulls" do not. In an essay, use this difference and one other difference to contrast Thurber's techniques with those of Aesop. Be sure to cite details from the stories in support of your points. End by contrasting the effects the two fables have on the reader.

Name _____   Date _____

"**Greyling**" by Jane Yolen

Selection Test

Critical Reading

On the line, write the letter of the one best answer.

_____ 1. Why does Greyling pull free from his mother's arms and dive off the cliff?
a. He is tired of his mother's worrying.
b. He wants to show the townspeople that he's not a coward.
c. He's already becoming a seal and he doesn't want his mother to see.
d. He wants to save his father.

_____ 2. Which pair of words best describes the townspeople?
a. enthusiastic and helpful   c. kindly and energetic
b. uninvolved and afraid   d. friendly and talkative

_____ 3. Which sentence best describes the fisherman's feelings at the end of the story?
a. He feels he'll never get over his grief.
b. He is more worried about his wife than himself.
c. He is angry at the townspeople.
d. He misses his son but accepts Greyling's decision.

_____ 4. Which of the following best describes Greyling's internal conflict while growing up with his human parents?
a. Greyling is very lonely, but he doesn't want his parents to know.
b. Greyling is drawn to the sea, but he doesn't understand why.
c. Greyling would like to swim, but he's afraid to jump from the cliff.
d. Greyling wants to forget all about his past life as a selchie, but he can't.

_____ 5. Choose the statement that best explains why the fisherman wrapped the seal in his shirt and hurried home to his wife.
a. He was afraid someone else would try to claim the seal.
b. He was tired of fishing that day.
c. He thought his wife would want to keep the seal in place of a child.
d. The fisherman had a feeling the seal was a selchie.

_____ 6. The fisherman's wife's conflict about Greyling returning to the sea is resolved
a. when Greyling returns to them forever
b. when she thinks Greyling has drowned
c. when she sees how determined Greyling is to rescue his father
d. when she realizes that Greyling, being part seal, will be happier in the sea

_____ 7. Once a year, when Greyling visits the waters near the hut of the fisherman and his wife,
a. they cry and tell him how much they miss him
b. Greyling feels the desire to become human again
c. Greyling watches his parents, but they don't know he's there
d. Greyling tells his parents about his adventures

_____ 8. Which of the following details best helps you predict that the townspeople will refuse to rescue the drowning fisherman?
   a. It is the worst storm the townspeople have ever seen.
   b. The townspeople gather to watch the storm on a very steep cliff.
   c. The townspeople ignore the repeated pleas of the fisherman's wife.
   d. The fisherman's boat is far from shore.

_____ 9. Which of the following best summarizes what the fisherman and his wife learn at the end of this story?
   a. Parents need to keep a closer watch on their children.
   b. Sometimes you need to let go of someone you love.
   c. Those who upset the balance of nature are punished.
   d. To have friends, you must be a friend.

_____ 10. Which of the following best explains the conflict between the fisherman's wife and the townspeople?
   a. They think her son is strange.
   b. They refuse to help her husband.
   c. They live in town and she lives on the shore.
   d. The sea storm has destroyed the family's hut.

_____ 11. The fisherman's wife wants to keep Greyling because
   a. her other children are grown up
   b. she wants a baby to hold in her arms
   c. she's bored by the townspeople
   d. she likes seals

_____ 12. Which of the following details best helps you predict that the fisherman and his wife will keep the selchie?
   a. The fisherman is at sea all day long.
   b. Greyling's eyes are the color of the sea.
   c. The fisherman and his wife long for a child of their own.
   d. Their moss-covered hut is close to the sea.

_____ 13. Greyling longs for the sea but loves the couple who raised him. Which statement best explains the resolution of this conflict?
   a. Greyling returns to the ocean but comes back to see his parents from time to time.
   b. Greyling chooses the sea and the life of a seal.
   c. After rescuing the fisherman, Greyling turns his back on the sea and lives the rest of his life on land.
   d. After the townspeople promise to take care of the couple, Greyling returns to the ocean.

Vocabulary, Spelling, and Grammar

_____ 14. Which of the following sentences contains a coordinating conjunction?
   a. The whole story was great, but the best part was when he dove from the cliff.
   b. I liked all the characters excepting the townspeople.
   c. Why didn't you like the townspeople?
   d. Now is the time to read more about selchies; they are part of an interesting legend.

_____ 15. The fisherman and his wife feel _grief_ when they lose Greyling. Choose the word or words that are closest in meaning to the word _grief_.
   a. disappointment
   b. greed
   c. deep sadness
   d. fear

____ 16. Which coordinating conjunction makes the most sense for completing this sentence?

Greyling has returned to the sea, _____ he visits his parents once a year.

a. for
b. and
c. but
d. so

____ 17. Which sentence does *not* contain a misspelled word?
a. We had rested enuff and were no longer tired.
b. I rolled up one shirt cuff and then the other.
c. The meat was too tuff to cut.
d. A cat's tongue feels as ruff as sandpaper.

____ 18. Greyling seemed to *slough* off his skin as he swam. The best definition for *slough* is
a. cast off
b. smooth out
c. shine up
d. scratch

____ 19. Which sentence below contains a misspelled word?
a. The wind made the sea very rough.
b. Greyling swam through the ruff waves.
c. The townspeople had heard enough from the fisherman's wife.
d. Unfortunately, the mast was not very tough.

____ 20. In which of the following passages from the story does the fisherman's wife feel grief?
a. She was afraid he would never return.
b. So he shrugged his shoulders and took off his shirt.
c. She would weep and wail and rock the cradle that stood by the hearth.
d. But the fisherman's wife clasped Greyling in her arms and held his ears with her hands.

Essay Questions

21. In a brief essay, explain two predictions you made while reading "Greyling." Which specific details in the story helped you make each prediction? Did new details make you change your original prediction? If so, which ones? End your essay by explaining how making predictions helped you stay interested in the story.

22. Write an essay comparing and contrasting the fisherman and his wife. How does each character express grief? Do they act the same or differently when faced with a conflict? At the end of the story, are they more like each other or less alike than at the beginning? Support your statements with details from the story.

23. Write an essay examining the conflicts Greyling experiences within himself. Describe the conflict with which he struggles as he grows up. Explain how this struggle becomes even more difficult as he watches his father's sinking boat. Does the action Greyling takes resolve his conflicts? End your essay by making a prediction about new conflicts you think Greyling might experience after he leaves his human parents.

"Abuelito Who" by Sandra Cisneros
"The Open Road" by Walt Whitman
"Life Doesn't Frighten Me" by Maya Angelou
"who knows if the moon's" by E.E. Cummings

Selection Test

Critical Reading

On the line, write the letter of the one best answer.

_____ 1. How do you know that the four poems are written in free verse?
   a. The poets say so.
   b. The poems have no rhyming words at all.
   c. The poems have no consistent structure and no regular pattern of rhyming lines.
   d. Most lines don't start with capital letters.

_____ 2. What two devices do all four poems use to create a sense of sound and rhythm of their own?
   a. verbs and adjectives
   b. questions and answers
   c. no punctuation and long lines
   d. rhyming words and repeated words

_____ 3. In "Abuelito Who," how has life changed for the speaker of the poem?
   a. The speaker no longer loves Abuelito.
   b. The speaker is too sad to enjoy life.
   c. The speaker's grandfather has died, so she must face everyday life without him.
   d. The speaker cannot sleep at night because of dreams that Abuelito is hiding underneath the bed.

_____ 4. What is the meaning of this line from "Abuelito Who"?

   who used to laugh like the letter k

   a. Abuelito's mouth looked like the letter k when he laughed.
   b. Abuelito's laugh used to sound like someone repeating the sound of the letter k.
   c. Abuelito had a very loud laugh.
   d. You could hardly hear Abuelito when he laughed.

_____ 5. In "Abuelito Who," the rain on the roof reminds the speaker of
   a. the coins Abuelito used to throw to the speaker
   b. Abuelito's tears
   c. Abuelito's little room
   d. the big brown shoes Abuelito used to wear

_____ 6. In "who knows if the moon's," what is the effect of the rhyme in the lines "who knows if the moon's / a balloon . . ."?
   a. The rhyme lets the reader know that this is a poem and not a prose selection.
   b. The rhyme gives the poem a musical sound and stimulates the reader's imagination.
   c. The rhyme helps the reader understand what the poem is about.
   d. The rhyme helps the reader visualize the beauty of the full moon at night.

_____ 7. In "who knows if the moon's," to where and with whom does the poet imagine that he might travel?
a. He imagines that he might be taken into a balloon by pretty people from a city in the sky and go sailing to that city.
b. He imagines that he might travel to the moon with friends where he could see a city in the sky.
c. He imagines that he might travel alone to visit people in a city in the sky.
d. He imagines that he might travel from the moon back to the earth to visit a city.

_____ 8. The poem "who knows if the moon's" expresses the speaker's desire to
a. take a trip to a foreign country
b. travel in a hot-air balloon
c. escape from the everyday world
d. travel in space

_____ 9. In "who knows if the moon's," the poet's choice of spring as the season in the "keen city" conveys the idea that
a. it is cold and uninviting there
b. it is nice but unfriendly there
c. it is always pleasant, friendly, fresh, and exciting there
d. it is pretty but things never change there

_____ 10. What can you infer about the speaker in "The Open Road" from these words: *I myself am good fortune*?
a. The speaker is very wealthy.
b. The speaker has friends who will bring good luck and happiness.
c. The speaker feels responsible for bringing good luck and happiness to others.
d. The speaker feels that people are responsible for their own happiness.

_____ 11. If things go wrong in the future for the speaker of "The Open Road," how might the speaker respond?
a. The speaker will become depressed and unhappy.
b. The speaker will take action to make things go better.
c. The speaker will ignore any problems that arise.
d. The speaker will ask others for advice.

_____ 12. The speaker in "Life Doesn't Frighten Me" describes her courage by
a. listing things that would scare some people but do not bother her
b. telling a story about how she learned to overcome her fear
c. naming the things that she tells herself when she is tempted to be afraid
d. telling how fear feels, sounds, and tastes

_____ 13. What is the "magic charm" owned by the speaker in "Life Doesn't Frighten Me"?
a. It is her love for her family.
b. It is a bracelet in the shape of a panther.
c. It is the word *boo.*
d. She does not say whether it is an object or an attitude.

_____ 14. According to "Life Doesn't Frighten Me," what do Mother Goose, dragons, and kissy little girls have in common?
a. They are beings that the speaker does not fear.
b. They are beings that only children fear.
c. They are imaginary beings.
d. They are beings that make the speaker laugh.

Vocabulary, Spelling, and Grammar

____ 15. In which of the following would the word *henceforth* correctly complete the sentence?
    a. I love chocolate; _____ it's bad for your teeth.
    b. The rain had left huge puddles; _____ he didn't wear boots.
    c. I got a bad sunburn; _____ I'll stay in the shade.
    d. The puppy was only four months old; _____ she was huge.

____ 16. Which subordinating conjunction would best complete the following sentence?

    The speakers in each poem share feelings about changes in their lives ____ the change each one faces is very different.

    a. because   c. when
    b. although   d. wherever

____ 17. In which sentence is the compound transition word misspelled?
    a. I closed the door; however, the dog escaped.
    b. I did the laundry; moreover, I washed the dishes.
    c. I'll help you this time, but henceforth you'll be on your own.
    d. I was late once this year; therafter I set my alarm clock every night.

____ 18. Which *clause* in this sentence expresses the less important idea?

    I've got a magic charm/That I keep up my sleeve . . .

    a. I've got a magic charm
    b. That I keep up my sleeve
    c. a magic charm
    d. keep up my sleeve

____ 19. Which word in the following sentence is a subordinating conjunction?

    The speaker in "Life Doesn't Frighten Me" is not afraid of anything because she has a magic charm that she keeps up her sleeve.

    a. in   b. that   c. because   d. has

____ 20. When the speaker in "The Open Road" says "I whimper no more," he means that
    a. he will no longer laugh
    b. he will no longer whine
    c. he will no longer listen to others
    d. he will no longer quarrel with others

Essay Questions

21. In poetry, the reader's inferences are usually based on the specific images the poet uses. In an essay, explain how the images in at least one of these four poems led you to make inferences about the poem's meaning. Use at least two specific quotations from the poem and clearly explain the inferences you made.

22. Each of the four poems in this group relates to the theme "A Road to Follow." Write an essay in which you compare and contrast the way in which at least two of the poems relate to the theme. In each poem you include, explain the "new road" the speaker will follow. Show how the changes in the speakers' lives are similar and different. Quote passages from the poems to support your points.

23. Each of the free verse poems in this group uses repeated words. In an essay, analyze how repetition of certain words or lines supports the poet's meaning in at least one of the four poems. Quote specific lines and words from the poem to demonstrate your ideas.

    Abuelito/The Open Road/Life Doesn't Frighten Me/Who Knows the Moon's **81**

"A Backwoods Boy" by Russell Freedman
"Jackie Robinson: Justice at Last" by Geoffrey C. Ward and Ken Burns

Critical Reading

On the line, write the letter of the one best answer.

_____ 1. In "A Backwoods Boy," Abraham Lincoln moved to New Salem in 1831 because he
    a. wanted to be with his family
    b. wanted to be on his own
    c. wanted to enter politics
    d. needed a job to help support his family

_____ 2. Which of the following is the main idea in "A Backwoods Boy"?
    a. Abraham Lincoln grew up in three states.
    b. Lincoln's mother died when he was young.
    c. Lincoln lost his first election in 1832.
    d. Lincoln was a hard-working and ambitious young man.

_____ 3. In "A Backwoods Boy," the job at Offutt's store was good for Lincoln because
    a. it gave him time to read and study
    b. Offutt paid him well
    c. he learned a lot about running a business
    d. he could close the store early and go home

_____ 4. Which detail in "A Backwoods Boy" explains the fact that the house on Knob Creek was the first home that Lincoln could remember?
    a. Lincoln was named after his pioneer grandfather.
    b. The family moved north to Indiana in 1816.
    c. Abraham's father was hard-working but uneducated.
    d. Young Abraham was still a toddler when his family moved there.

_____ 5. In "A Backwoods Boy," Lincoln's paying off a large debt when his business failed is a good example of his
    a. stubbornness   c. honesty
    b. poor judgment   d. sense of humor

_____ 6. Which of the following is *not* a main idea in "A Backwoods Boy"?
    a. Lincoln was briefly a captain in the militia.
    b. Lincoln's childhood was one of grinding poverty.
    c. Lincoln read and studied to improve himself.
    d. Lincoln's determination got him elected to the state legislature.

_____ 7. In "A Backwoods Boy," Abe got his gift for talking and storytelling from his
    a. mother   c. stepmother
    b. father   d. cousin Dennis Hanks

_____ 8. In "Jackie Robinson: Justice at Last," the authors use facts about racism to explain Robinson's
    a. great courage   c. distrust of whites
    b. batting average   d. anger

____ 9. In "Jackie Robinson: Justice at Last," why did Branch Rickey want Robinson to take abuse from whites?
   a. He didn't want him to be noticed.
   b. He was hoping Robinson would quit.
   c. He wanted the other players to like him.
   d. He wanted Robinson to be a dignified hero.

____ 10. In "Jackie Robinson: Justice at Last," Branch Rickey wanted baseball to be
   a. segregated   c. integrated
   b. all white   d. all black

____ 11. The authors think one main reason for Jackie Robinson's greatness was his
   a. playing ability   c. speaking ability
   b. color   d. loyalty

____ 12. Robinson's first season in the majors was difficult because
   a. he played poorly
   b. white fans and players rejected him
   c. he couldn't control his anger
   d. he was nervous all the time

____ 13. His teammates finally accepted Robinson because
   a. he was friendly   c. Rickey ordered them to
   b. he helped them win   d. he fought them

____ 14. The authors of "Jackie Robinson: Justice at Last" interpret the life of Robinson as an example of
   a. goodness destroyed by racism
   b. hard work over intelligence
   c. popularity over substance
   d. determination surmounting obstacles

____ 15. According to "Jackie Robinson: Justice at Last," Robinson largely succeeds
   a. on his own
   b. with the help of many people
   c. through one influential person
   d. with the financial help of his families

Vocabulary, Spelling, and Grammar

____ 16. What is the conjunction in this sentence from "A Backwoods Boy"?

   He tended the counter at Denton Offutt's store and slept in a room at the back.

   a. back   c. at
   b. the   d. and

____ 17. Which of the following best defines the word *treacherous* in this sentence?

   Its hopes for growth and prosperity had vanished when the Sangamon River proved too *treacherous* for steamboat travel.

   a. safe   c. dangerous
   b. easy   d. expensive

____ 18. Which of the following is spelled correctly?
   a. aptittude   c. atpitude
   b. aptitude   d. apptitude

____ 19. Which of these sentences from "A Backwoods Boy" has a conjunction that shows a *contrast* between two ideas?

      a. They regarded him as a good-humored, easy-going boy—a bookworm maybe, but smart and willing to oblige.

      b. He supported his family by living off his own land, and he watched for a chance to better himself.

      c. He would carry a book out to the field with him, so he could read at the end of each plow furrow. . . .

      d. Back in New Salem, folks would see him walking down the road, reciting aloud from one of his law books, or lying under a tree as he read. . . .

____ 20. What is the meaning of the italicized word in this sentence?

      No matter who insulted him, he never *retaliated*.

      a. gave up   c. remembered

      b. retreated   d. fought back

Essay Questions

21. Abraham Lincoln and Jackie Robinson both achieved greatness through their own efforts, but they also had some help along the way. In an essay about either Lincoln or Robinson, explain how a particular person helped Lincoln or Robinson in achieving his goals. Support your answer with examples from the text.

22. Both Abraham Lincoln and Jackie Robinson overcame difficult obstacles in order to achieve great success. Choose either Lincoln or Robinson, and write an essay explaining the obstacles one of them faced and how these obstacles were overcome. Use quotations and examples from the selection to support your ideas. If you prefer, write about both Lincoln and Robinson, comparing and contrasting their difficulties and how they overcame them.

23. Jackie Robinson agreed to follow Branch Rickey's advice not to fight back against the racism he experienced when he became a Dodger. Write an essay expressing your opinion of what might have happened if Robinson had ignored Rickey's advice and stood up for himself. How might this have affected Robinson's career and the history of baseball? Do you think, in general, people should follow such advice? Why or why not?

Unit 4: Seeing It Through

Unit Test

Critical Reading

On the line, write the letter of the one best answer.

_____ 1. What does the following passage from "Lob's Girl" foreshadow?

> Then she saw the train slide away out of sight around the next headland with a melancholy wail that sounded like Lob's last good-bye.

    a. The Pengellys will be happy without Lob.
    b. Sandy will have an accident.
    c. Lob will never enjoy train rides.
    d. Lob will miss Sandy and her family.

_____ 2. In "Lob's Girl," Mr. Dodsworth gives Lob to the Pengelly family because
    a. he is too old to keep a dog
    b. he cannot afford to keep the dog
    c. he realizes that Lob wants to be with the Pengellys
    d. he likes Sandy

_____ 3. In "Lob's Girl," how are Lob and Mrs. Pearce alike?
    a. They both have a great deal of determination.
    b. Both of them come from Liverpool.
    c. Both characters first meet Sandy at the beach.
    d. Both characters give up the thing that is dearest to them in order to save Sandy.

_____ 4. In "The Tiger Who Would Be King," what character trait is responsible for the downfall of the tiger?
    a. bad temper   b. dishonesty   c. ambition   d. cowardice

_____ 5. In "The Lion and the Bulls," the lion is able to defeat the bulls after he
    a. makes them feel overconfident
    b. makes them suspicious of each other
    c. waits until they are asleep
    d. makes them afraid of him

_____ 6. At the beginning of "Greyling," the fisherman and his wife have no children because
    a. they are too poor to afford them
    b. they work too hard and long to have time for them
    c. the wife has been ill
    d. they have never been able to have any

_____ 7. Greyling does not understand why he longs for the sea. Readers know, however, that his conflict comes from the fact that
    a. the fisherman, years earlier, found him on the beach
    b. he is destined to live his life on the sea as a fisherman
    c. he is a selchie and the sea is his true home
    d. he is destined to save his father from drowning some day

_____ 8. In "Greyling," what does the terrible storm that threatens to drown the fisherman lead you to predict?
   a. The townspeople will work together to save him.
   b. Grayling will save the fisherman by turning into a seal.
   c. The fisherman will be able to save himself.
   d. The fisherman's wife will attempt to save him.

_____ 9. In "Greyling," the fisherman's wife tries to keep her son from going to his father's rescue because
   a. she fears that he will become a seal again and that she will lose him
   b. Greyling has become more dear to her than her husband
   c. she fears that Greyling will drown in the storm
   d. she hopes that her husband will be able to save himself

_____ 10. Which fact from the beginning of "Greyling" would be most helpful for predicting the outcome of the story?
   a. The fisherman and his wife, despite their great desire to be parents, never had had a child of their own.
   b. It was the fisherman who took Greyling away from the sea.
   c. The fisherman agreed to keep Greyling away from the sea but sensed that doing so was wrong.
   d. The fisherman found the child on the beach the morning after a violent storm.

_____ 11. In "Abuelito Who," why does the rain remind the speaker of her grandfather?
   a. The speaker remembers a time when her grandfather wept tears like rain.
   b. The speaker knows that her grandfather used to love rainy weather.
   c. Her grandfather used to throw coins like rain.
   d. Her grandfather once gave her money to buy an umbrella.

_____ 12. Because "Abuelito Who" is a free verse poem, it does not rhyme. It captures the rhythms of speech, however, by
   a. packing many words into each line to suggest someone who is talking quickly
   b. listing the things that once were true of Abuelito
   c. repeating the question _who loves him_ throughout the poem
   d. repeating the name _Abuelito_ throughout the poem

_____ 13. In "who knows if the moon's," the speaker
   a. invites the reader to an imaginary world about the moon
   b. states his opinion about the nature of the moon
   c. describes a dream he had about the moon
   d. describes what he wishes were true about the moon

_____ 14. In "The Open Road," which of these inferences can you draw about the speaker?
   a. The speaker regards neatness and order as important factors in life.
   b. The speaker believes in planning everything carefully in advance.
   c. The speaker finds happiness in freedom from restriction.
   d. The speaker enjoys sightseeing.

_____ 15. In "Life Doesn't Frighten Me," the speaker may be frightened in dreams because
   a. the speaker has nightmares
   b. the creatures in dreams are scarier than the ones in real life
   c. nighttime is scarier than daytime
   d. the speaker is not in control when dreaming

_____ 16. In what ways are "Life Doesn't Frighten Me" and "who knows if the moon's" similar?
   a. Both poems repeat their titles several times.
   b. Both poems urge the reader to live life with courage.
   c. Both are free verse poems.
   d. Both use rhyme and rhythm to hold the reader's attention.

_____ 17. In "A Backwoods Boy," readers learn that formal education during Lincoln's boyhood
   a. was unheard-of   c. was less common than it is now
   b. was a new idea   d. was an unpopular idea

_____ 18. "A Backwoods Boy" shows that Lincoln
   a. had many lucky breaks that helped him in his early life
   b. knew from his early youth that he would become president of the United States
   c. was embarrassed by his humble birth
   d. overcame many hardships in early life

_____ 19. In "Jackie Robinson: Justice at Last," what is the most important fact brought out
   by the author as background to the article?
   a. World War II had just ended when Robinson came into major league baseball.
   b. Black men were not allowed to play in the major leagues until 1947.
   c. Jackie Robinson was a great athlete.
   d. Branch Rickey wanted to end the whites-only policy in major league baseball.

Vocabulary, Spelling, and Grammar

_____ 20. Which of the following words is a preposition?
   a. which   b. between   c. when   d. never

_____ 21. Which word is most nearly opposite in meaning to melancholy?
   a. cheerful   b. determined   c. kind   d. gloomy

_____ 22. Which of the following sentences contains a misspelled word?
   a. Some whales weigh over a hundred tons.
   b. I didn't believe that I would enjoy learning history, but I do.
   c. In baseball the pitcher tries to deceive the batter by throwing curve balls.
   d. Our neighbors just got a new car.

_____ 23. Which is the prepositional phrase in the sentence?

   We came inside, hung our coats in the closet, and watched our favorite television
   program.

   a. we came inside   c. in the closet
   b. hung our coats   d. our favorite television program

_____ 24. If a person is _treacherous_, it means that the person
   a. has little education   c. is very ambitious
   b. should not be trusted   d. has very few friends

_____ 25. Which is the coordinating conjunction in the following sentence?

   He spent hours trying to build the model ship, but he eventually lost interest.

   a. trying   b. to   c. eventually   d. but

_____ 26. Which of the following words is misspelled?
   a. tuff   b. enough   c. stuff   d. rough

_____ 27. Which word correctly completes the following sentence?

   If you make a decision, you have acted _____.

   a. decided   b. decisively   c. decision   d. decisive

____ 28. Which pair of words shows a subordinating conjunction and a coordinating conjunction that have a similar meaning?

a since/and   b. but/yet   c. because/for   d. so/unless

____ 29. A *querulous* person probably is not easy to

a. understand   b. please   c. identify   d. annoy

____ 30. Which of the following sentences has a subordinating conjunction linking two ideas?

a. At the party, they served ice cream and cake.

b. I traded two comic books for my friend's baseball card collection.

c. Some of the students tidied up the room and then left.

d. Although food was cold, we were hungry and ate it anyway.

Essay Questions

31. Do people use the same character traits to overcome hardships and obstacles, or does each person have a special mix of qualities? Choose two of the following characters from this unit: Lob in "Lob's Girl," Abraham Lincoln in "A Backwoods Boy," and Jackie Robinson in "Jackie Robinson: Justice at Last." In an essay, describe the difficulties that each character faces and describe the qualities he uses to overcome the challenges. Point out which qualities, if any, the two characters share, and state your opinion on whether certain abilities or characteristics are especially helpful in successfully dealing with hardship.

32. Some people see life as an adventure, full of promise; others get nervous about possible problems lying in wait around the next corner. Consider the speakers of two of these poems: "Life Doesn't Frighten Me," "who knows if the moon's," and "The Open Road." Write an essay in which you analyze the speakers of your chosen poems, to determine whether each should be placed among the hopeful ones or among the nervous and fearful. (It may be that a speaker can be hopeful under some conditions and fearful in others.) Use details from the selection to support your opinions. Conclude by saying what these poems suggest to readers about how to cope with fears.

33. In many stories and poems, characters overcome their fears, act in spite of their fears, or fall because of their fears. Choose two of the following selections: "The Lion and the Bulls," "Greyling," "The Open Road," "Life Doesn't Frighten Me," and "Jackie Robinson: Justice at Last." Write an essay in which you discuss how fear is an important element for the character or characters in that selection. Include a lesson that you think is taught in each of the selections that you choose.

34. Consider the title character of "Greyling" and Abraham Lincoln in "A Backwoods Boy," and write an essay in which you analyze the way in which either or both of them could be said to go through a transformation. Either compare and contrast both characters, or focus on one only. What changes do they go through, and how dramatic are the changes? How are the changes brought about? Are they the result of the character's inner qualities, or do the circumstances in which the characters find themselves play a part? Use details from the texts to support your conclusions.

35. What makes a challenge difficult, and how do writers convey that difficulty to their readers? Choose two of the following selections from this unit: "Lob's Girl," "Greyling," "Abuelito Who," and "Jackie Robinson: Justice at Last." Then write an essay in which you analyze how the authors make known the severity of the hardship faced by a character in the selection. Use details from the text to illustrate your analysis.

Unit 4: Seeing It Through

Alternative Unit Test

The two passages below are followed by questions based on their content and on the relationship between the two passages.

Passage 1

The following passage is about Joseph and Martine, an elderly couple who spend a night tending Rousa, their cow, who has injured herself in a fall.

from "Pig Earth" by John Berger

"I'm not leaving her alone all night," Martine insisted.

"A cow is an animal," he said.

"I'm staying with her. She could roll down there on to the rocks."

He walked away with his despondent walk.

"Twenty-seven years, and this is the first time I've had an accident with a cow." She said this quietly as she felt the cow's horns and ears. "A stupid accident. A stupid cow accident!"

With her complacent eyes, Rousa followed the woman's movement. Her horns were unhealthily cold.

Joseph came back with some blankets draped over his shoulders. Something had mollified him.

"I will stay with her," he said.

"I won't sleep anyway," said Martine.

They spread the blankets over Rousa, and then over themselves.

"She knows what's happening," said Martine.

Cows rarely make any sound when in pain. At the most they blow heavily through their immense nostrils.

From under the blankets the two of them looked down at the far lights in the valley. The sky was clear, the Milky Way like a vast misty white goose pecking at the lip of a jug.

"If only she'd move," whispered Martine. "I could milk her."

She lay by the cow's head, the halter rope coiled round her wrist. He lay between the cow's four legs.

"The lights stay on all night in the villages," he said. "One, two, three, four, five, six, seven, but none of them is my village."

From out of his pocket he took a mouth-organ. He had had this mouth-organ for fifty years, since he was a conscript in the army. At that time, when he was young, he used to pretend to play an invisible trumpet, using only his lips and hands. If asked, he would entertain the whole barrack room by playing this trumpet which did not exist. One evening a friendly sergeant said: "You play well enough to have something to play on. Here, I've got two. Take this."

And so he acquired a mouth-organ.

As he played now, he tapped his foot on the mountainside and looked at the tiny clusters of lights below—no larger than grains of sugar, fallen from a spoon.

He played a polka, a quadrille, a waltz, "The Nightingale of the Sweet Wood," a rigadoon. Neither she nor he could have said afterwards for how long he played. The night turned colder. As his foot beat time on the mountainside, his hands in the moonlight smoothed and ruffled each tune as if it were a bird miraculously perched on the instrument. All music is about survival, addressed to survivors.

Passage 2

"Dog and Papa's Fiddle" by Kristine O'Connell George

Papa polishes his fiddle

With a flannel cloth,

Whistles up Dog, who

Settles in, loose and soft.

Papa tucks his fiddle

Under his whiskery chin.

Dog stretches and yawns;

The night songs begin.

Dog scratches his ear.

The old moon climbs.

Papa's boots tap—

Each marking time.

Fiddle yowls like an alley cat.

Dog opens one eye,

Then Papa gentles into

Music of melting sky.

Critical Reading

On the line, write the letter of the one best answer.

_____ 1. After reading both passages, you know that
    a. all the characters get pleasure from music
    b. none of the characters have much interest in music
    c. the characters think of music as something only for special occasions
    d. the characters play music only because their animals like it
    e. the characters who play music are professional musicians

_____ 2. Which statement is true of both passages?
    a. Both take place in an isolated area.
    b. Both musicians are farmers.
    c. The characters in both passages are married.
    d. Both passages take place at night.
    e. The animals in both passages like the music.

_____ 3. In Passage 1, Martine says that Rousa "knows what's happening." What does this statement foreshadow?
    a. The cow will get up soon.
    b. The cow will die.
    c. Joseph and Martine will save Rousa's life.
    d. Joseph and Martine will fall asleep.
    e. Rousa will give birth to a calf.

_____ 4. After reading both passages, you can infer that
    a. all the characters are happy
    b. Papa is not as good a musician as Joseph
    c. all the characters care about their animals
    d. Papa is a trained musician, but Joseph is not
    e. Papa and Joseph are self-taught musicians

_____ 5. Which is closest in meaning to the statement in Passage 1 that music is "addressed to survivors"?
   a. Music is best appreciated by people who have a positive attitude toward life.
   b. Playing music professionally is a good way to earn a living.
   c. People who think they are about to die do not care for music.
   d. Musicians usually live long lives.
   e. Music can help people recover from illnesses.

_____ 6. Passage 2 is not an example of free verse because
   a. the lines are very short
   b. it uses simple words
   c. it is easy to understand
   d. it is divided into stanzas
   e. it uses rhyme and regular rhythm

_____ 7. In Passage 2, while Papa plays his fiddle, Dog
   a. lies nearby
   b. romps around happily
   c. howls along with the music
   d. goes to sleep
   e. sits in Papa's lap

_____ 8. On the basis of the information in Passage 1, which of the following is the most reasonable prediction that you can make about these characters?
   a. Martine and Joseph will get into a heated argument.
   b. Joseph will lose the mouth-organ.
   c. Joseph will become a professional musician.
   d. Rousa will survive her injury.
   e. Martine will give up taking care of cows.

_____ 9. In Passage 1, what does the music do for Martine and Joseph?
   a. It provides them with entertainment.
   b. It helps them to bear the long cold night.
   c. It reminds them that melodies sound beautiful.
   d. It gives them an opportunity to dance.
   e. It makes them laugh with joy.

_____ 10. In Passage 1, what is the conflict between Martine and Joseph?
   a. Martine thinks Rousa will live and Joseph thinks the cow will die.
   b. Martine thinks Joseph is to blame for Rousa's having fallen.
   c. Martine wants to stay all night with Rousa and Joseph does not.
   d. Joseph wants to play his mouth-organ and Martine doesn't want him to.
   e. Martine wants Joseph to help get Rousa on her feet and Joseph doesn't want to.

_____ 11. What is true of the animals in the two passages?
   a. They are important to the characters because they are worth a lot of money.
   b. They are unimportant to the characters.
   c. Rousa is important because she gives milk, but Dog doesn't matter much to Papa.
   d. Dog is important as a companion to Papa, but Rousa is just a farm animal.
   e. They are a part of the characters' lives.

_____ 12. In Passage 2, Papa resolves a potential conflict with Dog by
   a. stopping the tapping of his foot
   b. changing from a "yowling" fiddle tune to one that is "gentle"
   c. stopping his fiddle playing so that he can feed Dog
   d. stopping his fiddle playing so that Dog can go back to sleep
   e. letting Dog come in from the cold and warm himself by the fire

____ 13. Which statement about both passages is most likely to be true?
      a. All characters in both passages are city people.
      b. All characters in both passages probably work in factories.
      c. All characters in both passages live in rural areas.
      d. Martine and Joseph live in a rural area, and Papa lives in an apartment.
      e. Martine and Joseph live on a farm, and Papa lives in a suburban house.

____ 14. Which statement about both passages is most likely to be true?
      a. Papa plays music only occasionally but Joseph plays all the time.
      b. Joseph hasn't played his mouth organ for years, but Papa plays his fiddle most nights.
      c. Papa and Joseph would rather hear other people play music than play themselves.
      d. Papa and Joseph play music mostly when they need to cheer up.
      e. Papa and Joseph play music often.

____ 15. In Passage 1, how old is Joseph?
      a. in his twenties
      b. in his thirties
      c. in his fifties
      d. no younger than his late sixties
      e. there is no way to know how old Joseph is

Essay Questions

16. Music is important to the characters in these passages. In an essay, discuss the circumstances in which the characters play music. If the passages contain any clues, suggest reasons why the characters play and explain your reasoning. Compare and contrast the role of music in the passages, using only the material in the passages, if any, that may indicate what that role is. Use details from the passages to support your conclusions.

17. The theme for this unit is "seeing it through." Write an essay in which you analyze the ways in which that theme applies to the two passages. Include a comparison in which you describe differences and similarities between the applications of the theme. Support your conclusions with details from the passages.

18. In Passage 1, the author describes Joseph's mouth-organ playing by writing that "his hands in the moonlight smoothed and ruffled each tune as if it were a bird miraculously perched on the instrument." In Passage 2, Papa is said to play "Music of melting sky." Write an essay in which you suggest explanations for these images. What are they meant to say about Joseph's and Papa's playing? Could either image apply to the other musician? In what ways are the images similar, and in what ways are they different? Use details from the passages to support your observations.

"The Fun They Had" by Isaac Asimov

Selection Test

Critical Reading

On the line, write the letter of the one best answer.

____ 1. Margie hopes that her old teaching machine will be taken away because
    a. she wants one that works better
    b. she knows that the newer models can be used to play exciting games
    c. she is afraid that she will fail her next geography test
    d. she dislikes the way she is expected to learn information

____ 2. Which of the following passages shows that the story is science fiction?
    a. The inspector had smiled after he was finished and patted her head.
    b. On the page headed May 17, 2155, she wrote, "Today Tommy found a real book."
    c. He was a round little man with a red face.
    d. Margie always hated school, but now she hated it more than ever.

____ 3. Why does Tommy believe that a teaching machine is better than a human teacher?
    a. He does not want a teacher to give him lessons in his home.
    b. He thinks that a person could not be as intelligent as a machine.
    c. He thinks that the work is easier when it is assigned by a teaching machine.
    d. He thinks that a human teacher would make the students behave in class.

____ 4. The author makes us feel that this story is actually taking place in the future by
    a. telling us that the year is 2155
    b. showing how Margie feels about using the teaching machine
    c. explaining how Margie's mother feels about schoolwork
    d. giving details about how the children are taught and tested in subjects using the teaching machine

____ 5. Which passage from the story reveals the author's message about education?
    a. They turned the pages, which were yellow and crinkly, and it was awfully funny to read words that stood still instead of moving the way they were supposed to— on a screen, you know.
    b. "But my mother says a teacher has to be adjusted to fit the mind of each boy and girl it teaches and that each kid has to be taught differently."
    c. All the kids from the whole neighborhood came, laughing and shouting in the schoolyard, sitting together in the schoolroom, going home together at the end of the day. They learned the same things so they could help one another on the homework and talk about it.
    d. It was always on at the same time every day except Saturday and Sunday, because her mother said little girls learned better if they learned at regular hours.

____ 6. The author's strongest reason for thinking that the schools of today are better than the computerized schools of the future is that
    a. human teachers do not have to be repaired by professionals
    b. children find it hard to concentrate on their lessons when they learn at home
    c. children get more exercise by walking to their schools
    d. learning in a classroom with other children is enjoyable

Unit 5: Mysterious Worlds

7. Based on the information in the story, why would Margie enjoy attending the kind of school children attend today?
    a. She would like to spend time with other children during the school day.
    b. She is bored waiting for the inspector to fix her teaching machine.
    c. She would enjoy walking to school.
    d. She thinks a human teacher would be more informative than a computer.

8. What is the main reason that Margie wants to read the old book from Tommy's attic?
    a. She is curious to learn more about the schools of the past.
    b. She never has handled an old-fashioned book before.
    c. She thinks that it will help her with her schoolwork.
    d. She doesn't want Tommy to tease her about knowing less than he does.

9. The author sets the story in the future because
    a. he knows that the events in the story never really could take place at all
    b. he wants to promote the manufacture of computers and electronic machines
    c. he wants to show readers what might happen to the field of education if we let technology take over
    d. he believes in using computers to teach children

10. At the end of the story, which of the following best describes how Margie feels about the children who attended school in her grandparents' grandparents' time?
    a. She feels sorry for those children who had no computers.
    b. She envies the students of long ago and wishes to be one of them.
    c. She respects the children for being such good students.
    d. She dislikes the idea that those children were so noisy and lazy.

11. Which of the following best summarizes the plot of "The Fun They Had"?
    a. When two children find a book about the past, they both decide they are lucky to be growing up in the twenty-second century.
    b. While the inspector fixes Margie's teaching machine, the girl wishes the machine could be taken away forever.
    c. When Tommy shows Margie an old book he found, Margie finds herself wishing she could have gone to a real school the way her grandparents' grandparents did.
    d. When Margie and Tommy argue about the schools of the past, Margie realizes Tommy is not her true friend.

12. Which detail does *not* show that the story is set in the future?
    a. The children are not used to books printed on paper.
    b. Margie records her thoughts in a diary.
    c. The date is May 17, 2155.
    d. Schools with classrooms had not existed for centuries.

13. When Margie's mother says that each child has to be taught differently, she means
    a. the teaching machine has to be set in a special way for each child
    b. children sometimes do not get along with their human teachers
    c. some children do not have the patience to get through a long lesson
    d. children who have difficulty reading may prefer to listen to a recording of a lesson

14. We know that Margie feels much the same way the author does about her lonely "classroom" because she
    a. thinks about how much fun it would be to go to a regular school with other children
    b. hates school
    c. says her father is as smart as a teaching machine
    d. has trouble keeping up with her geography homework

____ 15. Which of the following questions is the most important to think about at the end of the story?
  a. Will Margie succeed at her lessons now that her teaching machine has been fixed?
  b. How much of their classroom time should students spend using the computer?
  c. How do we know our computers are working properly?
  d. Will using a computer for long periods of time cause health problems?

Vocabulary, Spelling, and Grammar

____ 16. Which best defines the word *nonchalantly* in this passage from the story?

> "Maybe," he said, *nonchalantly*. He walked away whistling, the dusty old book tucked beneath his arm.

  a. without seeming concerned   c. impolitely
  b. lazily   d. hurriedly

____ 17. An appropriate word to describe how Tommy speaks to Margie is
  a. kindly   c. angrily
  b. loftily   d. sweetly

____ 18. Which of the following words is pronounced using the *sh* sound?
  a. chef   c. church
  b. chief   d. choir

____ 19. Which word or words are the simple subject of this sentence?

> The students of the future do not learn in groups.

  a. groups   c. students
  b. do not learn   d. future

____ 20. In which of the following sentences is the simple predicate underlined?
  a. Margie and Tommy flipped through the book's yellowed pages.
  b. Margie and Tommy flipped through the book's yellowed pages.
  c. Margie and Tommy flipped through the book's yellowed pages.
  d. Margie and Tommy flipped through the book's yellowed pages.

Essay Questions

21. When Margie hears that the old book from the attic is about the schools of the past, she wants to read it as soon as she can. In an essay, discuss what Margie's interest in the past tells us about her personality. What kinds of things might she like and dislike? What might she most enjoy doing with her study time and free time? Use information from the story to back up your analysis of this character.

22. Write an essay in which you agree or disagree with this statement: "Students learn more by using computer programs than by being taught in traditional classrooms." Decide whether you agree with this idea or not; then make at least two points that support your opinion. Back up your argument using quotations and details from the story, personal experience, or information you have read on the subject.

23. The author of "The Fun They Had" has written a story set in the future to express his views about the best kind of education for young people. Why do you think he chose to deliver his message in a science fiction story rather than an essay on education? Write an essay in which you explain why Asimov chose this form of literature to express his views on the subject. Use quotations and examples from the story to support your explanation.

"A Dream Within a Dream" by Edgar Allan Poe
"The Spring and the Fall" by Edna St. Vincent Millay
"Ankylosaurus" by Jack Prelutsky

Selection Test

Critical Reading

On the line, write the letter of the one best answer.

____ 1. In "A Dream Within a Dream," when the speaker talks of sand slipping from his hand even as he tries to hold onto it, he is feeling
    a. that everything in his life is going wrong
    b. that things will get better soon
    c. that nothing he loves seems to last
    d. that bad will triumph over good

____ 2. Which pair of rhyming words is the only pair that occurs twice in "A Dream Within a Dream"?
    a. seem / dream   c. deep / weep
    b. deem / dream   d. brow / now

____ 3. The main idea of the poem "A Dream Within a Dream" is that
    a. there is no beauty in life
    b. nothing in life brings pleasure
    c. life is never easy
    d. nothing in life is lasting

____ 4. Which of the following is an inference you might draw about the speaker's feelings in "A Dream Within a Dream"?
    a. He feels life is a wonderful dream.
    b. The ocean makes him feel sad.
    c. He feels angry that he must part from someone he loves.
    d. He feels grief that he cannot hold onto life's precious things.

____ 5. In "The Spring and the Fall," the speaker's beloved
    a. was unkind in ways that seem small but really were important
    b. never talked to her unless he was angry
    c. refused to take walks with her
    d. stopped bringing her flowers

____ 6. Which set of words rhyme in the following lines from "The Spring and the Fall"?

    In the fall of the year, in the fall of the year, / I walked the road beside my dear. / The rooks went up with a raucous trill.

    a. roads, rook, raucous   c. fall, walked
    b. fall, trill   d. year, dear

____ 7. Which word below rhymes with the word *peach* in this line from "The Spring and the Fall"?

He broke me a bough of the blossoming peach / That was out of the way and hard to reach.

a. way   b. bough   c. hard   d. reach

____ 8. What is the meaning of this line from "The Spring and the Fall"?

He broke me a bough of the blossoming peach

a. The bough was a token of the man's love for the speaker.
b. The bough was in the way on the path.
c. The man's heart was broken.
d. The man was breaking off his relationship with the speaker.

____ 9. In "The Spring and the Fall," the speaker remembers that the person she loved
a. loved her in return in the beginning but then changed
b. loved her as much as she loved him
c. had to move away
d. liked long walks

____ 10. Which set of words below rhyme in the following lines from "Ankylosaurus"?

its hide was a fortress as sturdy as steel, / it tended to be an inedible meal.

a. sturdy, steel   c. steel, meal
b. tended, inedible   d. was, as

____ 11. In "Ankylosaurus," the prehistoric creature's body
a. was delicate and weak
b. had no tail
c. was tank-like and strong
d. had wings

____ 12. Which of the following is an inference you might draw based upon these lines from "Ankylosaurus"?

it waddled about on its four stubby legs, / nibbling on plants with a mouthful of pegs

a. Ankylosaurus was a vegetarian.
b. Ankylosaurus was a fierce hunter.
c. Ankylosaurus ate pegs.
d. Ankylosaurus was a swift runner.

____ 13. In "Ankylosaurus," the speaker believes that the dinosaur's brain
a. is intelligent and crafty   c is very complex
b. doesn't think very much   d. is enormous

Vocabulary, Spelling, and Grammar

____ 14. Which of the following is an incomplete sentence?
a. He kissed her goodbye.   c. The bough was bare.
b. When did they part?   d. Well, I never!

____ 15. Which of the following italicized words is spelled incorrectly?
a. His long hair grew over his *brough*.
b. Even *though* he hasn't succeeded, he is still trying.
c. I knew he was angry by his *frown*.
d. I *avow* that you are right.

_____ 16. Which of the following is an incomplete sentence?
   a. I see them yet, in the spring of the year.
   b. How few!
   c. Ankylosaurus was built like a tank.
   d. Take this kiss upon the brow!

_____ 17. Which of the following italicized words is spelled incorrectly?
   a. He didn't *allow* her to grieve.
   b. The tree *bow* broke.
   c. She remembers him *now*.
   d. He *thought* his days a dream.

_____ 18. In "A Dream Within a Dream," the speaker agrees with those who *deem* his days
   have been a dream. The best meaning for *deem* is
   a. feel
   b. hope
   c. judge
   d. allow the possibility

_____ 19. In "The Spring and the Fall," the rooks make *raucous* sounds, or sounds that are
   a. mocking
   b. soft and tender
   c. tapping
   d. loud and rowdy

_____ 20. In "Ankylosaurus," the ankylosaurus is *inedible*, or
   a. well protected from predators
   b. chewy and delicious to eat
   c. not able to be eaten
   d. strong

Essay Questions

21. Which of the three poems in this group of selections do you like the best? Choose "A Dream Within a Dream," "The Spring and the Fall," or "Ankylosaurus," and write an essay summarizing its ideas. Which words or passages from the poem stick in your mind? Quote those words or passages and explain what they mean.

22. Choose an image that you find particularly effective from "A Dream Within a Dream," "The Spring and the Fall," or "Ankylosaurus." In an essay, describe the image and explain its significance within the context of the poem. For example, if you chose the "pitiless wave" from "A Dream Within a Dream," you might explain that the wave represents time, which the speaker feels takes away everything that is beautiful and precious in life.

22. In an essay, compare and contrast "A Dream Within a Dream" and "The Spring and the Fall." Start by briefly stating the main idea of each poem. Then point out the ways in which the ideas in the two poems are similar and the ways they differ. Explain which poem seems to you more tragic, and why.

from *Exploring the* Titanic by Robert Ballard

Selection Test

Critical Reading

On the line, write the letter of the one best answer.

____ 1. Which of the following excerpts from the selection is the best example of a suspenseful detail?
    a. . . . water was pouring into the first five compartments.
    b. . . . it was Sunday and church services had been held.
    c. Jack ate alone in the first class dining room.
    d. Fred Fleet had passed a quiet watch.

____ 2. Which of the following excerpts from the story is an opinion?
    a. in the late afternoon, the temperature began to drop
    b. on Wednesday, April 10, the *Titanic* cast off
    c. the radio room received three more warnings
    d. such a close call . . . was a very bad omen

____ 3. After delivering the iceberg warning to the Captain, Bride thought that
    a. the captain had reacted too strongly
    b. the weather was beginning to change
    c. the captain seemed unconcerned
    d. Jack Phillips would be angry at him for taking so long

____ 4. Which of the following best describes the atmosphere as Jack Thayer hurries up on deck after the collision?
    a. frightening
    b. humorous
    c. outraged
    d. suspenseful

____ 5. Why does the *Titanic*'s near collision with another ship create suspense at the beginning of the story?
    a. because it was the fault of the *Titanic*'s crew
    b. because we know the *Titanic* will have a fatal collision on this voyage
    c. because the passengers don't know what's happening
    d. because Captain Smith seemed unconcerned

____ 6. Which of the following best describes the situation aboard ship immediately after the *Titanic* hit the iceberg?
    a. Passengers panicked and rushed to the lifeboats.
    b. Passengers and crew argued heatedly.
    c. Passengers were unaware of the seriousness of the collision.
    d. Passengers and crew braced themselves for another collision.

____ 7. Which of the following is an opinion rather than a fact?
    a. Darkness approached as the bugle call announced dinner.
    b. Then, in the late afternoon, the temperature began to drop rapidly.
    c. It was the kind of night that made one feel glad to be alive.
    d. He and his officers talked about how difficult it was to spot icebergs on a calm, clear, moonless night like this.

_____ 8. Which of the following details does the most to create an atmosphere of suspense to the story?
    a. There was a party going on in the captain's honor.
    b. There was so much confusion in the radio room that one of the iceberg warnings was never delivered.
    c. The day was sunny but cold.
    d. Harold Bride was exhausted.

_____ 9. The two wireless operators were tired Sunday morning because
    a. they had been arguing with each other all night
    b. they had been so seasick they hadn't sleep all night
    c. they'd been up for hours transmitting personal messages from passengers
    d. they had stayed up late at a party the night before

_____ 10. Which of the following excerpts is a fact and not an opinion?
    a. It was not a good sign.
    b. What danger could a few pieces of ice present?
    c. It looked as though they would miss it.
    d. At 7:30 P.M., the radio room received three more warnings.

_____ 11. According to the selection, why were some passengers on deck playing football with pieces of ice after the collision?
    a. They were sick of being confined to their cabins.
    b. They were trying to sneak into the lifeboats.
    c. The captain suggested they get some exercise.
    d. They didn't realize the seriousness of the accident.

_____ 12. Why does Bride's decision to take a nap late Sunday night add suspense to the story?
    a. You know that the disaster may happen at any moment.
    b. You wonder if the captain will be angry at Bride.
    c. Jack Phillips resents Bride's naps.
    d. He was supposed to meet Jack Thayer on deck.

_____ 13. The *Titanic*'s near collision at the beginning of the ship's maiden voyage was considered
    a. a sign of luck   c. a mechanical failure
    b. a bad omen   d. the other ship's fault

_____ 14. Which of the following best explains Phillips's words in this passage?

        . . . he cut off the California's radio operations with the words, 'Shut up, shut up, I'm busy.

    a. He was joking around.
    b. He was showing off in front of Bride.
    c. He was exhausted and irritable.
    d. He was following orders.

Vocabulary, Spelling, and Grammar

_____ 15. What is the best meaning of *majestically* in this passage from the selection?

        Moving *majestically* down the River Test, and watched by a crowd that had turned out for the occasion, the *Titanic* slowly passed two ships tied up to a dock.

    a. with splendor and dignity   c. slowly
    b. with disdain   d. nicely

_____ 16. Which of the following is an imperative sentence?
　　　　a. They were ordered to reverse the engines.
　　　　b. Reverse the engines.
　　　　c. Should I reverse the engines?
　　　　d. I can't believe they reversed the engines!

_____ 17. Which of the following contains a misspelled word?
　　　　a. The lookout had excellent vision.
　　　　b. It was a sad conclusion.
　　　　c. The captain's entrance was an intrusion.
　　　　d. No one expected the collizhun.

_____ 18. Which of the following is a declarative sentence?
　　　　a. Watch carefully for ice.
　　　　b. Send the call for assistance.
　　　　c. What did you see?
　　　　d. Bride had just awakened.

_____ 19. Which of the following best defines _novelty_ in this passage?

> In 1912, passengers . . . thought it was a real _novelty_ to send postcard-style messages . . .

　　　　a. a practical joke
　　　　b. something new and unusual
　　　　c. something boring and ordinary
　　　　d. an unpleasant task

_____ 20. Which kind of sentence is the following?

> Did it mean that the _Titanic_ might be too big a ship to handle safely?

　　　　a. interrogative　　　　　　　c. declarative
　　　　b. exclamatory　　　　　　　 d. imperative

Essay Questions

21. In an essay, imagine that you are either radio operator Harold Bride or Captain Smith. Give an account of events aboard the _Titanic_ as you see them. Use passages and quotations from the text to back up your account. Remember to keep events in the order that they are given in the story.

22. Write an essay explaining why you think the captain and crew ignored so many iceberg warnings. Start with the first warning received and describe the actions and reactions of the people involved. How might each person have made different choices? In your opinion, might this have changed the story's outcome?

23. Write an essay explaining how the author creates an atmosphere of suspense in the story. In your essay, cite at least three suspenseful details and describe how they drew you into the story's action. Tell how the suspenseful atmosphere made you question how or when the events would end. Was the sense of suspense over when the selection concluded?

Name _____ Date _____

"Breaker's Bridge" by Laurence Yep

Critical Reading

On the line, write the letter of the one best answer.

____ 1. Which sentence best summarizes "Breaker's Bridge"?
   a. Breaker almost loses his head.
   b. Breaker becomes friends with a strange old man.
   c. Breaker builds a bridge for the emperor with some help.
   d. Breaker's bridge is only half reliable.

____ 2. In the story, the failure of the second pier was due to
   a. Breaker's clumsiness
   b. the emperor's cunning
   c. the pellet's weak magic
   d. the river's wildness

____ 3. The main cause for the emperor wanting to build a bridge is so he can
   a. make his kingdom bigger
   b. get to his hunting palace easily
   c. visit the old man
   d. test Breaker's abilities

____ 4. The emperor and his officials knew the old man was magical when he
   a. spoke in a creaky voice
   b. carried a crutch
   c. made fun of the emperor
   d. appeared out of nowhere

____ 5. Breaker's determination to succeed against all odds was shown when he
   a. made the crutch for the old man
   b. accidentally crushed one of the pellets
   c. threw the pellets into the river
   d. befriended the old man

____ 6. The emperor was angry with Breaker because he
   a. hadn't built the bridge to last
   b. didn't finish the bridge
   c. used magic to build the bridge
   d. was friends with the old man

____ 7. The appearance of the old man before the emperor caused the emperor to
   a. forget about Breaker
   b. abandon the bridge
   c. become more cruel
   d. spare Breaker's life

____ 8. The main character trait of the emperor's official who brought the letter to Breaker was
   a. friendliness   c. thoughtfulness
   b. meanness   d. curiosity

____ 9. Breaker was afraid because he knew that if he failed
   a. the bridge would be destroyed
   b. he would be killed
   c. the emperor wouldn't hire him again
   d. he would be sent into exile

____ 10. What caused Breaker to make a crutch for the old man?
 a. The old man had broken his crutch.
 b. The old man had hurt his leg.
 c. Breaker wanted to be rid of him.
 d. Breaker wanted the old man to help him in return.

____ 11. What was the effect of Breaker's crushing the pellet?
 a. It made the second pier weak.
 b. It stopped the pier from materializing.
 c. It made both piers collapse.
 d. It made the bridge strong.

____ 12. The old man helped Breaker build the bridge with his
 a. technical skill
 b. magical powers
 c. practical advice
 d. great strength

____ 13. The emperor spared Breaker's life because
 a. Breaker was a powerful magician
 b. he felt sorry for Breaker
 c. Breaker had the support of an immortal
 d. Breaker had built a superb bridge

____ 14. The old man probably helped Breaker because Breaker had
 a. talked with him
 b. cut his fingers
 c. begged for his help
 d. made him a crutch

____ 15. One outstanding character trait of the old man is his
 a. foolishness   c. shyness
 b. fearlessness   d. wisdom

Vocabulary, Spelling, and Grammar

____ 16. Which is the indirect object in the following sentence?

 The old man gave him two pellets.

 a. man   c. pellets
 b. him   d. old

____ 17. Which word or words best define *piers* in this sentence from the story?

 The piers would support the bridge like miniature stone islands.

 a. supportive structures c. fishing docks
 b. islands   d. small bridges

____ 18. Which is spelled correctly?
 a. recieve   c. receive
 b. receeve   d. reiceve

____ 19. Which word is the direct object in this sentence from the story?

 Breaker shook his head in dismay.

 a. Breaker   c. his
 b. dismay   d. head

_____ 20. Which word best defines *writhing* in this sentence from the story?

> Pointed boulders thrust up like fangs, and the trees grew in twisted, *writhing* clumps.

    a. straight   c. turning
    b. tiny   d. neat

Essay Questions

21. In "Breaker's Bridge," Breaker is absolutely determined to build the bridge for the emperor, and he finally succeeds, despite many obstacles. Write an essay describing how Breaker shows determination at different times in the story. Support your explanation with details from the story.

22. It is easier to understand the events in "Breaker's Bridge" if you recognize the connections between causes and effects. A chief cause-and-effect relationship in "Breaker's Bridge" concerns how the emperor changes in the course of the story.Write an essay explaining how the old man's magic and his words change the emperor. Do you think the emperor will be a better ruler? Why or why not? Use details from the story to support your answers.

23. "Rivers are like people: Every now and then, they have to be reminded that change is the law that rules us all," the old man tells Breaker. In an essay, explain how the story supports this statement. Then explain why you agree or disagree with the statement.

"The Loch Ness Monster" by George Laycock
"Why the Tortoise's Shell Is Not Smooth" by Chinua Achebe

Selection Test

Critical Reading

On the line, write the letter of the one best answer.

_____ 1. According to "The Loch Ness Monster," officials in Scotland
    a. have taken steps to protect the Loch Ness monster
    b. have offered a reward to anyone who can capture the Loch Ness monster
    c. have issued warnings advising citizens and tourists to stay away from Loch Ness
    d. have repeatedly denied that the Loch Ness monster exists

_____ 2. What kinds of stories from oral tradition are mentioned in "The Loch Ness Monster"?
    a. stories that explain how Nessie came to live in Loch Ness
    b. stories that describe sightings of Nessie
    c. stories that tell about the terrible things that have happened to anyone who has ever claimed to see Nessie
    d. stories about how Nessie brings good luck to anyone who visits Loch Ness

_____ 3. George Laycock's purpose in writing "The Loch Ness Monster" is to
    a. persuade readers that the Loch Ness monster exists
    b. persuade readers that the Loch Ness monster does not exist
    c. inform readers about scientific research into the mystery of the Loch Ness monster
    d. entertain readers by sharing spooky and spine-tingling stories

_____ 4. Which phrase best describes the attitudes of the scientists whose work is discussed in "The Loch Ness Monster"?
    a. frustrated and disappointed
    b. unfair and biased
    c. skeptical and disbelieving
    d. curious and open-minded

_____ 5. According to "The Loch Ness Monster," photographs that are said to show the Loch Ness monster
    a. clearly reveal what the creature looks like
    b. contain indistinct images of a large, dark swimming creature
    c. have all been proved to be fakes
    d. are rumored to exist but have never been seen

_____ 6. After reading "The Loch Ness Monster," you can conclude that the depth of the water in Loch Ness
    a. provides support for those who think that the Loch Ness monster does not exist
    b. provides support for those who think that the Loch Ness monster does exist
    c. offers absolute proof that the Loch Ness monster exists
    d. has no bearing on the question of whether the Loch Ness monster exists

Unit 5: Mysterious Worlds

_____ 7. According to George Laycock in "The Loch Ness Monster,"
   a. the fact that Loch Ness has an abundant supply of fish proves that some large animals live there
   b. no one ever will be able to prove that Nessie is real
   c. the most persuasive evidence about Nessie comes from scientific study
   d. a driver's testimony is the best proof of Nessie's existence

_____ 8. Folk tales such as "Why the Tortoise's Shell Is Not Smooth" belong to the oral tradition. Which of the following also belongs to the oral tradition?
   a. a play based on a popular detective story
   b. a novel written one hundred and fifty years ago in New England
   c. a rhyme that young children chant while jumping rope
   d. a cartoon in today's newspaper

_____ 9. In "Why the Tortoise's Shell Is Not Smooth," the birds become angry at Tortoise because
   a. he claims that he is more beautiful than any of them
   b. he eats most of the food at a feast that they attend
   c. he steals their eggs
   d. he tricks them into making him their king

_____ 10. Which sentence best describes the lesson taught in "Why the Tortoise's Shell Is Not Smooth"?
   a. Patience and hard work are always rewarded.
   b. Never judge a person by his or her appearance.
   c. No one likes a person who is a smooth talker.
   d. A greedy and dishonest person may end up paying for his or her misdeeds.

_____ 11. "Why the Tortoise's Shell Is Not Smooth" is a traditional tale that explains
   a. how people should treat tortoises and other small animals
   b. how tortoises acquired their rough shells
   c. why it would be a bad thing for tortoises to have smooth shells
   d. why tortoises live on land

_____ 12. Why the Tortoise's Shell Is Not Smooth" shows that persuasive lies
   a. are not as powerful as the truth
   b. can fool someone who does not question their logic
   c. can be proven false by anyone who challenges them with the facts
   d. take place as often among animals as they do among people

_____ 13. In "Why the Tortoise's Shell Is Not Smooth," what trait does Tortoise reveal when he asks to be called _All of you_?
   a. cleverness   c. arrogance
   b. politeness   d. foolishness

_____ 14. Which of the following details from "Why the Tortoise's Shell Is Not Smooth" best suggests Tortoise's use of logic?
   a. "The custom here is to serve the spokesman first and the others later."
   b. Tortoise had no wings, but he went to the birds and asked to be allowed to go with them.
   c. His body rattled like a piece of dry stick in his empty shell.
   d. Tortoise had a sweet tongue . . .

Vocabulary, Spelling, and Grammar

____ 15. A creature that is *elusive* is
    a. familiar   c. remarkably intelligent
    b. tiny   d. always escaping

____ 16. Which sentence contains a predicate noun?
    a. Tortoises have rough shells.
    b. A tortoise's shell is hard.
    c. Tortoises are reptiles.
    d. The tortoise in the story was very sneaky.

____ 17. A subject complement follows a(n)
    a. action verb   c. adjective
    b. linking verb   d. noun

____ 18. Which words is not spelled correctly?
    a. independent   c. eloquant
    b. abundant   d. absent

____ 19. Which words is closest in meaning to *orator*?
    a. speaker   c. host
    b. author   d. guest

____ 20. In which sentence is the predicate adjective underlined?
    a. <u>Scotland</u> is beautiful at this time of year.
    b. The winters are quite <u>cold</u>.
    c. The people <u>are</u> helpful and friendly.
    d. Loch Ness is famous all over the <u>world</u>.

Essay Questions

21. Choose either "The Loch Ness Monster" or "Why the Tortoise's Shell Is Not Smooth" and explain in an essay how the work relates to the oral tradition. Briefly explain what the oral tradition is. Then explain how this tradition is reflected in the work you chose, citing specific passages or details to support your explanation.

22. Choose either "The Loch Ness Monster" or "Why the Tortoise's Shell Is Not Smooth" and write an essay in which you explain the author's purpose for writing. In addition to identifying the author's purpose, identify some of the details or passages that helped you recognize the purpose.

23. Write an essay in which you explain why you think it is important for writers and scholars to collect and preserve traditional tales such as "Why the Tortoises Shell Is Not Smooth." Where it is appropriate to do so, support your reasons with examples from the story.

Unit 5: Mysterious Worlds

Unit Test

Critical Reading

On the line, write the letter of the one best answer.

____ 1. In "The Fun They Had," Isaac Asimov gives a powerful message about education by
    a. presenting a summary of the history of education
    b. telling a sad story about a "classroom" that he does not like
    c. interviewing famous people about their memories of favorite teachers
    d. telling a fantastic story about life without classrooms or books

____ 2. Which detail from "The Fun They Had" shows that the story is science fiction?
    a. Margie hates school and is having a hard time learning history.
    b. Tommy has found a dusty old book in his attic.
    c. Tommy and Margie find it strange that the words in the old book do not move.
    d. Margie does not understand why anyone would write a book about school.

____ 3. In "The Fun They Had," people believe that one advantage of a teaching machine over a human teacher is that
    a. machines make learning more enjoyable
    b. machines can be adjusted to the ability of each individual student
    c. machines can work longer and harder
    d. students can take teaching machines wherever they go

____ 4. In "The Fun They Had," Margie hates school because
    a. she wishes she could be taught by a human being instead of a machine
    b. she doesn't think going to school is necessary
    c. she thinks history is boring
    d. she hates having to do her homework in a special code

____ 5. Which word best describes the speaker's attitude in "A Dream Within a Dream"?
    a. grieving
    b. uncertain
    c. optimistic
    d. amazed

____ 6. In "A Dream Within a Dream," what does the speaker claim to be holding?
    a. a cloud
    b. the heart of a loved one
    c. bitter tears
    d. golden sand

____ 7. Which inference can you draw about the speaker of "The Spring and the Fall"?
    a. She looks back on her lost love with amusement.
    b. She still feels pain when thinking about her lost love.
    c. She will never let herself fall in love again.
    d. She wants badly to find a new love.

____ 8. Which two adjectives best describe the creature in "Ankylosaurus"?

    I. ferocious   II. dim-witted   III. thick-skinned   IV. timid

    a. II and III   b. I and II   c. II and IV   d. I and III

____ 9. Which detail from *Exploring the* Titanic is an opinion?
    a. It was the kind of night that made one glad to be alive.
    b. Two more ice warnings were received from nearby ships around lunch time.
    c. Before going to bed, the captain ordered the lookouts to keep a sharp watch for ice.
    d. A few minutes later, the *Titanic* came to a stop.

____ 10. In *Exploring the* Titanic, it is suggested most strongly that
    a. the crew of the *Titanic* was very worried about icebergs
    b. if not for human error, the *Titanic* would not have gone down
    c. the *Titanic* was poorly designed
    d. the *Titanic* needed more watertight compartments

____ 11. In Exploring the *Titanic*, why was Harold Bride's job so important to the safety of the ship?
    a. He had to make sure the passengers were having a pleasant journey.
    b. He had to give directions to the captain about their destination.
    c. He had to bring messages to the captain regarding the ship.
    d. He was in charge of the men fueling the ship.

____ 12. As Robert Ballard describes it, the atmosphere on the *Titanic* during the day on Sunday was one of
    a. near panic
    b. easy relaxation
    c. cautious optimism
    d. growing anger

____ 13. Which is an outstanding character trait of the emperor in "Breaker's Bridge"?
    a. intelligence   b. honesty   c. inflexibility   d. loyalty

____ 14. In "Breaker's Bridge," when the old man first speaks to Breaker, Breaker is
    a. curious how the old man knows about the emperor's threat
    b. annoyed because the old man is distracting him
    c. angry because of the old man's disrespect
    d. respectful because the old man has great power

____ 15. In "Breaker's Bridge," the old man teaches Breaker and the emperor that
    a. selfishness is wrong, regardless of a person's position in society
    b. no man has the right to take another's life
    c. anything is possible if you try hard enough
    d. some things are meant to last and others are meant to change

____ 16. As George Laycock suggests in "The Loch Ness Monster," the most logical proof that Nessie exists is
  a. a sketch by an observer
  b. sounds recorded from an underwater microphone
  c. a sighting by a tugboat captain
  d. photographs from an underwater camera

____ 17. Which sentence best sums up "Why the Tortoise's Shell Is Not Smooth"?
  a. After the tortoise tricks the birds out of their food, they cause him to fall back to earth and break his shell.
  b. The tortoise tries to get the birds to share, but they make him fall back to earth and break his shell.
  c. After the tortoise tricks the birds into helping him fly, the birds make him fall.
  d. After the tortoise joins the birds for a feast, they make him fall to earth.

____ 18. Which of the following could be part of an oral tradition?
  a. a story about a star athlete
  b. an instruction manual for a computer
  c. a story about how the zebra got its stripes
  d. a news item about a recent election

____ 19. According to "The Loch Ness Monster," the most likely place in which a previously unknown animal is likely to be found is
  a. in a dense jungle   c. in an arid desert
  b. in a very deep body of water   d. near the North or South Pole

Vocabulary, Grammar, and Spelling

____ 20. Which word is the subject complement in the following sentence?

  He was tired after having spent the whole day working on the farm.

  a. whole   b. farm   c. He   d. tired

____ 21. A person who is a great *orator* is skilled in
  a. speaking   b. writing   c. painting   d. cooking

____ 22. Which of the following words is misspelled?
  a. thought   b. brawt   c. ought   d. straw

____ 23. Which of the following sentences contains *two* indirect objects?
  a. The teacher showed my friend and me the answer to the problem.
  b. For lunch yesterday, I ate a sandwich and an apple.
  c. She took her younger brother to the zoo and the planetarium.
  d. Our dog and cat are good friends.

____ 24. Which of the following words is a compound adjective?
  a. worthless   b. thankful   c. foolproof   d. laughable

____ 25. Which of the following words is spelled correctly?
  a. pierce   b. wieght   c. beleive   d. decieve

____ 26. What is the direct object in the following sentence?

  I drew a picture of my dog for art class.

  a. dog   b. I   c. class   d. picture

____ 27. Which word is most nearly opposite in meaning to *elusive*?
　　　　a. vague　　　　　　b. obvious　　　　　c. truthful　　　　　d. secret

____ 28. Which is *not* a complete sentence?
　　　　a. Give me the book.　　　　　　c. I am sorry.
　　　　b. He didn't know.　　　　　　　d. What a mess!

____ 29. Which word is misspelled?
　　　　a. shift　　　　　　b. mustache　　　　c. pistashio　　　　d. fresh

____ 30. What is the complete subject of the following sentence?

> Most of the people in the American colonies did not believe that
> England was treating them fairly.

　　　　a. most of the people in the American colonies
　　　　b. most of the people
　　　　c. the people in the American colonies
　　　　d. the people

Essay Questions

31. What might make a nonfiction article or essay "mysterious"? It could be suspense—the feeling that you want to know what is going to happen next; it might be a question to which no one knows the answer. Choose either "The Loch Ness Monster" or *Exploring the Titanic* and write an essay explaining what makes it mysterious. Explain what a reader might find exciting or fascinating in it. Use details from the selection to support your analysis.

32. Poems, like prose, can deal with the world of the imagination and create an air of mystery or even fear. In an essay, discuss why "A Dream Within a Dream" can be said to deal with the imaginary world. Describe the atmosphere that Poe creates, with an explanation of how he does so. Support your ideas with details from the poem.

33. Stories that focus on the world of the imagination always contain elements that do not exist in the real world, but they also include realistic aspects. This is true of "The Fun They Had," "Breaker's Bridge," and even "Why the Tortoise's Shell Is Not Smooth." Choose two of these stories and write an essay in which you identify those parts of the stories that are realistic and those that are imaginary. For each story, suggest a purpose the author may have had for using imaginary details. Refer to passages from the stories to illustrate your position.

34. Poets use the device of *repetition*—of a word or a phrase—for different purposes. Write an essay in which you describe the way in which repetition is used in "Ankylosaurus." Write which words or groups of words are repeated, and explain the effect the author wants to achieve by repeating the words. In your conclusion, explain how you rate the effectiveness of the repetition.

35. One of the minor themes of Unit 5 is "Dealing with Loss." The "loss" can refer to objects that are lost (or that are hard to find), to people who have been lost, to lost pleasures or plans that have fallen apart, and so on. Choose two selections from this unit that you think address this theme. In an essay, explain your choices—that is, tell why you think each selection can be said to be about a loss of some kind. Use details from the selections to support your ideas.

Unit 5: Mysterious Worlds

Alternative Unit Test

The two passages below are followed by questions based on their content and on the relationship between the two passages.

Passage 1

The following passage is from a science fiction story that takes place in the future, when the people of Earth are enslaved by aliens from Venus. Traveling in machines called Tripods, the aliens control humans' minds by placing Caps on people's heads. The speaker is about to attempt an escape from England to Switzerland, the only place where humans are still free.

from *The White Mountains* by John Christopher

There was heavy rain during the next two days, but after that it cleared, and a blazing hot afternoon dried up most of the mud. Everything went well. Before going to bed, I had hidden my clothes and pack and a couple of big loaves with them. After that it was only a matter of staying awake, and keyed up as I was, it did not prove difficult. Eventually Henry's breathing, on the far side of the room, became deep and even in sleep. I lay and thought about the journey: the sea, the strange lands beyond, the Great Lake, and the mountains on which snow lay all summer through. Even without what I had learned of the Tripods and the Caps, the idea was exciting.

The moon rose above the level of my window, and I slipped out of bed. Carefully I opened the bedroom door, and carefully closed it after me. The house was very quiet. The stairs creaked a little under my feet, but no one would pay attention even if they heard it. It was an old wooden house, and creakings at night were not unusual. I went through the big door to the mill room, found my clothes, and dressed quickly. Then out through the door by the river.

Passage 2

In the following passage the narrator, Steve, is about to tell his best friend Max that he has purchased a time machine.

from *Max and Me and the Time Machine* by Gerry Greer and Bob Ruddick

I guess I'm like everybody else. When I do something that's pretty terrific, I expect to get some credit for it. A little praise, a pat on the back, a bit of wild, thunderous applause—maybe even a chorus of "Bravo! Fantastic! Way to go!"

And that's just what I was expecting when I hauled that huge crate into our clubhouse and told my best friend, Max Zielinski, that it contained a time machine I had picked up at a garage sale down the street. For $2.50.

But Max did not applaud. He snorted.

"Who're you trying to kid, Steve?" he said, barely glancing up from the electronics book he was reading. "There's no such thing as time travel. Or time machines."

I wiped the sweat off my forehead with the back of my sleeve and slouched against the crate. "When have I ever lied to you?" I asked, trying to look hurt and sincere at the same time.

"An interesting question," said Max, carefully laying his book aside on the rumpled cot and holding up his fingers to count on. "Now, let me see, I can recall the Rotten Toboggan Affair..."

Critical Reading

On the line, write the letter of the one best answer.

_____ 1. How is the narrator of Passage 1 similar to the narrator in Passage 2?
   a. Both narrators are trying to escape to a new life of freedom.
   b. Both narrators seem open to new experiences.
   c. Both narrators share a need to be right.
   d. Both narrators are electronics experts.
   e. Both narrators share a good sense of humor.

_____ 2. Which of the following statements from Passage 1 expresses an opinion rather than a fact?
   a. There was heavy rain during the next two days . . .
   b. I lay and thought about the journey . . .
   c. The moon rose above the level of my window, and I slipped out of bed.
   d. Everything went well.
   e. Eventually Henry's breathing, on the far side of the room, became deep and even in sleep.

_____ 3. Which of the following statements best describes the mood of the narrator of Passage 1?
   a. He is depressed.
   b. He is lonely.
   c. He is excited about the journey.
   d. He is sorry that Henry can't accompany him.
   e. He regrets that he can't travel in the rain.

_____ 4. Steve believes that Max is
   a. afraid to try anything new
   b. a genius
   c. overly enthusiastic about the time machine
   d. easily distracted
   e. not giving him the praise he deserves

_____ 5. Based on your reading of both passages, how does science fiction sometimes resemble the real world?
   a. It reflects human emotions and desires.
   b. It takes you out of your own life.
   c. It can teach you about robots.
   d. It is imaginary.
   e. It is about places unlike anywhere on Earth.

_____ 6. Which of the following adjectives best describes the character of the narrator of Passage 1?
   a. sloppy
   b. careless
   c. fearful
   d. careful
   e. unpredictable

_____ 7. From Passage 2, you can infer that Max believes that Steve
   a. is boring
   b. can be too serious
   c. at times stretches the truth
   d. is of fine character
   e. can be believed at all times

____ 8. Which of the following contributes most to the atmosphere of suspense in Passage 1?
   a. the way the character pays attention to the weather
   b. the way the character must act in secret
   c. the fact that the Tripods might catch Henry sleeping
   d. the fact that a river flows near the old house
   e. the fact that the character is going away

____ 9. In which of the following ways are Steve and Max different from the narrator of Passage 1?
   a. The narrator of Passage 1 has a better sense of humor than Steve and Max.
   b. Steve and Max joke around more than the narrator of Passage 1.
   c. Steve and Max are more serious than the narrator of Passage 1.
   d. Steve and Max are less likely than the narrator of Passage 1 to do something foolish.
   e. Unlike the narrator of Passage 1, Steve and Max know how to prepare for anything.

____ 10. What effect is created by the repetition of the word *carefully* in the following sentence from Passage 1?

   Carefully I opened the bedroom door, and *carefully* closed it after me.

   a. It creates suspense by emphasizing how careful the narrator had to be.
   b. The words sound like a door opening and closing.
   c. It reminds the reader that it was the bedroom door that was opened and closed.
   d. It creates a monotonous effect that relaxes the reader.
   e. It surprises the reader.

____ 11. Which of the following choices contains clues that both Passage 1 and Passage 2 are science fiction pieces?
   a. The heavy rain of Passage 1 and the huge crate of Passage 2
   b. The moon rising in Passage 1 and the electronics book of Passage 2
   c. The Caps of Passage 1 and the Rotten Toboggan Affair of Passage 2
   d. the Tripods of Passage 1 and the time machine of Passage 2
   e. Henry's breathing in Passage 1 and the lack of applause in Passage 2

____ 12. Which of the following shows that the narrator of Passage 1 prepares carefully for his journey?
   a. He hides his clothes, some food and his pack.
   b. He gets a good night's rest.
   c. He doesn't wake Henry up.
   d. He waits until the rain stops.
   e. He waits until the moon rises.

____ 13. Which of the following is the best summary of both passages?
   a. In Passage 1, the narrator thinks about the dangers that await him. In Passage 2, Steve thinks of how excited Max will be.
   b. In Passage 1, the narrator waits for the rain to stop before he begins his journey. In Passage 2, Steve waits for applause.
   c. In Passage 1, the narrator describes how he begins his journey. In Passage 2, Steves brings a crated time machine into the clubhouse and Max scoffs at the idea of time travel.
   d. In Passage 1, the narrator hides his possessions. In Passage 2, Steve brings the crate into the clubhouse.
   e. In Passage 1, the narrator relates how important it is for him to stay awake and be quiet. In Passage 2, Max questions Steve's truthfulness by reminding him of the Rotten Toboggan Affair.

____ 14. The author of Passage 2 portrays Steve and Max as being
   a. lazy individuals who waste time
   b. typical friends who have shared adventures together
   c. deceitful enemies who are careful about what they say to each other
   d. two of the finest young people in the world
   e. individuals of little intelligence who are not interested in reading

____ 15. If there is a message common to both passages, it might be that people
   a. should keep an open mind about the possibility of life beyond the solar system
   b. should be cautious when dealing with space aliens
   c. in the future might participate in adventures and experiences that can now only be imagined
   d. should consider all the evidence before denouncing an idea
   e. in the distant past might have had the same experiences that we are having now

Essay Questions

16. In both passages, the author creates an atmosphere of suspense. In an essay, explain which specific details in each passage make you nervous or anxious to find out what will happen next. Tell which passage you find more suspenseful, and explain why you think that passage is more suspenseful than the other.

17. The narrator of Passage 1 and Steve, the narrator of Passage 2, are both characters in science fiction literature. They have certain character traits in common, but in some ways they are different. Write an essay in which you compare and contrast the traits of the two characters. Use specific quotations and examples from the two passages to support your points.

18. Both of these science-fiction passages hint at an anticipated adventure—that is, at an adventure yet to come.In an essay, compare and contrast the anticipated adventure of each passage. First, identify the anticipated adventure of each passage. Then, list clues from the passages that indicate what might happen during that adventure. Finally, indicate which anticipated adventure you think will be more exciting and explain why.

"Dragon, Dragon" by John Gardner

Selection Test

Critical Reading

On the line, write the letter of the best answer.

_____ 1. The king calls a meeting of everyone in the kingdom in order to
   a. praise his knights and his wizard
   b. find a way to stop the dragon that has been plaguing the kingdom
   c. find a husband for his daughter
   d. announce his intention to retire

_____ 2. Which statement tells how the king's knights and the king's wizard are similar?
   a. Both have helped the king solve many problems in the past.
   b. Both are devoted to the queen.
   c. Both are away from the kingdom when the dragon starts his rampage.
   d. Both fail to stand up to the dragon.

_____ 3. Which word best describes the wizard?
   a. powerful   c. bad
   b. incompetent   d. skillful

_____ 4. Who is the cause of the main problem that the characters in the story face?
   a. the queen   c. the dragon
   b. the king   d. the wizard

_____ 5. Read the following passage. Then choose the statement that best explains why John Gardner includes this detail in his story.

   "Oh yes," said the king. "I'll tell you what I'll do. I'll give the princess's hand in marriage to anyone who can make the dragon stop."

   "It's not enough," said the cobbler. "She's a nice enough girl, you understand. But how would an ordinary person support her? Also, what about those of us that are already married?"

   a. It adds suspense to the story.
   b. It adds humor to the story.
   c. It helps to show how ineffective and foolish the king is.
   d. It makes the story sound like a traditional fairy tale.

_____ 6. The cobbler feels that he, unlike the other people at the king's meeting,
   a. is the only one that knows there is no way to kill the dragon
   b. has children who are brave enough to face the dragon
   c. has the best plan for solving the kingdom's problem
   d. does not deserve to attend the meeting

_____ 7. What elements of the story do the details in the following passage provide?

> Every time there was a full moon the dragon came out of his lair and ravaged the countryside. He frightened maidens and stopped up chimneys and broke store windows and set people's clocks back and made dogs bark until no one could hear himself think.

    a. background—the way things normally are in the kingdom
    b. character—the dragon's physical appearance
    c. problem—the trouble that the dragon is causing
    d. conclusion—the way that the story ends

_____ 8. When the youngest son recites his poem, the dragon
    a. turns into a mouse
    b. trembles with fear
    c. cries with laughter
    d. expresses his admiration for the young man's talents

_____ 9. Suppose that a television reporter interviewed the youngest son at the end of the story. Which quality would the young man say held the secret to his success?
    a. strength   c. courage
    b. cleverness   d. loyalty

_____ 10. The climax, or turning point, of the story occurs when
    a. the eldest son is eaten by the dragon
    b. the middle son is eaten by the dragon
    c. the youngest son puts on his armor
    d. the youngest son kills the dragon

_____ 11. How does the dragon respond to the coming of the three sons?
    a. He keeps the first son waiting outside but waits for the other two inside.
    b. He runs from the first son but stands his ground against the other two.
    c. He rushes out to attack the first two sons but hides from the third.
    d. He expects the coming of the first son but is surprised by the coming of the other two.

_____ 12. Which of the following occurs during the resolution, or conclusion, of the story?
    a. The king calls a meeting of everyone in the kingdom.
    b. The wizard changes the queen into a rosebush.
    c. The youngest son kills the dragon.
    d. The youngest son returns the wizard's book of spells.

_____ 13. Who follows the wise old cobbler's advice?
    a. the eldest son   c. the youngest son
    b. the middle son   d. the king

_____ 14. Which of the following best sums up the lesson that the three sons learn as a result of their experiences?
    a. It pays to listen to a wise old person's advice, even if the advice doesn't seem to make sense.
    b. Never listen to anyone else's advice, no matter how wise and useful it may seem.
    c. Never confront a dragon in his own lair.
    d. People who have confidence in themselves always succeed.

Vocabulary, Spelling, and Grammar

____ 15. Which of the underlined words does not contain a long *i* sound that is spelled with a *y*?
   a. These cookies are very tasty.
   b. They should satisfy your craving for something sweet.
   c. It is illegal to park in front of a fire hydrant.
   d. Is this your typewriter?

____ 16. Which of the following sentences contains a subordinate clause?
   a. There once was a dragon who frightened many people.
   b. The dragon's name was Gorgon.
   c. It lived in a cave.
   d. One day, a brave princess challenged the dragon.

____ 17. If you seem to be *reflecting* about something, you seem to be
   a. asking about it   c. singing about it
   b. speaking about it   d. thinking about it

____ 18. In which sentence is the underlined word misspelled?
   a. The king was a tyrant.
   b. His tierannical actions made him very unpopular.
   c. The people in his kingdom became tired of living under such tyranny.
   d. They had been tyrannized long enough.

____ 19. If a dragon *ravages* a town, it
   a. destroys the town   c. avoids the town
   b. visits the town   d. protects the town

____ 20. In which sentence is the subordinate clause underlined?
   a. Please come to our party, even if you can't stay very long.
   b. After she comes home from school, Shelley feeds her cat and walks her dog.
   c. Ted plans to buy a new bicycle as soon as he has saved enough money.
   d. Aunt Alice sends me a postcard whenever she goes on a trip.

Essay Questions

21. In an essay, explain the plot of "Dragon, Dragon." In your explanation, define the term *plot* and identify the basic parts of a plot. Use examples from the story to support your explanation.

22. Write an essay in which you compare and contrast "Dragon, Dragon" with a traditional fairy tale, such as "Little Red Riding Hood" or "Beauty and the Beast." Point out the similarities and differences in the problems the characters face and how they solve their problems. Cite specific events and details from the stories to support your comparison.

23. In an essay, identify two reading strategies that you applied while reading "Dragon, Dragon." Then explain how each strategy helped you understand the story. For example, explain how you identified with a character or situation; made predictions about what might happen further along in the story; drew inferences, or guesses, based on details in the story; or used details to envision the action and setting. Use specific examples from the text to support your explanation.

"Becky and the Wheels-and-Brake Boys" by James Berry

Selection Test

Critical Reading

On the line, write the letter of the best answer.

_____ 1. The main force opposing Becky in her campaign to get a bicycle is
   a. Becky's cousin Ben
   b. Mr. Dean
   c. Becky's mother
   d. the boys in town

_____ 2. Becky thinks that if she had a bike of her own,
   a. she would be able to ride faster than the boys
   b. the boys would want her to ride with them
   c. the boys would envy her new bike
   d. she wouldn't have to stay home all the time

_____ 3. Which of the following best describes the main conflict in the story?
   a. Becky wants to learn how to ride a bike, but the boys won't teach her.
   b. Becky wants a bike, but her mother doesn't want her to have one.
   c. Becky wants to make up with Shirnette, but Shirnette won't talk to her.
   d. Becky wants a bike, but her mother can't afford one and thinks that bikes are
      only for boys.

_____ 4. Becky's mother agrees to Mr. Dean's offer to sell Becky a bicycle because
   a. she can afford the small payments and she wants Becky to be happy
   b. she doesn't want Mr. Dean to know how poor the family is
   c. she no longer thinks that girls shouldn't ride bikes
   d. she is afraid that Becky will be angry if she refuses

_____ 5. What does Granny-Liz mean in this line from the story?

   A tomboy's like a whistling woman and a crowing hen, who can only come to a
   bad end.

   a. Only men can whistle, and only roosters can crow.
   b. If Becky had a bike, she probably would fall down and hurt herself.
   c. Some things are just for boys, and girls should not try to do them.
   d. It's bad luck for a woman to whistle.

_____ 6. Becky's mother must work especially hard because
   a. Becky wants to buy so many expensive things
   b. Granny-Liz lives with her
   c. she wants her sons and daughters to have everything they want
   d. she has to support her family without a husband to help her

_____ 7. Which sentence best expresses the relationship between Becky and her mother?
   a. They love and respect each other, but they don't always agree.
   b. They barely speak to each other.
   c. Becky's mother loves her but doesn't care if Becky is happy.
   d. Becky is so selfish that all she cares about is getting her way.

____ 8. What might the following passage of the story lead you to predict?

> By Saturday morning I felt real sorry for Mum. I could see Mum really had it hard for money. I had to try and help. I knew anything of Dad's—anything—would be worth a great mighty hundred dollars.

   a. Becky will try to sell one of her father's possessions.
   b. Becky will try to earn money by getting a part-time job.
   c. Becky will tell her mother she doesn't really need a bike after all.
   d. Becky will find a hundred dollars that her father left for her.

____ 9. Which of the sentences below most clearly states the conflict between Becky and the Wheels-and-Brake Boys?
   a. Becky wants the boys to let her watch them ride, but they always ride away.
   b. Becky wants to ride with the boys, but the boys don't like her.
   c. Becky wants the boys to teach her how to ride, but they refuse.
   d. The boys are envious of Becky's new bike.

____ 10. The person in the story who first helps Becky to resolve her conflict is
   a. Mr. Dean, the fireman
   b. Becky's cousin Ben
   c. Shirnette, Becky's friend
   d. Becky's mother

____ 11. What would the following words, spoken by Becky's mother, lead you to predict about Becky's chances of getting a bike?

> Becky, d'you think you're a boy? Eh? D'you think you're a boy? In any case, where's the money to come from? Eh?

   a. Becky's mother will never let her have a bike.
   b. Becky's mother will get her a bike if Becky promises not to ride with the boys.
   c. Becky's mother may agree to let Becky have a bike if she can afford it.
   d. Becky's mother will give in if Becky promises to help more at home.

____ 12. Why does Mr. Dean laugh when Becky asks him to buy her father's sun helmet to use as a fireman's hat?
   a. He thinks Becky is joking.
   b. He already has a fireman's hat and has no need for the sun helmet.
   c. Although he would like to buy the sun helmet, he doesn't have enough money to pay for it.
   d. Although he can't use the hat, he is impressed by Becky's spunk and determination.

____ 13. Which of the following observations about Becky best helps you to predict the ending of the story?
   a. She misses her father, who has died.
   b. She decides to improve her appearance after her mother criticizes her.
   c. She thinks Shirnette could help persuade the boys to teach her to ride a bike.
   d. She never gives up trying to persuade her mother to let her have a bike.

____ 14. At the end of the story, which prediction might you make about Becky's future?
   a. Becky's friends will become jealous of her because she now has a bicycle.
   b. Becky will realize that having a bicycle is not as wonderful as she thought.
   c. Becky will succeed at reaching other goals that are important to her.
   d. Becky and Shirnette will decide to form their own bicycle club.

____ 15. Why doesn't Becky's mother want her to have a bike?

    a. The family cannot afford a bike.

    b. The family cannot afford a bike, and she thinks bikes are only for boys.

    c. She thinks that bikes are only for boys.

    d. She thinks that Becky asks for too many expensive things.

Vocabulary, Spelling, and Grammar

____ 16. Which of the phrases below best defines the word *reckless* in the following sentence from the story?

> Next, most reckless and fierce, all the boys raced against each other.

    a. brave and daring   c. not caring about danger

    b. unskilled and clumsy   d. not caring about winning

____ 17. Which word comes closest in meaning to *veranda*?

    a. pond   c. roof

    b. porch   d. sidewalk

____ 18. In which of the following sentences is the independent clause underlined?

    a. <u>After dinner</u> Becky carefully combed her hair.

    b. After dinner <u>Becky carefully combed her hair.</u>

    c. After dinner Becky <u>carefully combed her</u> hair.

    d. <u>After dinner Becky</u> carefully combed her hair.

____ 19. Which of the following words is *not* spelled correctly?

    a. tennis   c. neckliss

    b. menace   d. furnace

____ 20. Which of the following is an independent clause in this sentence?

> When she can borrow a bike, Shirnette comes too.

    a. Shirnette comes too   c. borrow a bike

    b. can borrow   d. When she can borrow a bike

Essay Questions

21. Do you think Becky is right or wrong to try so hard to get a bicycle for herself? Is she just being selfish in trying to obtain something her family cannot afford, or are there good reasons for her actions in the story? Write an essay expressing your opinion. Use examples from the story and what you have learned from your own experience to back up your point of view.

22. How do Becky's ideas of what a girl's life should be differ from her mother's? How do their different opinions contribute to the conflict between mother and daughter? Write an essay contrasting their ideas and explaining how and why a conflict develops between the two characters. Use quotes, details, and examples from the story to support your ideas. Conclude your essay by explaining how the conflict is resolved in the story.

23. In "Becky and the Wheels-and-Brake Boys," we learn about the conflict through Becky's point of view. If the story were being told by Becky's mother, how might events be presented? In an essay, explain how Becky's mother would see the situation as it unfolds. Concentrate on the main events surrounding the conflict between Becky and her mother. Use quotes and examples from the story to support your ideas.

"**Overdoing It**" by Anton Chekhov
"**Eleven**" by Sandra Cisneros

Selection Test

Critical Reading

On the line, write the letter of the best answer.

_____ 1. In "Overdoing It," which of the following best describes the train station?
     a. new and shiny   c. lonely and forsaken
     b. cheerful and comfortable   d. beautiful and fancy

_____ 2. In "Overdoing It," why is the surveyor scared?
     a. He is a coward.
     b. The wagon driver doesn't know how to drive.
     c. He is alone on a lonely road with a stranger.
     d. The wagon driver is rude to him.

_____ 3. In "Overdoing It," which words best describe the personality of Klim, the wagon driver?
     a. friendly and outgoing   c. sad and depressed
     b. nasty and rude   d. bored and indifferent

_____ 4. In "Overdoing It," how does Gleb Smirnov overdo it?
     a. He talks too much.
     b. He becomes so frightened that he runs into the forest in the middle of the trip.
     c. He has to take a long trip to a strange place.
     d. Trying to hide his own fear, he scares the driver away.

_____ 5. Which of the following describes how the surveyor says he deals with troublemakers?
     a. with forgiveness
     b. with violence
     c. with hatred
     d. with kindness

_____ 6. Why do you suppose that, at the end of "Overdoing It," the road and Klim no longer seem threatening to the surveyor?
     a. The surveyor finally learns the way to the estate.
     b. The surveyor and Klim become friends.
     c. Klim promises to protect the surveyor.
     d. The surveyor discovers that Klim actually is afraid of him.

_____ 7. Which of the following is an example of direct characterization of Gleb Smirnov in "Overdoing It"?
     a. "Where are you, Klimushka?"
     b. "You'll ki-i-i-ill me!"
     c. The road and Klim no longer seemed to him threatening.
     d. "I was just kidding, and got scared."

_____ 8. In what place does Rachel, in "Eleven," want to put the red sweater?
  a. desk
  b. garbage can
  c. alley
  d. box

_____ 9. In "Eleven," why does Rachel wish she were one-hundred-and-two instead of eleven?
  a. If she were very old, she wouldn't have to go to school.
  b. She doesn't like being eleven.
  c. She wishes she could grow up faster.
  d. If she were older, she would know what to say to Mrs. Price.

_____ 10. In "Eleven," why doesn't Rachel want her classmates to think she owns the red sweater?
  a. It doesn't fit her properly, and she doesn't want to look silly in it.
  b. It is an ugly, smelly sweater, and she doesn't want to have anything to do with it.
  c. She doesn't want her friends to think she lost her sweater.
  d. She doesn't like the color red.

_____ 11. In "Eleven," which sentence best explains why Rachel's teacher, Mrs. Price, is so sure the sweater belongs to Rachel?
  a. The sweater has Rachel's name on it.
  b. Rachel doesn't speak up immediately to say the sweater isn't hers.
  c. All the students in the class agree that the sweater belongs to Rachel.
  d. Mrs. Price saw Rachel wearing the sweater.

_____ 12. In "Eleven," which statement best summarizes why Rachel says you can be eleven, but also younger ages at the same time?
  a. People sometimes behave in ways they did at younger ages.
  b. You never forget what it was like to be a child.
  c. Some people never really act their age.
  d. Young children are always wishing they were older.

_____ 13. When Rachel is made to wear the red sweater, she feels
  a. bored   c. embarrassed and miserable
  b. guilty   d. hot and itchy

_____ 14. In "Eleven," what does Rachel mean by "too late," when she says

  There'll be candles and presents and everybody will sing happy birthday, . . . only it's too late.

  a. Her birthday party is happening too late at night.
  b. The party won't matter because her day has already been ruined.
  c. Her party won't be a surprise, because she already knows about it.
  d. She's too embarrassed for her classmates to come to the party.

Vocabulary, Spelling, and Grammar

_____ 15. Which is closest in meaning to _prolonged_?
  a. longer than expected
  b. helpful
  c. short and quick
  d. long and drawn out

_____ 16. Which is the subordinate clause in this sentence?

We didn't go outside all day because it rained without stopping.

    a. We didn't go outside all day
    b. because it rained without stopping
    c. it rained without stopping
    d. without stopping

_____ 17. In which sentence should a homophone be used in place of the word in italics?
    a. When the man heard the bad joke, he made a _rye_ face.
    b. Please _wrap_ the present for me.
    c. _Wring_ out the wet towel before you hang it up to dry.
    d. I'll _write_ my thank-you letter tomorrow.

_____ 18. Why is the underlined clause in this sentence a subordinate clause?

Rachel's birthday was ruined <u>because Mrs. Price made her wear the red sweater</u>.

    a. There is no verb.
    b. There is no subject.
    c. The words don't come at the beginning of the sentence.
    d. The words depend on the rest of the sentence for their meaning.

_____ 19. Which words are a subordinate clause in this sentence?

She held in her tears until she could no longer stop them.

    a. stop them
    b. her tears
    c. until she could no longer stop them
    d. She held in her tears

_____ 20. Which is the best meaning for the word _emerged_ in this line from "Overdoing It"?

Klim . . . _emerged_ from the thicket and hesitantly approached his passenger.

    a. jumped up and down   c. crawled like a snake
    b. came out   d. bent down low

Essay Questions

21. When you identify with a character, you try to understand what it would feel like to be that character and have the same experiences. In an essay, explain how you would feel if you were Gleb Smirnov in "Overdoing It" or Rachel in "Eleven." Choose several events from the story and tell how you would feel during or after each one.

22. Each of these stories relates to the theme "Difficult Days." Choose either "Overdoing It" or "Eleven" and in an essay explain how the story relates to this theme. For the story you choose, explain how the day is difficult and how the character resolves the difficulty or difficulties. Quote passages from the story to support your points.

23. In "Overdoing It" and "Eleven," each author uses a different type of characterization to develop the main characters. In an essay, compare and contrast the two authors' use of direct and indirect characterization. Back up your ideas with examples from each story.

"The Lawyer and the Ghost" by Charles Dickens
"The Wounded Wolf" by Jean Craighead George

Selection Test

Critical Reading

On the line, write the letter of the best answer.

____ 1. In "The Lawyer and the Ghost," the ghost probably appears because the lawyer
    a. called him forth
    b. threatened to destroy the press
    c. was careless with the fire
    d. was about to leave

____ 2. What is the setting of "The Lawyer and the Ghost"?
    a. a tavern   c. a graveyard
    b. a court of law   d. the rooms of a poor lawyer

____ 3. To which sense do the details in this passage from "The Lawyer and the Ghost" appeal?

> "Who are you?" said the new tenant, turning very pale, poising the poker in his hand, however, and taking a very decent aim at the countenance of the figure — "Who are you?"

    a. touch   c. smell
    b. taste   d. sight

____ 4. In "The Lawyer and the Ghost," the ghost haunts the rooms because he
    a. wants to return to the place where he lived his life
    b. is trapped in the press
    c. likes cold, drafty places
    d. is cursed to remain there forever

____ 5. In "The Lawyer and the Ghost," which detail in this passage is a clue that the story takes place in the past?

> "And, pray, what do you want here?" faltered the tenant.

> "In this room," replied the apparition, "my worldly ruin was worked, and I and my children beggared. In this press, the papers in a long, long suit which accumulated for years, were deposited."

    a. the appearance of a ghost
    b. a lawsuit that lasts for years
    c. old-fashioned words like *pray* and *press*
    d. a person called a tenant

____ 6. In "The Lawyer and the Ghost," the ghost appears to the lawyer in order to
    a. make friends with him   c. warm himself by the fire
    b. drive him away   d. seek his advice

_____ 7. In "The Lawyer and the Ghost," the tenant's arguments for the ghost to live elsewhere is a sign of his
      a. cleverness   c. anger
      b. kindheartedness   d. foolishness

_____ 8. To what sense do the details in this excerpt from "The Wounded Wolf" appeal?

       The music wails and sobs, wilder than the bleating wind.

      a. sight   c. hearing
      b. taste   d. smell

_____ 9. In "The Wounded Wolf," what time of year is indicated in the details of this passage?

       Roko snarls and hurries toward the shelter rock. A cloud of snow envelops him. He limps in blinding whiteness now.

      a. spring   c. fall
      b. summer   d. winter

_____ 10. The animals and birds in "The Wounded Wolf" follow the wounded Roko in order to
      a. eat him   c. escape the cold
      b. help him   d. be led to food

_____ 11. When you read about the sounds in this passage, what feeling do you share with Roko in "The Wounded Wolf"?

       Suddenly he hears the musk-oxen thundering into their circle. The ice cracks as the grizzly leaves. The ravens burst into the air. The white fox runs. The snowy owl flaps to the top of the shelter rock. And Kiglo rounds the knoll.

      a. fear   c. relief
      b. sadness   d. awe

_____ 12. The wolves in "The Wounded Wolf" are led to Roko by
      a. Roko's cries   c. a helpful bear
      b. the raven's cries   d. the smell of death

_____ 13. The ending of "The Wounded Wolf" makes you think that that wolves are
      a. caring   c. fierce
      b. independent   d. cowardly

_____ 14. In "The Wounded Wolf," how much time passes in the course of the story?
      a. several hours   c. two days
      b. one day   d. several days or more

_____ 15. Which best describes the feeling evoked by envisioning this passage from "The Wounded Wolf"?

       Roko sees the shelter rock. He strains to reach it. He stumbles. The ravens move in closer. The white fox boldly walks beside him. "Hahaha," he yaps. The snowy owl flies ahead, alights, and waits.

      a. happiness   c. confusion
      b. tension   d. sadness

Vocabulary, Spelling, and Grammar

_____ 16. Which word or words best defines *expend* in the sentence?

> If you hurled it with ever so sure an aim, it would pass through me, without resistance, and expend its force on the wood behind.

  a. use up   c. seize
  b. find   d. renew

_____ 17. Which of the following best describes this sentence from "The Wounded Wolf"?

> They scream and peck and stab at his eyes.

  a. simple sentence with one subject and verb
  b. simple sentence with compound subject
  c. simple sentence with compound verb
  d. compound sentence

_____ 18. Which of the following is spelled correctly?
  a. sufficient   c. suficient
  b. suffishent   d. sufficeint

_____ 19. Which of the following is closest in meaning to *massive*?
  a. tiny   c. colorful
  b. strange   d. huge

_____ 20. Which of the following is a simple sentence with one subject and verb?
  a. The snowy owl flies ahead, alights, and waits.
  b. The wounded wolf wags his tail.
  c. Only yards from the shelter rock, Roko falls.
  d. "Kong, kong, kong," he tolls—this is the end.

Essay Questions

21. "The Lawyer and the Ghost" and "The Wounded Wolf" both have endings that fool our expectations. Choose one of the stories and write an essay telling how you expected the story to end. If the story ended as you expected, explain which details in the story lead you to predict the ending correctly. If you did not predict the ending correctly, contrast your expected ending with the actual ending. Tell if the ending surprised, disappointed, or pleased you, and why.

22. Both stories in this selection have well-defined settings. Choose one of the stories and write an essay explaining how the setting of the story contributes to the action or influences the characters' actions. Use details from the story to support your explanation.

23. Many animals come to watch and hasten Roko's death. In an essay, explain how you react to these animal characters. In your explanation, answer the following questions: Do you find the animals cruel, or do you see them behaving as nature requires them? How would you consider these characters if they were human and not animals? Conclude your essay by analyzing what the story says about the difference between humans and other animals.

Name _____ Date _____

Selection Test

Critical Reading

On the line, write the letter of the best answer.

_____ 1. Which of the following best summarizes "The All-American Slurp"?
   a. The narrator makes a best friend and adjusts to her new country.
   b. The narrator's parents have more trouble adjusting to change than their children.
   c. The members of the Lin family encounter problems and challenges as they adapt to their new home.
   d. The Gleason family discovers that their new Chinese neighbors are really just like an American family.

_____ 2. Which of the following best states the theme of "The All-American Slurp"?
   a. It is not wise to move to a strange land.
   b. Cultures and customs may be different, but people's needs and feelings are similar everywhere.
   c. No matter where a person travels, good manners are important.
   d. Change is an important part of growing up.

_____ 3. In "The All-American Slurp," the narrator's purpose in explaining how each person in the Lin family learns English is to
   a. demonstrate how Chinese people learn English
   b. prove that children learn new languages more easily than adults
   c. show the personality of each family member
   d. point out that English is a difficult language to learn

_____ 4. The theme of "The All-American Slurp" can best be inferred by comparing
   a. the way Mr. and Mrs. Lin learn to speak English
   b. Chinese clothing to American clothing
   c. the brother and sister in the Lin family
   d. the problems the Lins and the Gleasons have during dinner at each other's homes

_____ 5. At the conclusion of "The All-American Slurp," how have the Lins adjusted to life in America?
   a. They are willing to give up Chinese customs for American ways.
   b. They are becoming more comfortable with American ways, but they will still keep some of their Chinese customs.
   c. They do not know which Chinese customs to follow and which to give up.
   d. They have not adjusted well to American life and plan to return to China.

_____ 6. In "The All-American Slurp," you can infer that when the Gleasons have trouble eating Chinese-style, the narrator of the story feels
   a. amused and relieved that the Lins are not the only ones to have trouble with unfamiliar etiquette
   b. annoyed because Mrs. Lin did not serve American food
   c. sorry for the Gleasons because they are having difficulty with their chopsticks
   d. disgusted by the Gleasons' lack of table manners

____ 7. By the end of the "The All-American Slurp," what does the narrator discover about the habit of slurping?
   a. It is regarded as bad manners throughout the world.
   b. It is considered normal behavior in most restaurants.
   c. Americans and Chinese share this habit but find it acceptable at different times.
   d. It is considered acceptable only in America.

____ 8. Which of the following best summarizes the events in "The Stone"?
   a. Maibon and his wife quarrel about Maibon's wish to remain young.
   b. Maibon is granted his wish to remain unchanged, but soon learns that change is necessary to all living things.
   c. People should not ask for gifts from magical beings.
   d. If a man does not change, his children will grow older than their father.

____ 9. In "The Stone," the disagreement between Maibon and Madrona shows that
   a. they really do not get along well together
   b. Madrona is an unpleasant person
   c. the wife is wiser and more practical than the husband
   d. Maibon has made other foolish decisions that annoyed Madrona

____ 10. What inference can you draw from this sentence in "The Stone"?

   Never again did Maibon meet any of the Fair Folk, and he was just as glad of it.

   a. Maibon is finally content to let nature take its course without any magical interference.
   b. Human beings should not trust the cruel Fair Folk.
   c. Maibon stayed close to home and did not have any further adventures.
   d. Maibon now has more respect for his wife.

____ 11. In "The Stone," Maibon wishes to remain young forever because
   a. he is afraid of growing old and weak
   b. he wants to live longer than anyone else on earth
   c. he is afraid he will die before his wife does
   d. he cannot think of any other wishes to make

____ 12. Which of the following best states the theme of "The Stone"?
   a. Wishes are dangerous things.
   b. Old age is frightening to all people.
   c. Human beings are ungrateful creatures.
   d. Wisdom means accepting that life will bring many changes.

____ 13. In "The Stone," you can infer that the stone keeps coming back to Maibon because
   a. Maibon has secretly hidden it and only pretended to throw it away
   b. a magic stone can never be parted from its owner
   c. Maibon still has not accepted the need for change and growth in his life
   d. Doli keeps returning it to Maibon

____ 14. In "The Stone," Doli hesitates to give Maibon the wishing stone because
   a. he thinks Maibon is too greedy to be rewarded
   b. he knows that people have made foolish or dangerous wishes in the past
   c. he believes people should not try to change their lives by magic
   d. he is angry about being asked for gifts by so many human beings

Vocabulary, Spelling, and Grammar

____ 15. Which of the following words comes closest in meaning to *mortified*?
a. dead
c. scared
b. ashamed
d. depressed

____ 16. Which of the following words contains the *k* sound spelled as *qu*?
a. question
c. etiquette
b. racket
d. quarrel

____ 17. Which of the following sentences is a compound sentence?
a. The girl was embarrassed by her family's table manners.
b. The waiter was surprised and displeased.
c. The narrator glanced around, understood the situation, and hid in the ladies' room.
d. The diners looked up, and they saw an unfamiliar sight.

____ 18. Which of the following words best defines the word *jubilation* in this sentence?

> Instead of sharing Maibon's jubilation, Madrona flung up her hands and burst out:
> Maibon you're a greater fool than I ever supposed!

a. rue
c. plight
b. triumph
d. fallow

____ 19. Which of the following words contains the *k* sound spelled as *qu*?
a. quick
c. question
b. quality
d. physique

____ 20. Which of the following is a compound sentence?
a. Maibon worried about growing old without thought to the future.
b. Maibon worried about growing old, for he feared losing his strength.
c. Maibon worried about growing old, losing his strong physique, and becoming unable to work.
d. Maibon worried about growing old, as if worrying could change anything.

Essay Questions

21. The narrator in "The All-American Slurp" and Maibon in "The Stone" each learn an important lesson about life. Choose one of the stories and, in an essay, explain what you think the character learns. How does the character learn it? Back up your ideas with details and examples from the story.

22. The narrator in "The All-American Slurp" and Maibon in "The Stone" have trouble making or accepting changes in their lives. Write an essay explaining how they deal with change. What kinds of problems does each character face? How are these problems solved? Use details and examples from the stories that back up your ideas.

23. Choose either "The All-American Slurp" or 'The Stone" and write an essay about the story's theme of change. Explain the theme; then describe what the main characters learn. Use details, examples, and your own experiences to support your analysis.

Unit 6: Short Stories

Unit Test

Critical Reading

On the line, write the letter of the one best answer.

____ 1. In "Dragon, Dragon," you can predict that the oldest and middle sons will fail to defeat the dragon because they
   a. go to face the beast without weapons
   b. boast a great deal before going to meet the dragon
   c. ignore their father's advice
   d. make fun of the wizard and the knights

____ 2. "Dragon, Dragon" seems to take place
   a. in ancient times   c. in modern times
   b. in no real time   d. several hundred years ago

____ 3. Which word best describes the youngest son?
   a. brave   c. ambitious
   b. sly   d. dutiful

____ 4. In "Becky and the Wheels-and-Brake Boys," Becky and Granny-Liz are in conflict because
   a. Granny-Liz does not like Becky
   b. Granny-Liz has old-fashioned ideas about how girls should behave
   c. Becky is always rude to Granny-Liz
   d. Granny-Liz thinks Becky spends too much money on herself

____ 5. In "Becky and the Wheels-and-Brake Boys," Becky feels that her dad
   a. was easier to get favors from than her mother
   b. loved her more than her mother did
   c. would have helped her be accepted by the Wheels-and-Brake Boys
   d. liked her more than he liked her brothers and sisters

____ 6. In "Becky and the Wheels-and-Brake Boys," Ben agrees to teach Becky to ride a bike because
   a. she bullies him into doing it
   b. he feels he has to help out his cousin
   c. he feels sorry for her
   d. he is impressed by her new bike

____ 7. In "Overdoing It," how are Klim and the station guard most alike?
   a. Both are frightened by the land surveyor's threats.
   b. Both are peasants with little love for upper-class people.
   c. Both seem unimpressed when they meet the land surveyor.
   d. Both wish that they could run away from the land surveyor.

____ 8. In "Overdoing It," when Gleb realizes that he has frightened Klim,
   a. he gets scared about being alone
   b. he feels proud of himself for having frightened Klim
   c. he feels guilty for having scared the other man
   d. he worries about Klim coming back to get revenge

_____ 9. In "Eleven," which word best describes the narrator of the story?
    a. angry   c. shy
    b. stubborn   d. quick-witted

_____ 10. In "Eleven," Mrs. Price insists that Rachel put the sweater on because
    a. she does not want Rachel to catch a cold
    b. she thinks the sweater is pretty
    c. she is worried that Rachel will forget to take the sweater home
    d. she believes that Rachel is just being difficult

_____ 11. In "The Lawyer and the Ghost," why does the lawyer resent the press?
    a. It cost him money that he didn't want to spend.
    b. It is too old and rickety to be of any practical good.
    c. It takes up too much space in his new office.
    d. It is haunted.

_____ 12. In "The Lawyer and the Ghost," what word best describes the story's setting?
    a. cheerful   c. deluxe
    b. shabby   d. comfortable

_____ 13. In "The Lawyer and the Ghost," the ghost has never been anywhere except his old office because
    a. he has not wanted to go anywhere else
    b. he did not know he could go anywhere else
    c. he was afraid to go anywhere else
    d. he had never thought of going anywhere else

_____ 14. In "The Wounded Wolf," which of the following sentences best explains this passage?

    A frigid blast picks up long shawls of snow and drapes them between young Roko and his pack. And so his message is not read.

    a. Heavy snow keeps Roko's distress signal from being seen by the other wolves.
    b. The noise of the wind is too loud for Roko's call to be heard by the other wolves.
    c. Roko is almost buried in snow and cannot signal the other wolves.
    d. The pack knows that Roko is badly hurt and decides to abandon him, despite his signal for help.

_____ 15. In "The Wounded Wolf," the pack realizes that something is wrong with Roko when
    a. they see that he is missing
    b. they hear his call for help
    c. he fails to answer their roll call
    d. they find him under attack

_____ 16. Which of the following best states the theme of "The All-American Slurp"?
    a. It is important to learn how to behave in a new culture as quickly as possible.
    b. Good manners and behavior are different in different cultures.
    c. It is not polite to make fun of people who do not know how to behave properly.
    d. Until people learn how to behave in a new culture, they should keep to themselves.

_____ 17. The narrator of "The All-American Slurp"
    a. is always getting angry at the rest of her family for embarrassing her
    b. finds American habits and manners silly
    c. is more easily embarrassed by social mistakes than the others in her family
    d. has no trouble getting used to American ways

_____ 18. In "The Stone," what can you infer about how the Fair Folk regard human beings?
 a. They like human beings but find them odd.
 b. They hate and fear human beings.
 c. They admire human beings and try to behave like them.
 d. They have little respect for human beings and think they behave foolishly.

_____ 19. In "The Stone," change is shown to be
 a. a necessary aspect of life
 b. a terrible aspect of life that humans must endure
 c. something that people can avoid, if they are willing to make sacrifices
 d. something to fight against as hard as possible

Vocabulary, Spelling, and Grammar

_____ 20. Which of the following is a compound sentence?
 a. As soon as the guests had left the house, the hosts started cleaning up.
 b. We drove to the beach but did not go into the water.
 c. The class boarded the bus and sat down, talking happily.
 d. I had planned to write a letter, but we had to work all day.

_____ 21. Which word is most nearly the opposite of *jubilation*?
 a. anger   c. boredom
 b. sorrow   d. curiosity

_____ 22. Which of the following words is misspelled?
 a. lake   c. physique
 b. plak   d. antique

_____ 23. Which of the following is *not* a simple sentence?
 a. His brother and sister live in another city.
 b. She likes to play soccer and swim.
 c. After the game ended, both teams met to shake hands.
 d. We used to play and march in the school band.

_____ 24. A *massive* object is very
 a. large   c. ugly
 b. delicate   d. smooth

_____ 25. Which group of underlined words is a subordinate clause?
 a. He wanted to find the book, but the library was closed.
 b. We went to the supermarket and bought a birthday cake.
 c. The curtain went up after the orchestra played the overture.
 d. After sunset, we could see thousands of stars.

_____ 26. Which of the following words is misspelled?
 a. wrist   c. written
 b. wrong   d. wrag

_____ 27. Which group of underlined words is not a subordinate clause?
 a. The class was dismissed after the bell rang.
 b. She opened the door quietly and she peered inside.
 c. We stayed inside until the storm was over.
 d. As soon as the doors opened, the crowd raced toward the seats.

_____ 28. If a man is a *reckless* driver,
 a. you should not ride with him
 b. you should not worry about riding with him
 c. he never gets lost
 d. he has never had an accident

____ 29. Which of the following words is spelled correctly?
    a. hidrant   c. gyant
    b. bicicle   d. supply

____ 30. Which group of underlined words is an independent clause?
    a. <u>Until the television set is fixed</u>, we cannot watch our favorite shows.
    b. After they came in through the open doorway, <u>they walked across the room</u>.
    c. He bought his ticket at the window <u>and entered the theater</u>.
    d. She rowed the boat out into the lake <u>and sat watching the water</u>.

Essay Questions

31. In stories, *conflict* means "struggle," or "disagreement." Conflicts may take place between different characters, or within a single character, or between a character and his or her environment. Choose two of the following characters: Becky in "The Wheels-and-Brake Boys," Rachel in "Eleven," Roko in "The Wounded Wolf," or Gleb in "Overdoing It." Write an essay in which you describe a conflict that your chosen characters must deal with. Indicate whether the conflicts are with other characters, within themselves, or with their environment. Compare and contrast the kinds of conflicts involved in the stories and the extent to which the characters are successful in meeting the challenges caused by their conflicts. Use details from the selections to support your position.

32. Humor is an important ingredient in several stories in this unit. Chose two of the following stories: "Dragon, Dragon," "The Lawyer and the Ghost," or "Overdoing It," and write an essay in which you analyze how the authors make use of humor to entertain their readers. Point out ways in which the authors use similar ways to make their stories amusing and ways in which they use contrasting methods. Support your analysis with details from the selections.

33. The central characters in some of the stories in this selection are children. Write an essay in which you compare and contrast the personalities of Becky in "The Wheels-and-Brake Boys" and Rachel in "Eleven." Include a short description of each character; then point out the ways in which the characters differ from each other and are alike. Illustrate your conclusions with details from the text.

34. One kind of conflict most common in literature and movies is the struggle between "good" and "bad." Choose two of the following stories: "Eleven," "Becky and the Wheels-and-Brake Boys," "The Wounded Wolf," or "The All-American Slurp." In an essay, analyze whether the conflicts faced by the central characters in the stories are struggles between "good" and "bad." Support your conclusions with reasons and with examples from the stories.

35. The setting for a story can often be an important part of the effect the story has on readers. Choose two of these stories: "Overdoing It," "The Wounded Wolf," and "The Lawyer and the Ghost," and write an essay in which you analyze the way in which the setting and the writer's description of it contribute to the story's final effect. Use details from the selections to support your points.

Unit 6: Short Stories

Alternative Unit Test

The two passages below are followed by questions based on their content and on the relationship between the two passages.

Passage 1

from "The Fish Angel" by Myron Levoy

Noreen Callahan was convinced that her father's fish store on Second Avenue was, without a doubt, the ugliest fish store on the East Side. The sawdust on the floor was always slimy with fish drippings; the fish were piled in random heaps on the ice; the paint on the walls was peeling off in layers; even the cat sleeping in the window was filthy. Mr. Callahan's apron was always dirty, and he wore an old battered hat that was in worse shape than the cat, if such a thing were possible. Often, fish heads would drop on the floor right under the customers' feet, and Mr. Callahan wouldn't bother to sweep them up. And as time passed, most of his customers went elsewhere for their fish.

Mr. Callahan had never wanted to sell fish in a fish store. He had wanted to be an actor, to do great, heroic, marvelous things on the stage. He tried, but was unsuccessful, and had to come back to work in his father's fish store, the store which was now his. But he took no pride in it; for what beauty was possible, what marvelous, heroic things could be done in a fish store?

Noreen's mother helped in the store most of the week, but Saturday was Noreen's day to help while her mother cleaned the house. To Noreen, it was the worst day of the week. She was ashamed to be seen in the store by any of her friends and classmates, ashamed of the smells, ashamed of the fish heads and fish tails, ashamed of the scruffy cat, and of her father's dirty apron. To Noreen, the fish store seemed a scar across her face, a scar she'd been born with.

And like a scar, Noreen carried the fish store with her everywhere, even into the schoolroom. *Fish Girl! Fish Girl! Dirty Fish Girl!* some of the girls would call her. When they did, Noreen wished she could run into the dark clothes closet at the back of the room and cry. And once or twice, she did.

Passage 2

The following passage is about a boy named Colm who is on his way to a lake where he is to fetch a cow and guide it home.

from "The Wild Duck's Nest" by Michael McLaverty

The lake faced west and was fed by a stream, the drainings of the semicircling hills. One side was open to the winds from the sea and in winter a little outlet trickled over the cliffs making a black vein in their gray sides. The boy lifted stones and began throwing them into the lake, weaving web after web on its calm surface. Then he skimmed the water with flat stones, some of them jumping the surface and coming to rest on the other side. He was delighted with himself and after listening to his echoing shouts of delight he ran to fetch his cow. Gently he tapped her on the side and reluctantly she went towards the brown-mudded path that led out of the valley. The boy was about to throw a final stone into the lake when a bird flew low over his head, its neck astrain, and its orange-colored legs clear in the soft light. It was a wild duck. It circled the lake twice, thrice, coming lower each time and then with a nervous flapping of wings it skidded along the surface, its legs breaking the water into a series of silvery arcs. Its wings closed, it lit silently, gave a slight shiver, and began pecking indifferently at the water.

Colm with dilated eyes eagerly watched it making for the farther end of the lake. It meandered between tall bulrushes, its body black and solid as stone against the graying water. Then as if it had sunk it was gone. The boy ran stealthily along the bank looking away from the lake, pretending indifference. When he came opposite to where he had last seen the bird he stopped and peered through the sighing reeds whose shadows streaked the water in a maze of black strokes. In front of him was a soddy islet guarded by the spears of sedge and separated from the bank by a narrow channel of water. The water wasn't too deep—he could wade across with care.

Rolling up his short trousers he began to wade, his arms outstretched, and his legs brown and stunted in the mountain water. As he drew near the islet, his feet sank in the cold mud and bubbles winked up at him. He went more carefully and nervously. Then one trouser leg fell and dipped into the water: the boy dropped his hands to roll it up, he unbalanced, made a splashing sound, and the bird arose with a squawk and whirred away over the cliffs.

Critical Reading

On the line, write the letter of the one best answer.

_____ 1. After reading both passages, which statement to you know to be true about both of the central characters?
  a. They are happy with their lives.
  b. They are both young.
  c. They are unhappy living where they do.
  d. They love nature.
  e. They are intelligent and ambitious.

_____ 2. From what you learn in the two passages, which activity would the central character from Passage 2 be more likely to do than the central character from Passage 1?
  a. read a book
  b. take care of a young brother or sister
  c. go to school
  d. clean a room
  e. feed chickens

_____ 3. Based on your reading of Passage 2, you might predict that, in the rest of the story, Colm
  a. will get more involved with the bird
  b. will never return to the lake
  c. will be interested mostly in the cow
  d. will never see the bird again
  e. will go fishing in the lake

_____ 4. In Passage 1, Noreen's father's fish store is shown to be
  a. like most other fish stores
  b. unusually busy
  c. unusually neglected and dirty
  d. in an out-of-the-way location
  e. a place in which she takes pride

_____ 5. Which statement is true of the settings of both passages?
  a. They are described in detail.
  b. They are only briefly described.
  c. The setting of Passage 1 is described in detail but the setting of Passage 2 is not.
  d. The setting of Passage 2 is described in detail but the setting of Passage 1 is not.
  e. Neither of the settings is likely to be important in the complete stories.

_____ 6. After reading both passages, which inference do you find most likely to be true?
   a. Colm is more likely to get into a conflict with classmates than Noreen.
   b. Noreen is more likely to enjoy spending time with her family than Colm.
   c. Neither Colm nor Noreen is likely to reveal their emotions.
   d. Noreen feels more frustrated with her life than Colm.
   e. Both Colm and Noreen have hot tempers.

_____ 7. In Passage 2, what adjective best describes Colm's attitude on seeing the bird?
   a. frightened
   b. fascinated
   c. amused
   d. bored
   e. angry

_____ 8. In Passage 1, Mr. Callahan
   a. lost interest in being an actor when he got the chance to work in his father's fish store
   b. hated selling fish at first but has come to like it more
   c. thinks of having come to work in the fish store as a defeat
   d. still has hopes of succeeding as an actor
   e. would like to sell the fish store

_____ 9. Which statement is true of both passages?
   a. There is no hint of the conflict that drives the story plot in either passage.
   b. The conflicts of the stories are made clear in both passages.
   c. The conflict of both passages is between two people.
   d. Passage 2 clearly states the story's conflict.
   e. Passage 1 clearly states the story's conflict.

_____ 10. Based on Passage 1, which of the following is the most logical prediction you can make for this story?
   a. Noreen will agree to clean the house on Saturdays so that her mother can help at the fish store.
   b. Mr. Callahan will get an acting job and close the fish store.
   c. The girl who teases her the most will move away.
   d. Noreen will do something to prove that she is more than a "Fish Girl."

_____ 11. Which details from the two passages are examples of indirect characterization?
   a. Noreen being ashamed of the fish store and Colm throwing stones into the lake
   b. Noreen's crying in the closet and Colm's fascination with the duck
   c. Noreen hating to work in the fish store and Colm skimming stones
   d. Mr. Callahan taking no pride in his fish store and Colm's fascination with the duck
   e. Noreen's mother helping in the store and Colm's pleasure at skipping stones across the lake

_____ 12. Which sense or senses help you envision the settings of both passages?
   a. sight only
   b. sight and hearing
   c. sight and smell
   d. sight, hearing, and smell
   e. sight and touch

_____ 13. In Passage 2, when the wild duck first lands on the lake, it
   a. appears indifferent to its surroundings
   b. shows signs of being very hungry
   c. appears friendly to people
   d. appears cautious
   e. seems curious about Colm

_____ 14. In which way do the two passages show Colm and Noreen to be most different from each other?
   a. in intelligence
   b. in mood
   c. in courage
   d. in level of education
   e. in common sense

_____ 15 Noreen is ashamed of the fish store because
   a. it is dirty
   b. it smells terrible
   c. it does little business
   d. it is ugly
   e. all of the above

Essay Questions

16. Although these two passages present only small parts of their full stories, they provide enough information about the central characters, Noreen and Colm, to help you form an idea of what they are like. In an essay, write character descriptions of Noreen and Colm, using what the two passages tell you about them. Use their actions, thoughts, and feelings to help you reach your conclusions. Conclude your essay by comparing and contrasting the two characters. In what ways, if any, do you think they are alike, and in what ways are they different? Use details from the passages to support your conclusions.

17. Story plots often focus on how the story's central character copes with some kind of problem or conflict. Write an essay in which you describe the problems the central characters in the two passages might face in their stories. If either or both of the passages do not give a clear indication of what this problem might be, look for clues that at least suggest an answer. Compare and contrast the characters' problems: make predictions as to whether they may involve conflicts with other people, with nature, or within themselves. Support your conclusions with details from the passages.

18. The setting of a story often has a great deal to do with the problems a character must face. Write an essay in which you describe the settings of the two passages and indicate the ways in which they differ from each other. Suggest how the setting for each passage might affect the development of the plot, Support your conclusions with details from the passages.

"The Shutout" by Patricia C. McKissack and Frederick McKissack, Jr.

Selection Test

Critical Reading

On the line, write the letter of the best answer.

_____ 1. Which of the following is the most important point for the author's meaning in
"The Shutout"?
   a. The New York Knickerbocker Club was organized in 1845.
   b. After the Civil War, African American players were excluded from major-league
   baseball.
   c. Slave owners liked to make money betting at sports events.
   d. After 1858, baseball became a business.

_____ 2. In "The Shutout," which of the following facts does this passage explain?

   Slave owners preferred these individual sports [boxing, wrestling, footracing, horse-
   racing] because they could enter their slaves in competitions, watch the event from
   a safe distance, pocket the winnings, and personally never raise a sweat.

   a. Baseball was not a popular southern sport.
   b. There is little information about the role of African Americans in the early development of baseball.
   c. Baseball is more popular in the South today than it was in 1860.
   d. By 1858, baseball was becoming the nation's number-one sport.

_____ 3. In "The Shutout," which of the following facts provides the evidence to this passage?

   So, from the start, organized baseball tried to limit or exclude African American
   participation.

   a. Several West African cultures had stick-and-ball and running games.
   b. The National Association of Baseball Players voted to exclude African American
   players in 1867.
   c. The press ignored African American ball clubs.
   d. African Americans played on integrated teams in the North before the Civil War.

_____ 4. Which of the following best explains why the Negro Leagues were organized?
   a. Talented African American athletes wanted to play baseball, despite the racism of
   the day.
   b. African American players knew they'd get good press coverage in the Negro Leagues.
   c. African American players didn't want to play on teams with whites.
   d. There was a lot of money to be made playing in the Negro Leagues.

_____ 5. What is the authors' purpose in reporting that Abner Doubleday's diaries never
recorded a visit to Cooperstown, New York?
   a. to explain why Doubleday is famous for inventing baseball
   b. to offer an insight into Doubleday's life
   c. to cite evidence to support their belief that Doubleday did not invent baseball at
   Cooperstown
   d. to cite evidence that Cooperstown hadn't yet been founded in the 1830s

_____ 6. In 1867, the National Association of Baseball Players ruled that
   a. teams with African American players would not be allowed in the Association
   b. teams that excluded African Americans would be fined
   c. only integrated teams would be allowed to join the Association
   d. teams with white players would not be allowed to join the Association

____ 7. Which of the following best describes public opinion of early professional baseball?
   a. It was some time before the public grew to enjoy the game.
   b. Professional baseball had an enthusiastic audience from the very beginning.
   c. Audiences were small due to the lack of press coverage.
   d. The public enjoyed individual sports better than professional baseball.

____ 8. What insight do the authors express in this passage?

   > Slave owners preferred these individual sports because they could enter their slaves in competitions, watch events from a safe distance, pocket the winnings and personally never raise a sweat.

   a. Slave owners had no athletic abilities themselves.
   b. Slave owners encouraged slaves to develop athletic abilities.
   c. Slave owners enjoyed watching sports more than participating in them.
   d. Slave owners used their slaves for entertainment and profit.

____ 9. In 1860, none of the sixty teams participating in the National Association of Baseball Players were from the South. This was because
   a. Southerners didn't want to play against teams that included African Americans.
   b. Southerners preferred individual sports such as boxing and wrestling.
   c. The southern states were seceding from the Union, so they would not be joining any national association.
   d. The North and the South couldn't come to an agreement on rules of the game.

____ 10. Researchers are not able to find out much about the early Negro Leagues because
   a. the Negro Leagues were not recognized by the National Association of Baseball Players
   b. there were too few participants to keep records
   c. no one is sure if the Negro Leagues really existed
   d. records were not well kept and the white press generally ignored the Negro Leagues

____ 11. If you wanted to evaluate the author's message about segregation in "The Shutout," which of the following facts would be of special interest to you?
   a. During the Civil War there were no southern teams in the National Association of Baseball Players.
   b. In the 1840s, the "pitch" was thrown underhanded.
   c. Free African Americans played baseball on integrated teams during the Civil War.
   d. West African cultures had stick-and-ball and running games.

____ 12. Which of the following best describes the racial situation in baseball before the Civil War?
   a. There was general tolerance for integrated teams in the North.
   b. There were no integrated teams in the North.
   c. Slave owners allowed segregated teams in the South.
   d. Slave owners allowed integrated teams in the South.

____ 13. Which of the following was given by the National Association of Base Ball Players as reason for not allowing Association teams to be integrated?
   a. The Association thought that African American players were better than white players.
   b. The Association wanted to avoid personal and political conflict.
   c. The Association thought that white players were better than African American players.
   d. The Association didn't want African American and white players to play together.

_____ 14. What is the authors' opinion of the exclusion of African Americans by the National Association of Base Ball Players?
  a. They think the decision made sense in 1867, but not at the present time.
  b. They think the decision made sense for southern teams, but not northern.
  c. They think the decision was fair, as long as African Americans could have their own teams.
  d. They consider the decision to have been wrong and based on racist ideas.

Vocabulary, Spelling, and Grammar

_____ 15. There are wonderful anecdotes about the early history of baseball. The word _anecdotes_ means
  a. details   b. mysteries   c. long descriptions   d. short, amusing tales

_____ 16. Which of the underlined words in these sentences is spelled incorrectly?
  a. The antique was irreplaceable.
  b. It was iresponsible of her to leave the key.
  c. It was an irresistible dessert.
  d. The edge was jagged and irregular.

_____ 17. The rule that excluded African American players was irrational. _Irrational_ means
  a. unreasonable   b. unfair   c. out of date   d. new

_____ 18. Which of the following is a compound sentence?
  a. African Americans wanted to play, but the association denied them permission.
  b. Returning soldiers helped to inspire a new interest in baseball.
  c. Some emancipated slaves learned how to play baseball.
  d. Sometimes between battles, Union soldiers chose up teams and played baseball games.

_____ 19. Major League baseball was not racially diverse until after Word War II. _Diverse_ means
  a. similar   b. segregated   c. confused   d. varied

_____ 20. Which of the following is a complex sentence?
  a. In 1857–1858 an association was formed, and baseball became a business.
  b. The association met and authorized an admission fee for games.
  c. The fans, who had paid fifty cents to see the game, cheered loudly.
  d. By 1860, there were about sixty teams in the association.

Essay Questions

21. In an essay, summarize African Americans' involvement in baseball from the Civil War up until the end of World War II. Base your summary on information from the selection, and organize your summary in chronological order.

22. In an essay, demonstrate why "The Shutout" is a good example of a historical essay. Remember that a historical essay is a short piece of nonfiction that gives facts, evidence to back up factual claims, explanations, and insights about historical events. In your essay, provide examples of all the elements of a historical essay to show that "The Shutout" is a good model for this kind of writing.

23. In an essay, develop an argument that could have been used against the decision by the National Association of Base Ball Players to exclude African Americans from their teams. Begin by stating that you believe the decision is wrong. Then go on to state at least one reason for the decision to be reversed, backing up your reason with facts and examples. End your essay by summarizing your points or making a final statement to emphasize your opinion.

Name _____ Date _____

"Letter to Scottie" by F. Scott Fitzgerald
"Olympic Diary" by Amanda Borden

Selection Test

Critical Reading

On the line, write the letter of the best answer.

_____ 1. "Letter to Scottie" shows that F. Scott Fitzgerald's relationship with his daughter is
   a. indifferent   c. hostile
   b. loving   d. difficult

_____ 2. In "Letter to Scottie," the author writes that doing one's duty
   a. is not as important as being happy
   b. is important for adults, but less so for children
   c. is not as important as many people think
   d. is the most important goal anyone can have

_____ 3. F. Scott Fitzgerald's primary purpose in writing the "Letter to Scottie" is to
   a. advise his daughter on how to lead a worthwhile life
   b. express his love for his daughter
   c. joke with his daughter about nicknames
   d. confide in his daughter about his problems in writing a story

_____ 4. Which of the following sentences is nearest in meaning to this line quoted by the author in "Letter to Scottie"?

   Lilies that fester smell far worse than weeds.

   a. When lilies lose their bloom, they sometimes smell terrible.
   b. Outward beauty can be misleading.
   c. There is no reason to assume that lilies are superior to weeds.
   d. The more promise one shows, the more clearly his or her failings stand out.

_____ 5. In "Letter to Scottie," F. Scott Fitzgerald tells his daughter that he is busy writing
   a. a long novel   c. a speech
   b. a screenplay   d. a magazine story

_____ 6. The author of "Letter to Scottie" is annoyed when his daughter calls him
   a. Egg
   b. Pappy
   c. Daddy
   d. Pops

_____ 7. In "Olympic Diary," at the end of 1995 Amanda Borden had to stop training and competing because
   a. her coach told her she would not qualify for the Olympics
   b. she broke her toe and her hand
   c. she had to return to school full-time
   d. her routine on the bars received a low score

_____ 8. According to "Olympic Diary," the 1996 Olympic Games were held in
   a. Sydney
   b. Barcelona
   c. Atlanta
   d. Los Angeles

_____ 9. In "Olympic Diary," what sentence best sums up Amanda Borden's attitude toward the difficult times she has experienced?
   a. She wishes they had never happened.
   b. She thinks that she has had more than her share of bad luck.
   c. She thinks that she has been unusually lucky.
   d. She believes that difficult times build character.

_____ 10. Amanda Borden's purpose in writing "Olympic Diary" is
   a. to make a record of the way in which she became an Olympic athlete
   b. to show how difficult it is to be a skilled gymnast
   c. to thank the people who helped her make it to the Olympics
   d. to develop her skills as a writer

_____ 11. In "Olympic Diary," Amanda Borden writes that when she works in front of a large crowd
   a. she is terrified   c. she ignores them
   b. she is thrilled   d. she performs better

_____ 12. According to "Olympic Diary," Amanda Borden first gets involved in gymnastics because
   a. she thinks she can win an Olympic gold medal
   b. she is better at it than she is as a ballet dancer
   c. she wants to do something that she believes she will enjoy
   d. it is more challenging than ballet

_____ 13. Which of the following passages from "Olympic Diary" is the most informal?
   a. A friend of the family suggested gymnastics.
   b. We received lots of great clothes and other goodies.
   c. It was my first time away from home, and I didn't like it.
   d. I began training and "slowly" I got everything back.

_____ 14. Which of the following qualities would the author of "Olympic Diary" consider most important to achieving success?
   I. self-confidence
   II. attractiveness
   III. determination
   IV. friendliness

   a. I and IV   c. II and IV
   b. II and III   d. I and III

Vocabulary, Spelling, and Grammar

____ 15. Which of the following words is *not* spelled correctly?
    a. niece
    b. weight
    c. acheive
    d. perceive

____ 16. Which of the following films could be a *documentary*?
    a. a film about life in the desert
    b. a feature-length cartoon
    c. an action thriller
    d. a musical

____ 17. How is the underlined pronoun used in the following sentence?

The competitor with the best score was <u>she</u>.

    a. subject   c. indirect object
    b. direct object   d. subject complement

____ 18. In which of the following sentences is the object pronoun used correctly?
    a. The dentist told she that her teeth were perfect.
    b. Our dog likes me but she will not fetch the sticks I throw.
    c. Their parents wanted they to clean up the living room after the party.
    d. The ball bounced up and hit he in the chest.

____ 19. If an activity is *compulsory*, it means that
    a. you must do it
    b. you are forbidden to do it
    c. it is dangerous
    d. it is very difficult

____ 20. In which sentence is the object pronoun used correctly?
    a. She gave the book to my brother and I.
    b. I helped they with their arithmetic homework.
    c. He invited my friends and me to go to the ball game.
    d. We gave a party for her cousin and she.

Essay Questions

21. Each selection in this grouping is concerned with how someone reached or could reach a particular goal. Choose one of the selections and write an essay in which you describe the goal and explain the steps the author outlines to achieving that goal. Do you agree with the author? Why or why not?

22. Both selections are examples of "private writing," usually not intended for publication. Choose one of the selections and write an essay in which you analyze the author's use of personal details, an informal tone, and colloquial language. In your essay, comment on how the type of private writing (letter or diary) reveals the personality of the writer.

23. In each of these selections, the writer states directly or implies what he or she thinks is most important in life. Choose one of the pieces and, in an essay, analyze what is most important to the writer. Back up your thoughts with specific examples from the text. If you wish, compare and contrast two or more of the pieces, showing how the writers are similar or different in what they consider important.

"My Papa, Mark Twain" by Susy Clemens
"The Drive-In Movies" by Gary Soto
"Space Shuttle *Challenger*" by William Harwood

Selection Test

Critical Reading

On the line, write the letter of the best answer.

_____ 1. What evidence does the author of "My Papa, Mark Twain" offer to prove that her father was not just a humorist joking at everything?
   a. Many people enjoyed reading his famous book *Huckleberry Finn*.
   b. There is always a streak of humor in each of Twain's books.
   c. His book *The Prince and the Pauper* is full of serious and touching scenes as well as humor.
   d. Twain went into a printing office to learn a trade.

_____ 2. What does Susy Clemens mean by this line in "My Papa, Mark Twain"?

   I never saw a man with so much variety of feeling as papa has.

   a. Mark Twain was more sensitive than the average person.
   b. Mark Twain had trouble expressing his feelings.
   c. Mark Twain could express many different emotions in his writing.
   d. Mark Twain had stronger feelings than the average person.

_____ 3. According to the information Susy Clemens presents in "My Papa, Mark Twain," her father could best be described as
   a. strict, proper, and predictable
   b. practical, energetic, and lively
   c. quiet, shy, and serious
   d. humorous, absentminded, and affectionate

_____ 4. Susy Clemens proves that she is a good biographer in "My Papa, Mark Twain" because she
   a. gives specific examples that support the points she makes about her subject
   b. is the subject's daughter and obviously knows the man she is writing about
   c. has read many of the books her father wrote
   d. praises her father's talent

_____ 5. What can you tell about Mark Twain from the evidence in this passage from "My Papa, Mark Twain"?

   . . . he told us the other day that he could listen to himself talk for hours without getting tired, of course he said this in joke, but I've no dought it was founded on truth.

   a. Twain was a good and sympathetic listener.
   b. Twain enjoyed talking more than listening to others.
   c. Twain liked to make fun of himself.
   d. Twain preferred writing to speaking.

6. On the Saturday morning described in "The Drive-In Movies," why does the narrator decide to work especially hard?
   a. He wants to earn a larger allowance.
   b. He wants to impress his brother and sister and set a good example for them.
   c. He feels sorry for his mother because she works so hard.
   d. He wants to go to the local drive-in movie theater.

7. When she sees the work the boys have done that morning, how does the mother in "The Drive-In Movies" seem to feel?
   a. grateful and pleased
   b. amused and surprised
   c. annoyed and impatient
   d. shocked and concerned

8. In "The Drive-In Movies," the boys' experience with waxing the family car is evidence that
   a. they really did not work hard enough to be successful
   b. they did not have the proper tools and know-how to be completely successful
   c. the wax they used was the wrong kind for the job
   d. they loved their mother and were devoted to her

9. If someone else had described the author's experiences in "The Drive-In Movies," the story would probably
   a. be more accurate and precise
   b. include fewer personal details and examples
   c. have a different central character
   d. give more information about Soto's family

10. There is enough evidence in "The Drive-In Movies" to conclude that the author is
    a. a person with great energy and determination
    b. a person who avoids hard work whenever possible
    c. a person who does not understand the importance of relaxation
    d. a person with little sympathy or feeling for others

11. "Space Shuttle *Challenger*" explains that *Challenger*
    a. lifted off and returned to Earth safely
    b. exploded during liftoff
    c. went dangerously off course during an orbit around Earth
    d. never lifted off because of technical problems

12. According to "Space Shuttle *Challenger*," how does the author usually feel when he covers the launch of a spacecraft?
    a. nervous   b. bored   c. happy   d. angry

13. In "Space Shuttle *Challenger*," the author supports his statement that Rob Navias was a veteran reporter by telling us that
    a. Navias always hesitated to push the SEND button
    b. Navias had covered fourteen straight missions together with the author
    c. Navias worked for NASA public affairs
    d. Navias knew as much space trivia as UPI Science Editor Al Rossiter did

14. Which of the following best describes how reading "Space Shuttle *Challenger*" can help a reader broaden his or her experience?
    I. It will help him or her learn about the history of space flight.
    II. It will help him or her understand what it is like to report on space flight.
    III. It will help him or her understand the risks involved in space flight.
    IV. It will help him or her understand the scientific importance of the space shuttle missions.
    a. I only   b. I and IV   c. II only   d. II and III

____ 15. Which of the following statements from "Space Shuttle *Challenger*" conveys a personal reaction that the author shares with his readers?

    a. It was bitterly cold that night.

    b. I would occasionally glance toward the launch pad where *Challenger* stood bathed in high power spotlights, clearly visible for dozens of miles around.

    c. Off to the side, a brilliant tongue of orange flame periodically flared into the night as excess hydrogen was vented harmlessly into the atmosphere.

    d. I held the enormity of the disaster at bay; I knew if I relaxed my guard for an instant it could paralyze me.

Vocabulary, Spelling, and Grammar

____ 16. Which of the following words is closest in meaning to *consequently*?

    a. finally   c. to begin with

    b. as a result   d. surprisingly

____ 17. Which of the following words is spelled correctly?

    a. exccess   c. recces

    b. neccessary   d. incessantly

____ 18. A continuous, logical series of events may be defined as

    a. sequential   c. inconsequential

    b. random   d. jumbled

____ 19. Which of the following words best describes how the narrator of "The Drive-In Movies" polished the family car?

    a. hastily   c. incessantly

    b. vigorously   d. sloppily

____ 20. Which is the object of a preposition in the following sentence?

Susy Clemens wrote a story about her father.

    a. story   c. father

    b. Susy Clemens   d. about

Essay Questions

21. What does Susy Clemens believe people ought to know about her famous father, the subject of "My Papa, Mark Twain"? Write an essay explaining the main points of this biographical sketch. Use quotes and examples from the selection to support your points.

22. In all three selections, the writers present evidence that shows they are keen observers. Choose one of the selections and write an essay in which you discuss how the author uses details and examples to support important observations about characters and actions. Use examples from the selection to illustrate your points.

23. In "The Drive-In Movies," Gary Soto narrates a day in his childhood and makes the memory come alive by including vivid details. Yet, he does not make many direct statements about the characters and events that he describes. Write an essay in which you interpret and explain how the author's use of details and examples allows you to make inferences about characters and action in the selection.

"Restoring the Circle" by Joseph Bruchac
"How the Internet Works" by Kerry Cochrane
"Turkeys" by Bailey White

Selection Test

Critical Reading

On the line, write the letter of the best answer.

____ 1. In "Restoring the Circle," which of the following best describes the author's thoughts about imaginative portrayals of Native Americans in literature and history?
   a. Inaccurate portrayals that stereotype Native Americans are harmful to Native American culture.
   b. Only Native American authors should be permitted to write about Native American life and culture.
   c. Literary portrayals of Native Americans should be written in one of the Native American languages.
   d. All fiction about Native Americans is insulting to Native American culture.

____ 2. Using context clues, how would you define the word *aggressive* in the passage from "Restoring the Circle" below?

> Native American men were pictured as savage and dangerous people who were *aggressive* for no good reason.

   a. quarrelsome   c. sensitive
   b. hesitant   d. illogical

____ 3. According to the author of "Restoring the Circle," which of the following best describes literature written by Native American authors today?
   a. It portrays all Native Americans as being honest and noble.
   b. It is more imaginative than literature written by non-Native people.
   c. It portrays Native Americans as real human beings with both positive and negative traits.
   d. It is written in Native American languages.

____ 4. Which of the following passages from "Restoring the Circle" lets you know that the work is a persuasive essay?
   a. One of the most prominent Native American writers is N. Scott Momaday, who is of Kiowa Indian ancestry.
   b. . . . imaginative portrayals of Native American people and Native American cultures become painful stereotypes and distorted history.
   c. In many Native American traditions, life is seen as a circle.
   d. More than 400 different languages are spoken by the various Native Americans of North America.

____ 5. In "Restoring the Circle," the author admires N. Scott Momaday's novel *House Made of Dawn* because Momaday's work
   a. is thrilling and suspenseful
   b. helps preserve cultural traditions
   c. won the Pulitzer Prize
   d. is written in a poetic style

_____ 6. Which of the following pairs of words best describe the author's mother in "Turkeys"?
   a. tolerant and good-humored
   b. cold and distant
   c. angry and loud
   d. weak and impatient

_____ 7. One of the main points in "Turkeys" is that
   a. the author's mother had a good sense of humor
   b. there was no vaccine for measles back in the 1950's
   c. human beings can hatch eggs in an emergency
   d. the ornithologists would go to almost any length to save the wild turkeys

_____ 8. In "Turkeys," the ornithologists are interested in the wild turkeys that live near the author's childhood home because
   a. they are interested in preserving the species
   b. they are seeking to control the wild turkey population
   c. they want to experiment with hatching the eggs
   d. they want to capture wild turkeys for a study they are conducting

_____ 9. Which of the following lets you know that "Turkeys" is a narrative essay?
   a. The author tells about a memorable event in her life.
   b. Wild turkeys really were on the verge of extinction at the time the essay was written.
   c. The author uses dialogue in the essay.
   d. The ornithologists were scientists.

_____ 10. Which of the following lets you know that "How the Internet Works" is an informational essay?
   a. The essay is a work of nonfiction.
   b. The essay tells how to send information on the Internet.
   c. The essay explains or informs about use of the Internet.
   d. The author has his own personal Internet address.

_____ 11. In "How the Internet Works," one of the author's main points is that
   a. every computer connected to the Internet must have an IP address
   b. the Internet is a great research resource for students
   c. the Internet can be compared to the postal system
   d. a domain is part of an Internet address

_____ 12. In "How the Internet Works," which of the following statements reflects the author's opinion of Internet use for students?
   a. The Internet is not worthwhile for students, because it is too difficult to use.
   b. Schools cannot afford to use the Internet, because it is too expensive.
   c. Education was better before students had access to the Internet.
   d. The Internet offers students tremendous opportunities for learning.

_____ 13. Which of the following best defines _protocols_, as defined in "How the Internet Works"?
   a. Protocols work similarly to the postal system.
   b. Protocols have the name of the host computer along with the domain name.
   c. Protocols are a set of rules that standardize procedures for computer use.
   d. Protocols are rules for playing games.

_____ 14. In "Turkeys," how might you best describe the author's attitude toward the birds?
   a. fascinated and sympathetic
   b. angry and vengeful
   c. bored and frustrated
   d. puzzled and shy

_____ 15. Considering the context, how would you define the word *acceleration* in the following passage from "Turkeys"?

> One ornithologist had devised a formula to compute the ratio of domestic to pure-strain wild turkey in an individual bird by comparing the angle of flight at takeoff and the rate of *acceleration*. And in those sad days, the turkeys were flying low and slow.

    a. level of climbing   c. loudness of call
    b. increase in speed   d. duration of flight

Vocabulary, Spelling, and Grammar

_____ 16. Which of the following pairs of words are both spelled correctly?
    a. insistent, insistance   c. reverent, reverence
    b. resistant, resistence   d. resident, residince

_____ 17. In this sentence, what is the meaning of the word *destination*?
> Almost instantly the message sent on the Internet reached its *destination*.

    a. address
    b. place to which something or someone is going
    c. Web page
    d. place from which something or someone is leaving

_____ 18. In which of the following sentences are the quotation marks used incorrectly?
    a. "Yes," said my mother.
    b. "I'll be right over," said the ornithologist.
    c. "I love Thoreau's writing," I told him.
    d. Yes, I understand the protocols, "I told the teacher."

_____ 19. What is the best meaning for the italicized word in this sentence?
> It is *detrimental* to portray a culture in a distorted way.

    a. harmful   b. unwise   c. ignorant   d. understandable

_____ 20. Which of the following sentences contains correct punctuation and capitalization?
    a. I said, "The Internet is a great resource."
    b. "I love that poem", she said.
    c. He said "that author had great wisdom."
    d. Native American culture is incredible, "I" whispered.

Essay Questions

21. In "Restoring the Circle," the author mentions three mistaken impressions people have formed about Native Americans from reading literature written by people who did not understand Native American culture. In an essay, identify these three incorrect stereotypes, and explain how the author persuades readers to change their ideas.

22. Each selection in this grouping is an example of a different type of essay. Choose one of the selections, and write an essay in which you identify its type and explain what makes it a persuasive, narrative, or informational essay. Use quotations and examples from the piece to back up your points.

23. Choose one of the selections in this grouping and, in an essay, explain the author's message and identify the main ideas he or she uses to get that message across. Support your explanation with examples from the text.

Unit 7: Nonfiction

Unit Test

Critical Reading

On the line, write the letter of the best answer.

_____ 1. Which of the following facts is supported by this passage from "The Shutout"?

> Samuel Hopkins Adams (1871–1958), an American historical novelist, stated that his grandfather "played base ball in Mr. Mumford's pasture" in the 1820's.

   a. Baseball originated in the United States.
   b. Baseball did not originate in Cooperstown, NY, in 1839.
   c. Baseball was the most popular sport in the United States in the early nineteenth century.
   d. Samuel Hopkins Adams's grandfather invented baseball.

_____ 2. In "The Shutout," the exclusion of African American athletes from the National Association of Base Ball Players is explained on the grounds that
   a. barring African Americans would avoid conflict and keep politics out of baseball
   b. African Americans could not play baseball as well as other athletes
   c. no integrated sports events had ever taken place in the United States
   d. teams with African American players would have an edge over teams that did not

_____ 3. According to "The Shutout," it is difficult to learn facts about baseball as played by African Americans during the time they were excluded from Major League Baseball because
   a. African Americans did not play in organized leagues
   b. records were poorly kept and the mainstream press did not cover it well
   c. African Americans played baseball by different rules
   d. few people ever watched games played by African Americans

_____ 4. If your purpose in reading "The Shutout" was to learn about the origins of baseball, which fact would be of particular interest to you?
   a. The "Negro Leagues" kept erratic records of their games.
   b. The Baseball Hall of Fame did not honor "Negro League" players for many years.
   c. Slave owners in the old South especially enjoyed boxing, wrestling, and racing.
   d. Many cultures have had games involving bats and balls.

_____ 5. In "Letter to Scottie," the White Cat is
   a. a nickname Fitzgerald gives his daughter
   b. a nickname Scottie has given her father
   c. something that Fitzgerald and Scottie know about, but other readers do not
   d. a Fitzgerald family pet

_____ 6. The tone of F. Scott Fitzgerald's "Letter to Scottie" is
   a. informal and affectionate
   b. formal and reserved
   c. angry and critical
   d. sad and depressing

_____ 7. In "Olympic Diary," Amanda Borden's purpose in writing about the injuries and hardships she suffered is
   a. to discourage readers from becoming gymnasts
   b. to demonstrate to readers how tough she is
   c. to make the diary exciting and suspenseful
   d. to show how difficult it is to become a world-class gymnast

_____ 8. In "Letter to Scottie," Fitzgerald's use of informal language, lists of items, nicknames, and personal feelings shows that the selection
   a. was not edited and proofread properly
   b. was written hastily and carelessly
   c. is an example of "private" writing
   d. reflects Fitzgerald's lack of concern for his daughter

_____ 9. In "My Papa, Mark Twain," Twain's problem with the burglar alarm shows that
   a. Twain does not care about keeping his house secure from burglary
   b. Twain has trouble understanding how such devices work
   c. Twain has a good imagination
   d. Twain is very nervous about burglars breaking into his house

_____ 10. Which detail from "My Papa, Mark Twain" shows most clearly that it was written by a family member?
   a. Clara and I are sure that papa played the trick on Grandma about the whipping that is related in _The Adventures of Tom Sawyer._
   b. . . . _The Prince and the Pauper_ is full of touching places, but there is always a streak of humor in them somewhere.
   c. His complexion is very fair, and he doesn't ware a beard.
   d. He has beautiful gray hair, not any too thick or any too long . . .

_____ 11. In "My Papa, Mark Twain," the number of cats in the Twain home is evidence that
   a. Twain is very absent-minded
   b. Twain does not care about keeping a neat home
   c. Twain loves animals
   d. Twain was writing a book about cats

_____ 12. In "The Drive-In Movies," the brothers work so hard all Saturday because
   a. they have been raised very strictly
   b. they need to earn extra money
   c. they are doing it as a gift for their mother
   d. they want to put their mother in a good mood

_____ 13. "Space Shuttle _Challenger_" makes it clear that space shuttle launches
   a. can always turn into disasters   c. have become boring routines
   b. are always fun   d. are completely safe these days

_____ 14. From "Space Shuttle _Challenger_," you can conclude that two important values for a news reporter are
   a. courtesy and efficiency   c. accuracy and speed
   b. intelligence and sympathy   d. memory and logic

_____ 15. In "Space Shuttle _Challenger_," the author says that detailed profiles of each crew member were written before every shuttle mission
   a. to be printed in newspapers around the country
   b. to compare and contrast the skills and training of the crew members
   c. to serve as instant obituaries in the event of a disaster
   d. to be broadcast in case of a launch delay

_____ 16. In "Restoring the Circle," the author says that fictional portrayals of Native American cultures by people of other cultures
    a. are inaccurate because no written records of Native American history exist
    b. lack the authentic quality that only Native American writers could create
    c. have become closer to reality in recent years
    d. will be more possible in a hundred years than they are now

_____ 17. From the context, how would you define the word *authentically* in this passage from "Restoring the Circle"?

Writing can become a window into another reality, offering to non-Natives the opportunity to *authentically* experience something of Native American culture.

    a. briefly   c. reliably
    b. deeply   d. occasionally

_____ 18. "How the Internet Works" offers an explanation of the workings of the Internet because
    a. many people have mistaken ideas about the Internet
    b. many people know little or nothing about the Internet
    c. the author thinks it is vital that everyone know how the Internet works
    d. the author wants everyone to use the Internet

_____ 19. In "Turkeys," which of the following best describes the author's opinion of the ornithologists?
    a. cautious and wise   c. cautious and scientific
    b. fussy and impractical   d. arrogant and rude

Vocabulary, Spelling, and Grammar

_____ 20. Which of the following sentences is correctly punctuated?
    a. "Is anybody home"? she called.
    b. "I read a book every week" said the man.
    c. "That's ridiculous!" snapped the woman.
    d. "We want to go to the movies", whined the boys.

_____ 21. The word *incessantly* means
    a. never sounding   c. always loud
    b. never ceasing   d. intolerant

_____ 22. Which word is misspelled?
    a. irregular   b. irrational   c. irritate   d. ireverent

_____ 23. Which sentence uses an *incorrect* subject pronoun?
    a. The person who called you was me.
    b. If the book is here, you can have it.
    c. It was she who voted against going on the field trip.
    d. All day long, they worked at the factory.

_____ 24. The word closest in meaning to *anecdotes* is
    a. medicines   b. stories   c. desserts   d. maps

_____ 25. Which sentence has two object pronouns?
    a. The teacher should give the assignment to you and me.
    b. She and I would like to join you for lunch.
    c. They played soccer with us after school.
    d. I will be glad to share some of this ice cream with you.

_____ 26. Which of the following words is *incorrectly* spelled?
    a. beg   b. league   c. drag   d. intrige

____ 27. Which is the object of the preposition in this sentence?

        The photograph was taken of her when she was a young woman.

        a. she   b. her   c. woman   d. photograph

____ 28. The *prelude* to an event
    a. happens after the event
    b. happens at the same time as the event
    c. happens before the event
    d. happens instead of the event

____ 29. Which of the following titles contains *incorrect* capitalization or punctuation?
    a. "Restoring the circle"   c. *A Tale of Two Cities*
    b. "How the Internet Works"   d. "Turkeys"

____ 30. Which of the following words is *not* correctly spelled?
    a. niece   c. pierce
    b. decieve   d. reign

Essay Questions

31. Writers are capable of creating vivid portraits of the people they write about. Choose either "My Papa, Mark Twain," or "The Drive-In Movies," and write a descriptive essay about the subject the author has chosen. Conclude your essay by suggesting what the author's purpose was in writing the piece.

32. Nonfiction often consists of a mixture of fact and insight, and readers need to be able to distinguish between the two. Choose either "The Shutout" or "Space Shuttle *Challenger*" and, in an essay, summarize the facts and the insights the author presents. Explain how the facts relate to the insights, and conclude by giving your opinion as to whether the insights would have been convincing to you if the facts had not been part of the article.

33. In autobiographical writing, authors can reveal a good deal about their personalities without actually describing themselves directly. Write an essay to point out what the authors reveal about themselves in two of these selections: "Olympic Diary," "The Drive-in Movies," and "Turkeys." Compare and contrast the ways in which the authors wrote about themselves; in what ways, if any, were they similar, and in what ways, if any, were they different? Use details from the selections to support your statements.

34. Nonfiction writing, whether intended for the public or for one other person, often says much about how the writer feels toward his or her subject, or the person to whom the writing is addressed. Write an essay in which you analyze what you learn about this kind of relationship in two of the following selections: "Letter to Scottie," "My Papa, Mark Twain," and "Restoring the Circle." In your essay include both facts about the relationships and insights you can make based on these facts. Use details from the selection as needed to support your analysis. Conclude the essay by comparing and contrasting the connections the pieces reveal. In what ways are they alike, and in what ways are they different from each other?

35. An author does not necessarily have to state an opinion on a subject directly; he or she can suggest an opinion about a subject by hints and suggestions. Choose two of the following selections: "Space Shuttle *Challenger*," "How the Internet Works," and "Turkeys." Then, write an essay in which you state the author's message and how it is delivered. Use details from the selections to support your analysis.

Name _____ Date _____

Unit 7: Nonfiction

Alternative Unit Test

The two passages below are followed by questions based on their content and on the relationship between the two passages.

Passage 1

In this excerpt from her autobiography, naturalist Jane Goodall describes her first day in an African National Park.

from *My Life With the Chimpanzees* by Jane Goodall

July 16, 1960, was a day I shall remember all my life. It was when I first set foot on the shingle and sand beach of Chimpanzee Land—that is, Gombe National Park. I was twenty-six years old.

Mum and I were greeted by the two African game scouts who were responsible for protecting the thirty square miles of the park. They helped us to find a place where we could put up our old ex-army tent.

We chose a lovely spot under some shady trees near the small, fast-flowing Kakombe Stream. In Kigoma (before setting out), we had found a cook, Dominic. He put up his little tent some distance from ours and quite near the lake.

When camp was ready I set off to explore. It was already late afternoon, so I could not go far. There had been a grass fire not long before, so all the vegetation of the more open ridges and peaks had burned away. This made it quite easy to move around, except that the slopes above the valley were very steep in places, and I slipped several times on the loose, gravelly soil.

I shall never forget the thrill of that first exploration. Soon after leaving camp I met a troop of baboons. They were afraid of the strange, white-skinned creature (that was I) and gave their barking alarm call, "Waa-hoo! Waa-hoo!" again and again. I left them, hoping that they would become used to me soon—otherwise, I thought, all the creatures of Gombe would be frightened. As I crossed a narrow ravine crowded with low trees and bushes I got very close to a beautiful red-gold bushbuck—a forest antelope about the size of a long-legged goat. I knew it was female because she had no horns. When she scented me she kept quite still for a moment and stared toward me with her big dark eyes. Then, with a loud barking call, she turned and bounded away.

Passage 2

The following excerpt from a biography of artist Georgia O'Keeffe describes one of her earliest memories.

from Georgia O'Keeffe: The "Wideness and Wonder of Her World"
by Beverly Gherman

Georgia's uncanny appreciation for her surroundings began in infancy. She insisted she could remember her very first outing, when she was carried from the hazy rooms of the family's farmhouse into sunlight. Propped against large pillows on a familiar red and black quilt, her eyes filled with a blueness that seemed to stretch forever over her head. She was dazzled by the brilliance of the sun. It warmed her face and arms. It skipped along the stars and flowers of the quilt and glistened against the prickly grass beyond her.

Georgia noticed her mother's friend Winnie, whose long dress was dotted with dainty blue flowers and gathered together into a puffy bustle. She was startled by Winnie's mass of curly blond hair after having seen only the straight, dark hair of her mother and aunts.

Most vivid of all to Georgia, then scarcely a year old, was the brightness of that day. It forced her to squint at the white farmhouse glaring against the dark, curving drive. It collided with the high hedge and formed shadows that crawled along the path before her.

Years later, when Georgia related her earliest memory, her mother kept insisting it was impossible to remember things that happened before you could walk or talk. But Georgia was adamant and described the scene in such sharp detail that her unbelieving mother finally had to admit Georgia's memory was not only accurate, but quite amazing.

Critical Reading

On the line, write the letter of the best answer.

_____ 1. Based on these passages, which statement is common to both Jane Goodall and Georgia O'Keeffe?
   a. They have special memories of their childhoods.
   b. They like to explore their surroundings.
   c. They are observant of their surroundings.
   d. They like to observe animals.
   e. They appreciate the play of light and shadows.

_____ 2. The author's purpose that is common to both passages is
   a. to describe an important memory
   b. to explain how the woman becomes an artist
   c. to explain how the woman becomes a naturalist
   d. to reveal how the woman becomes famous
   e. to show the importance of childhood events

_____ 3. Which of the following statements indicates the kind of nonfiction that applies to both passages?
   a. Both are history essays.
   b. Passage 1 is a letter, and Passage 2 is a journal.
   c. Both passages are media accounts.
   d. Both passages are persuasive essays.
   e. Passage 2 is a biography, and Passage 1 is an autobiography.

_____ 4. Identify one of the author's main points that applies to both passages.
   a. The passage explains how family members influence the woman in her work.
   b. The description helps to explain the woman's dedication to her work.
   c. The passage describes the woman's conflict with nature.
   d. The description explains the importance of animals in the woman's work.
   e. The description explains the importance of light in the woman's work.

_____ 5. In Passage 1, what evidence shows that Jane Goodall is dedicated to her work as a naturalist?
   a. She sets up camp near Kakombe Stream.
   b. She frightens baboons on her first day in the park.
   c. She continues exploring despite the burned vegetation.
   d. She is able to identify a female bushbuck on her first day.
   e. She goes exploring as soon as the camp is set up.

6. Why is July 16, 1960, a day Jane Goodall says she will always remember?
   a. It was the day she saw her first baboons in the wild.
   b. It was the day she saw her first bushbuck in the wild.
   c. It was the day she turned twenty-six.
   d. It was the day she first arrived in Chimpanzee Land.
   e. It was the day she first met the game scouts in the national park.

7. In Passage 1, why does Jane Goodall hope the baboons will get used to her soon?
   a. She hopes to be able to observe them without being seen.
   b. She thinks they may frighten all the animals of Gombe National Park with their alarm call.
   c. She is afraid they will keep her from observing the chimpanzees.
   d. She doesn't want to hear their alarm call again.
   e. She is afraid they will harm her and her mother.

8. In Passage 2, what does this early memory tell the reader about Georgia O'Keeffe as an artist?
   a. She was impressed by Winnie's curly blond hair.
   b. She didn't get to leave the house until she was nearly one year old.
   c. She had powers of observation at a very young age.
   d. She was impressed by flowers at an early age.
   e. She is stubborn when she believes she is right.

9. In Passage 2, a detail not included in O'Keeffe's early memory is
   a. the shadow of the barn
   b. the brilliance of the sun
   c. the stars on her quilt
   d. the blueness of the sky
   e. the prickly grass beyond her

10. In Passage 2, O'Keeffe was struck by the contrast between
    a. the white farmhouse and the dark driveway
    b. the hazy rooms of the house and the sunlight outside
    c. Winnie's blond hair and her mother's dark hair
    d. all of the above
    e. none of the above

11. A purpose for reading both passages would be
    a. to learn about important events in exceptional women's lives
    b. to understand how women can become successful
    c. to find out how memories affect women's lives
    d. to learn how families affect women's success in different fields
    e. to learn how women succeed in different fields

12. Which statement best compares the nonfiction forms of Passage 1 and Passage 2?
    a. Passage 1 is part of a biography and Passage 2 is part of an autobiography.
    b. Passage 1 is part of an autobiography and Passage 2 is part of a biography.
    c. Passage 1 is part of a journal and Passage 2 is part of a letter.
    d. Passage 1 is a narrative essay and Passage 2 is a media account.
    e. Passage 1 is an informational essay and Passage 2 is a persuasive essay.

13. What role does nature play for the women in these passages?
    a. Goodall is interested in animals, while O'Keeffe is interested in plants.
    b. Goodall is interested in vegetation, while O'Keeffe is interested in sunlight.
    c. Each woman attempts to change some element of nature.
    d. Each woman appreciates details of nature that are connected with her work.
    e. Each woman struggles against the elements of nature.

____ 14. Which statement best identifies the most important problems mentioned in both passages?
  a. In Passage 1, the animals are afraid of Goodall; in Passage 2, O'Keeffe's mother refuses to believe her daughter's first memory.
  b. In Passage 1, much vegetation is burned away; in Passage 2, the sun is too bright for O'Keeffe's eyes.
  c. In Passage 1, Goodall is too inexperienced to explore the national park; in Passage 2, Winnie's hair is too curly.
  d. In Passage 1, the terrain is too slippery; in Passage 2, the farmhouse is too hazy.
  e. In Passage 1, Goodall is afraid of animals; in Passage 2, O'Keeffe has difficulty remembering things.

____ 15. These two passages might have been placed together
  a. to show the similarities between Africa and the United States
  b. to show the similarities between naturalists and artists
  c. because both describe a woman's memory of her surroundings
  d. because both are written by women who are important in their fields
  e. to show the differences between naturalists and artists

Essay Questions – Select One

16. Write an essay telling two ways in which Jane Goodall and Georgia O'Keeffe are alike and two ways in which they are different, based on these passages. Give examples from the passages to support your views.

17. In an essay, compare and contrast Passage 1, which is from an autobiography, with Passage 2, which is from a biography. What elements of Passage 1 show that it is an autobiography? What elements of Passage 2 show that it is a biography? What elements do an autobiography and a biography have in common? Give examples from the passages to support your views.

18. Nature plays a large part in the lives of both Jane Goodall and Georgia O'Keeffe. Write an essay explaining how each woman is affected by nature in these passages. Explain how nature has an influence on their lives.

Name _____   Date _____

The Phantom Tollbooth, Act I based on the book by Norton Juster,
by Susan Nanus

Selection Test

Critical Reading

On the line, write the letter of the best answer.

_____ 1. Which of the following best summarizes what an audience learns from the first scene
of "The Phantom Tollbooth"?
a. Milo does not like school.
b. Milo watches television too much.
c. Some people are never satisfied with what they have.
d. Milo is about to begin an unusual adventure.

_____ 2. As the drama begins, why is Milo always bored?
a. He already knows everything and has nothing more to learn.
b. He does not know how to make good use of his time.
c. He does not enjoy games.
d. He dislikes reading.

_____ 3. No one stays at the Royal Banquet long enough to hear King Azaz's closing speech
because
a. the King no longer makes much sense when he speaks
b. the people prefer to listen to the Mathemagician
c. everyone wants to spend more time with Milo
d. they are all exhausted and want to go home

_____ 4. What does the Whether Man really mean in this line?

Of course, some people never go beyond Expectations . . .

a. Some people are very hopeful and optimistic.
b. Some people are too pessimistic to have any real expectations.
c. Some people know it is better to expect good fortune than fear bad luck.
d. Some people dream about the future without doing anything about it.

_____ 5. The Princesses Rhyme and Reason are banished from Dictionopolis after they
a. say that words are more important than numbers
b. lose their power to make sensible decisions
c. judge numbers and words to be of equal importance
d. say that numbers are more important than words

_____ 6. Without Rhyme and Reason, Dictionopolis will most likely remain a place where
a. numbers are more respected than words
b. people understand the value of language
c. words have lost much of their power because they are overused
d. many people will write poetry

_____ 7. A good summary of *The Phantom Tollbooth*, Act I, would include
    a. details about Milo's mysterious package at the beginning of the drama
    b. information about the particular taste of every letter in the alphabet
    c. a word-for-word copy of the argument between King Azaz and the Mathemagician
    d. a description of King Azaz's costume

_____ 8. In the scene in which Milo meets the Lethargarians, the stage directions call for the actors to
    a. perform with slow, exhausted actions
    b. speak crisply and with energy
    c. welcome Milo enthusiastically
    d. look angrily at Milo when he asks where he is

_____ 9. The people who buy words by the bag at the Word Market are probably
    a. trying to save money by purchasing large quantities at a time
    b. in the process of writing a dictionary
    c. too lazy to make up their own words
    d. talented poets and short story writers

_____ 10. What do you learn from these stage directions that announce the entrance of Tock the Watchdog?

> *They all run off and ENTER a large dog with the head, feet, and tail of a dog, and the body of a clock, having the same face as the character The Clock.*

    a. The Lethargarians are terrified of dogs.
    b. Tock represents Time and is the enemy of laziness.
    c. Milo is worrying about wasting his time.
    d. A new act of the drama is about to begin.

_____ 11. When Tock remarks to Milo that words "are fine if you have something to say," he really means,
    a. Words are fine unless you have something to say.
    b. Words are not fine if you have something to say.
    c. Words are fine if you have something worthwhile to say.
    d. Words are fine if you have nothing to say.

_____ 12. After Tock explains to Milo that there had been a great disagreement between Azaz and the Mathemagician, the stage directions call for the lights to dim on Tock and Milo and to come up on Azaz. The purpose of this stage direction is to show that
    a. Milo and Azaz are about to meet
    b. the action being shown actually occurred at an earlier time
    c. the disagreement will occur later in the play
    d. night is falling where Milo is

_____ 13. The best point at which to stop and summarize some of the action in Act I would be
    a. after the Clock makes the opening speech about time
    b. at the end of Act I, Scene i
    c. in the middle of the argument between Azaz and the Mathemagician
    d. after Azaz serves a light snack

_____ 14. Azaz gives Milo a box of letters of the alphabet in order to
    a. help him know what to say when he meets the Mathemagician
    b. win his battle with the Mathemagician
    c. teach him to be a better reader
    d. protect Milo on his journey to Digitopolis

____ 15. Drama is different from other forms of literature because
   a. it is intended to be represented on stage by performers
   b. it is meant to be read aloud
   c. it uses dialogue to express meaning
   d. it can use musical devices

Vocabulary, Grammar, and Spelling

____ 16. The word *ignorance* means
   a. a strong warning   c. a lack of knowledge
   b. a misunderstanding   d. a dangerous situation

____ 17. Which sentence contains a misspelled word?
   a. Ignorance can be corrected by careful attention to the world around us.
   b. The package contained three precautionary signs for Milo's journey.
   c. The Humbug only contributed to the confusion in the realm.
   d. Milo had the misapprehention that there was nothing interesting to do with his time.

____ 18. Which of the following sentences shows correct subject-verb agreement?
   a. Tock want to show Milo that time is precious.
   b. Milo learns the value of time through his experiences in Dictionopolis.
   c. The Lethargarians sleeps most of the day and night.
   d. The words Milo hear are confusing.

____ 19. In the word precautionary, the prefix *pre-* shows that the word means cautionary measures taken
   a. *before* danger is present   c. *after* a danger is past
   b. *during* the dangerous situation   d. cautionary measures taken *more than once*

____ 20. Which of the following sentences includes a plural subject with a plural verb?
   a. A half-baked idea is rarely useful to anyone.
   b. Dictionopolis seems to be a place of great confusion.
   c. The word merchants show their goods to Milo.
   d. Idleness is not the path to knowledge.

Essays

21. As Milo makes his journey, he meets quite a few unusual characters. Milo learns something from the attitude and behavior of each of these characters. Select one character or group of similar characters, and write an essay explaining what Milo learns from meeting this individual or group. In your essay, include details and examples of dialogue that support your ideas.

22. Although *The Phantom Tollbooth* is an entertaining drama, its author also has a particular viewpoint to express. What do you think the drama tells us about the relationship between how a person uses time and how that person becomes educated? In an essay, discuss how the characters and situations Milo encounters relate to this question. Use examples of dialogue and details from the drama to back up your ideas.

23. The staging of a play is an important element of drama. In an essay, analyze how the stage directions written for *The Phantom Tollbooth*, Act I, help the audience to better understand the action of the play. Be specific in your discussion of various stage directions and connect them to the overall meaning of the scene or passage for which the directions were written.

Name _____ Date _____

The Phantom Tollbooth, Act II based on the book by Norton Juster,
by Susan Nanus

Selection Test

Critical Reading

On the line, write the letter of the best answer.

_____ 1. Which of the following stage directions provides important information about Kakafo-
nous A. Dischord, Doctor of Dissonance?
   a. *He opens a large dusty book and thumbs through the pages.*
   b. *Surprised at the question*
   c. *Hands MILO a package*
   d. *Several small explosions and a grinding crash are heard.*

_____ 2. Why doesn't it matter whether Milo, Humbug, and Tock choose to travel in miles,
rods, yards, feet, inches, or half-inches ?
   a. They don't know which direction to go in.
   b. There are so many obstacles, they will never get to Digitopolis, anyway.
   c. All the distances on the sign are really the same.
   d. Digitopolis is only an imaginary place.

_____ 3. Which is a key detail in helping a reader envision the Dodecaheron?
   a. a stethoscope around his neck and big ears
   b. Yellow Gleaming Eyes
   c. a 12-sided figure with a different fact on each side
   d. a beautifully-dressed man holding an eye dropper

_____ 4. What does the Dodecaheron mean when he tells Milo that numbers are not made,
but that "You have to dig for them"?
   a. Numbers grow in the ground.
   b. Numbers exist, but you have to find the ones you need to figure out a specific
      problem.
   c. Numbers are not important if you are good at using words.
   d. Numbers are more important than words.

_____ 5. Why do the numbers that the Mathemagician scoops up include only numbers from
1 to 9 and an assortment of zeros?
   a. The numbers mine had only those numbers.
   b. The Mathemagician could not hold any more numbers.
   c. The Mathemagician thought that Milo wouldn't understand other numbers.
   d. These are the numbers from which all other numbers are formed.

_____ 6. Which of the following details help you envision the measuring room?
   a. The interior is dark.
   b. Iridescent and glittery numbers seem to sparkle from everywhere.
   c. Hundreds of Yellow Gleaming Eyes can be seen.
   d. All walls, tables, chairs, desks, cabinets, and blackboards are labeled to show
      their heights, widths, depths, and distances from one another.

_____ 7. What detail in the stage directions helps you to envision the Mathemagician's facial expressions when he speaks about Rhyme and Reason?
   a. *Opening a closet door.*
   b. *Puts the letter on the easel.*
   c. *Sadness turns to fury.*
   d. *Door reveals an "8" that is as wide as the "3" was high.*

_____ 8. Which is the best reason for rescuing the princesses Rhyme and Reason?
   a. Azaz and the Mathemagician will stop arguing and act reasonable.
   b. King Azaz is offering a reward for their rescue.
   c. The Mathemagician will be happy again.
   d. The princesses are imprisoned by demons.

_____ 9. Which of the following best explains why the Mathemagician calls his pencil a magic staff?
   a. The pencil can make demons disappear.
   b. Magic will turn the pencil into anything Milo wants or needs.
   c. You can make numbers disappear with a pencil.
   d. You can solve problems with a pencil.

_____ 10. Which of the following explains the double meaning of the name "Senses Taker"?
   a. The Senses Taker can take away your senses, but doesn't make sense.
   b. A *census taker* helps keep records about population; this *Senses Taker* also takes away people's senses.
   c. Everything the Senses Taker says is nonsense.
   d. A real senses taker should be sensible, but the Senses Taker has no sense.

_____ 11. Which prop helps Milo to gain entrance to the Castle-in-the-Air?
   a. the Mathemagician
   b. lights, indicating the passage of time
   c. the magic staff
   d. a package of letters

_____ 12. What is the obstacle the Mathemagician mentions when Milo sets out to rescue the princesses?
   a. the castle walls
   b. the Senses Taker
   c. the demons
   d. the Everpresent Wordsnatcher

_____ 13. Why is the loud sound of the ticking clock in Milo's room at the end so important?
   a. It reminds Milo how long he has been gone.
   b. It reminds Milo of the importance of time and that time is continually passing.
   c. Clocks always make ticking sounds, so this just makes the scene more real.
   d. This sound helps introduce Clock as a character.

_____ 14. How has Milo changed from the beginning of Act II?
   a. He is braver than he was at the beginning.
   b. He is more unsure of himself about numbers and time.
   c. He is looking forward to being busy and making good use of his time in the future.
   d. He is more tired and bored than in the beginning.

Vocabulary, Spelling, and Grammar

_____ 15. Which of the following sentences would be correctly completed by adding the word *admonishing*?
   a. You can compliment someone by giving them an _____ look.
   b. That was the most _____ thing I've ever seen!
   c. "Well done," she said, _____ us for our excellent performance.
   d. "Be sure to stay out of trouble," he said, with an _____ look.

_____ 16. The indefinite pronoun *each*
   a. is always singular
   b. is always plural
   c. may be either singular or plural
   d. may never be used with the verb *be*

_____ 17. Which of the underlined words is misspelled in these sentences?
   a. Dodecaheron is not a <u>gratius</u> host to Milo and his friends.
   b. The numbers mine was very <u>spacious</u>.
   c. The senses taker is an <u>obnoxious</u> character.
   d. Milo was so hungry after eating subtraction stew that he had a <u>voracious</u> appetite.

_____ 18. Use what you know about the meaning of the root -son- to help determine the correct meaning of the italicized word in this sentence.

   The *resonance* of the piano is beautiful.

   a. shiny wood   c. gleaming ivory
   b. graceful shape   d. full and rich sound

_____ 19. Use the meaning of the root -son- and sentence context to identify the correct meaning of *sonorous* in the following sentence.

   It was not only what the speaker said, but his *sonorous* voice that captivated the audience.

   a. difficult to hear   c. full, deep, rich-sounding
   b. happy   d. scratchy, croaking

_____ 20. Which of the following sentences does *not* show correct subject-verb agreement?
   a. Sooner or later, everyone loses patience with Dodecahedron.
   b. Each of the characters want the princess to be rescued.
   c. Everything is possible as long as you try.
   d. Nobody likes to waste time.

Essay Questions

21. Many of the characters in Act II of *The Phantom Tollbooth* represent either a desirable human quality or a human fault. Choose one character and identify the quality or fault he or she represents. Explain why the trait is a desirable quality or a fault. Use situations that could possibly arise in real life as examples to back up your ideas.

22. In your opinion, what is the most important lesson Milo learns from his experiences in Act II of *The Phantom Tollbooth*? State the lesson, explain how Milo learns the lesson, and tell why you think the lesson would help someone get along in life.

23. A classic story is a story of such high quality and excellence, and which focuses on such important universal themes, that people continue to read it for many years after it is written. In an essay, explain why *The Phantom Tollbooth* should be considered a classic. Use examples from the play to support your reasons.

Grandpa and the Statue by Arthur Miller

Selection Test

Critical Reading

On the line, write the letter of the best answer.

____ 1. Young Monaghan likes to look at the Statue of Liberty because
    a. it represents freedom for all
    b. it reminds him of his grandfather
    c. it reminds him of his days in the army
    d. it reminds him of his brother

____ 2. Which of the following do you find out about Grandpa Monaghan from his grandson's dialogue with August in the hospital?
    a. Grandpa Monaghan was stingy.
    b. Grandpa Monaghan had many friends.
    c. Grandpa Monaghan came from Ireland.
    d. Grandpa Monaghan was rich.

____ 3. Which of the following do you find out about Grandpa Monaghan from his dialogue with Sheean?
    a. He doesn't like Sheean.
    b. He is ashamed of being stingy.
    c. He doesn't believe what he reads in the newspapers.
    d. He likes to ride on the Staten Island Ferry.

____ 4. Grandpa Monaghan thinks the statue is broken because
    a. it has no base to stand on
    c. he hasn't had a chance to see it
    b. it is hidden in a warehouse
    d. it hasn't been put together yet

____ 5. When Young Monaghan tells August that his grandpa was called the stingiest man in Brooklyn, you can predict that
    a. his grandpa will end up giving money for the base of the statue
    b. his grandpa will not want to subscribe to the fund for the statue's base
    c. his grandpa will become rich
    d. his grandpa will change and become generous

____ 6. When Grandpa Monaghan agrees to take his grandson to see the Statue of Liberty, you can predict that
    a. they will meet the other boys there
    b. he will never change his mind about the statue
    c. he will change his mind about the statue
    d. the statue will be blown down

____ 7. Sheean donates a dime to the fund in Monaghan's name because
    a. Sheean wants every name on the street on the subscription list
    b. Sheean likes Monaghan
    c. Sheean owes Monaghan money
    d. Sheean is stingy

_____ 8. Which of these statements helps you predict that grandpa's opinion of the statue will change?
  a. You've stranded me!
  b. That's the date the country was made!
  c. No, the stairs are this way!
  d. Go on now, I want to study this a minute.

_____ 9. Why does Grandpa Monaghan put a coin on the base of the statue?
  a. He sees that the statue has not fallen down.
  b. He thinks the statue is beautiful.
  c. He finally understands the real meaning of the statue.
  d. He wants to make his grandson proud of him.

_____ 10. Which of the following does Young Monaghan's dialogue let you know about Child Monaghan's feelings?
  a. He felt attached to his grandfather.
  b. He was ashamed of his grandfather.
  c. He was afraid of his grandfather.
  d. He thought his grandfather was funny.

_____ 11. Why does Child Monaghan hope that the wind blows the statue down?
  a. He doesn't like the statue.
  b. His grandfather won't take him to see the statue.
  c. He doesn't want the other boys to think his grandfather is stingy.
  d. He thinks the statue is dangerous.

_____ 12. Which statement best describes Young Monaghan's feelings toward his grandfather?
  a. He is embarrassed by him.   c. He wants to be like him.
  b. He admires his stinginess.   d. He sees his faults and loves him.

_____ 13. The reason Grandpa Monaghan doesn't want to give money for the base of the statue is that
  a. he doesn't like the statue   c. he doesn't believe in liberty
  b. he is too stingy   d. the statue comes from France

_____ 14. Why does Grandpa Monaghan tell his grandson not to let anyone know they went to see the Statue of Liberty?
  a. He doesn't want people to know he spent the money for the trip.
  b. He wants people to think he went to Staten Island.
  c. He likes his life to be private.
  d. He is embarrassed because he told everyone he had no interest in the statue.

_____ 15. Why does Grandpa Monaghan say that the statue had "Welcome All on it all the time"?
  a. He sees the words, "Welcome All" on the base of the statue.
  b. The veteran tells him that the statue's purpose is to welcome immigrants to the United States.
  c. Those are the words he thinks should be on the statue.
  d. That is the real meaning of the words on the statue.

Vocabulary, Spelling, and Grammar

____ 16. Which of the following is closest in meaning to *peeved*?
   a. annoyed   c. inscribed
   b. subscribed   d. amused

____ 17. In which of these sentences does the pronoun agree in gender and number with its antecedent?
   a. Each boy said they wanted to see the statue.
   b. Each boy said he wanted to see the statue.
   c. Each boy said she wanted to see the statue.
   d. Each boy said they wanted to see it.

____ 18. In which of the following sentences is the word *uncomprehending* used correctly?
   a. The grandfather was *uncomprehending* enough to understand the meaning of the words on the base of the statue.
   b. The grandfather in the play was so *uncomprehending*, he saved broken umbrella handles.
   c. At first, the boy's grandfather was *uncomprehending* about the meaning of the Statue of Liberty.
   d. The most *uncomprehending* thing about the statue was its real meaning.

____ 19. Which of the following sentences can be completed with the word *they*?
   a. I asked the girl a question, but _____ didn't answer.
   b. Each boy said _____ didn't know the answer.
   c. Ask the girls if _____ enjoyed seeing the Statue of Liberty.
   d. Ask each girl if _____ enjoyed the trip to the Statue of Liberty.

____ 20. Which of the following words is spelled *incorrectly*?
   a. braver   c. happier
   b. prettier   d. graier

Essay Questions

21. Grandpa Monaghan says that the words on the base of the Statue of Liberty mean "Welcome All." In an essay, give your interpretation of the words on the base of the statue. Do you agree with Grandpa Monaghan? Why or why not? Use specific quotes from the words on the statue's base to back up your interpretation.

22. Young Monaghan's dialogue reveals much about how he felt toward his grandfather. In an essay, analyze Young Monaghan's feelings for his grandfather. Support your analysis with examples of dialogue.

23. In the play, Monaghan is represented as a young man in an army hospital and also as a young boy. In an essay, contrast Child Monaghan with Monaghan the young man. How has he changed as he grew up? Use details from the dialogue to back up your ideas. You might guess at what experiences in Young Monaghan's life changed him.

Unit 8: Drama

Unit 8: Drama

Unit Test

Critical Reading

On the line, write the letter of the best answer.

_____ 1. In *The Phantom Tollbooth*, Act I, the five Ministers of Dictionopolis are costumed to look
    a. handsome and impressive   c. pompous and foolish
    b. poor and ragged   d. intelligent and thoughtful

_____ 2. In *The Phantom Tollbooth*, Act I, which of the following is the best definition of a *half-baked idea*?
    a. an idea that makes no sense because it has not been completely thought out
    b. an idea that would be correct if it were expressed more clearly
    c. a funny idea
    d. an idea that used to be considered true but is not any more

_____ 3. In *The Phantom Tollbooth*, Act I, it is illegal to think in the Doldrums because
    a. thinking is considered dangerous   c. thinking is considered impossible
    b. thinking is considered unhealthy   d. thinking is considered to be work

_____ 4. In *The Phantom Tollbooth*, Act I, how would you summarize the contest between King Azaz and the Mathemagician?
    a. Rhyme and Reason declare it a tie and neither one is happy.
    b. Rhyme and Reason declare Azaz the winner.
    c. Rhyme and Reason declare the Mathemagician the winner.
    d. Rhyme and Reason declare that Azaz wins first place and the Mathemagician wins second place.

_____ 5. In *The Phantom Tollbooth*, Act I, which adjective most accurately describes Milo at the beginning of the selection?
    a. tired   b. bored   c. angry   d. curious

_____ 6. In *The Phantom Tollbooth*, Act I, what is the most likely prediction you can make at the end of the selection?
    a. Humbug will be of great help to Milo in the next act.
    b. Milo will fail to accomplish his goal.
    c. Milo will have more strange adventures in the next act.
    d. Milo will change his mind and refuse to continue on his journey.

_____ 7. Which detail in *The Phantom Tollbooth*, Act II, is most helpful in envisioning Dr. Kakafonos A. Dischord?
    a. his mortar and pestle   c. his mirror
    b. his stethoscope   d. his big ears

_____ 8. Why is Sense of Humor in *The Phantom Tollbooth*, Act II, so powerful?
    a. because everyone enjoys laughing at a good joke
    b. because being able to laugh at situations can inspire people to action
    c. because the demons are afraid of laughter
    d. because laughing is good exercise

9. In *The Phantom Tollbooth*, Act II, why can Milo accomplish the impossible?
   a. He doesn't know that it is impossible.
   b. He is able to use magic.
   c. He has the help of the Watchdog.
   d. It is only a dream.

10. In *The Phantom Tollbooth*, Act II, it is important that the Senses Taker look mild and harmless at first because
   a. he is not really dangerous
   b. he wants to be friendly
   c. he can help Milo, the Watchdog, and the Humbug on their way
   d. distracting people from focusing on their goals seems harmless, at first

11. In *The Phantom Tollbooth*, Act II, the Mathemagician does not show Milo the biggest number there is because
   a. the number is too big to fit into a room
   b. there is no such thing as the biggest number there is
   c. Milo would not be able to grasp such a huge number
   d. he doesn't want to

12. In *The Phantom Toll Booth*, Act II, envisioning the demons as hundreds of eyes serves to show
   a. that they are evil
   b. that they are dangerous
   c. that there are many of them
   d. that they are imaginary

13. In *Grandpa and the Statue*, Sheean wants everyone on Butler Street to contribute to the Statue of Liberty Fund because
   a. he thinks it is a beautiful statue
   b. he doesn't want the neighborhood to get into trouble
   c. he sees it as a patriotic gesture that is being done all over the country
   d. he wants to feel that Butler Street has played an important part in getting the statue put up

14. In *Grandpa and the Statue*, August thinks Monaghan is feeling blue because
   a. he spends a lot of time staring out the window
   b. he never talks
   c. he won't play checkers
   d. he is in a hospital

15. In *Grandpa and the Statue*, what does Monaghan's final speech reveal about his feelings?
   a. He feels depressed about his grandpa's stinginess.
   b. He feels angry because his grandpa misled him.
   c. He wishes his grandpa was there to talk with him.
   d. He enjoys thinking back to what he and his grandpa did together.

16. Grandpa Monaghan in *Grandpa and the Statue* first starts to see the statue in a different light when
   a. he reads the poem on the tablet
   b. he talks to the veteran
   c. he goes to the warehouse
   d. he learns that his grandson's class is going to visit the statue

© Prentice-Hall, Inc.

Unit 8: Drama

____ 17. In *Grandpa and the Statue*, what do you predict will happen when Grandpa talks to the veteran?
    a. Grandpa Monaghan will be moved by what the veteran says about the statue.
    b. Grandpa Monaghan will feel that he was right in not giving any money.
    c. Grandpa Monaghan will give the veteran some money.
    d. Grandpa Monaghan and the veteran will become good friends.

____ 18. In *Grandpa and the Statue*, Grandpa places the fifty-cent piece near the tablet of the Statue of Liberty because he feels
    a. miserable   b. angry   c. guilty   d. happy

____ 19. In *Grandpa and the Statue*, when Monaghan says that his grandfather ". . . got all twisted up with the Statue of Liberty," he means that his grandfather
    a. had problems because he refused to contribute to the Statue of Liberty fund
    b. became trapped in the interior stairway of the Statue of Liberty
    c. went bankrupt from contributing to the Statue of Liberty fund
    d. missed the last boat of the day heading from the Statue of Liberty to Brooklyn

Vocabulary, Spelling, and Grammar

____ 20. The indefinite pronoun *all* is
    a. always singular
    b. always plural
    c. sometimes singular and sometimes plural
    d. used with people but not with things

____ 21. When people have a *misapprehension* about an idea, it means that
    a. they are miserable   c. they support it
    b. they disagree with it   d. they misunderstand it

____ 22. Which of the following sentences contains a misspelled word?
    a. We followed the direcsions and managed to find the address.
    b. Thomas Edison was responsible for many inventions.
    c. The class had a discussion about the book after they had read it.
    d. We called the theater to get information about when the movie started.

____ 23. Which of the following sentences uses correct subject-verb agreement?
    a. Both of the characters has a conversation with the Spelling Bee.
    b. All of the Watchdog's advice is worth taking seriously.
    c. Many of the characters in the play has funny names.
    d. Each of the five ministers have a fancy costume.

____ 24. If a machine were to run *perpetually*,
    a. it would make a lot of noise   c. it would never stop
    b. it would not need any electricity   d. it would be very delicate

____ 25. In which of the following sentences is the verb *not* correct?
    a. Everyone who wants to can come to the rehearsal.
    b. Anyone is welcome to try out for the part of Dodecahedron.
    c. In the numbers mine, everything is shining and glittery.
    d. Every one of the performers were happy with the performance of the play.

____ 26. Which of the following sentences contains a misspelled word?
    a. She was a gracious hostess and made us welcome.
    b. That apple pie is delicious.
    c. The living room is very spasious.
    d. The museum is showing a collection of precious jewels.

____ 27. Which sentence does *not* show correct pronoun-antecedent agreement?
        a. The players took his seat on the bench.
        b. My grandparents wore their best clothes to the birthday party.
        c. My sister and I handed our tickets to the conductor.
        d. The musician asked the orchestra to wait until her instrument was tuned.

____ 28. To say that someone is the *stingiest* person in town means that he or she is
        a. the least intelligent   c. the most unfriendly
        b. the least willing to spend money   d. the most ambitious

____ 29. *Another, both, few, much,* and *some* are examples of what kind of pronoun?
        a. personal   c. indefinite
        b. relative   d. interrogative

____ 30. Which of the following words is correctly spelled?
        a. happyest   b. funnyer   c. sillyest   d. mightiest

Essay Questions

31. One of the important elements of drama is *dialogue*, the words spoken by the characters. Dialogue reveals things about the ones who speak it, not only through what they say but the way in which they say it. Choose two of the following characters from this unit: Grandpa Monaghan from *Grandpa and the Statue*, the Mathemagician and Insincerity from *The Phantom Tollbooth*, and write an essay in which you describe some different aspects of their style of speech, and what it says about the characters. Support your conclusions with details from the selections.

32. *The Phantom Tollbooth* seems to be a completely unrealistic piece of writing, but is it? Write an essay in which you analyze whether this play is totally separate from the way the world and its people actually exist. Perhaps the only "realistic" aspect of this play is its message to readers or audience members. Include any "realistic" elements you find in the play, and explain your reasoning for this opinion. Use details from the selection to support your conclusions.

33. Plays are written to be performed. How could *The Phantom Tollbooth* and *Grandpa and the Statue* be performed on a stage? Write an essay in which you analyze the challenges of creating stage productions of these two plays, and suggest whether you think that either might work better as a radio play or a movie. Give reasons for your conclusions, and use details from the selections to support your position.

34. In *The Phantom Tollbooth* and *Grandpa and the Statue*, characters gain valuable insights during the course of the play. Choose one of the plays, and write an essay in which you explain what the main character learns. Point out why the lesson is of value, and how the lesson is taught. Support your conclusion with details from the text if necessary.

35. In *Grandpa and the Statue*, the Statue of Liberty is a symbol for the welcome which the United States has traditionally extended to the "huddled masses" from other nations. *The Phantom Tollbooth* also makes use of symbols. Write an essay in which you suggest meanings for either the Castle-in-the-Air or the Pit in which Milo and his friends are trapped for a time. Explain the reasoning that led you to your conclusion, and use details from the selection to support your analysis. (HINT: If you choose the Castle-in-the-Air, consider why such a castle, traditionally a symbol for impracticality, should be used in this play as a *prison*.)

Unit 8: Drama

Alternative Unit Test

The two passages below are followed by questions based on their content and on the relationship between the two passages.

Passage 1

from *The Girl Whose Fortune Sought Her* by Patricia Clapp

Characters

MELINDA   WIDOW   CLOWN   PEDDLER   GIRL   MAN

TIME: *A spring morning.*

SETTING: *The yard in front of the WIDOW'S cottage. The cottage stands upstage center, and there is a bench on either side of the door. Everywhere one looks, beautiful flowers grow.*

AT RISE: MELINDA *comes out of the front door; leaves it open behind her. She carries small gardening tools and starts to prune the flowers in the window boxes, and carefully to loosen the earth around them. A moment later her mother, the WIDOW, follows her.*

WIDOW: That's right, be gentle with them. Careful of those new little leaves.

MELINDA: Yes, Mother.

WIDOW: We must be gentle with all living things, Melinda, whether they're plants or people.

MELINDA: Yes, Mother.

WIDOW: You have a nice touch with flowers, child.

MELINDA: Thank you, Mother.

WIDOW: What's the matter, child? You don't seem very happy. Is something wrong?

MELINDA: No, Mother.

WIDOW: "Yes, Mother; no, Mother; thank you, Mother";—what is it, Melinda? It isn't like you to be so quiet. Tell me what the trouble is.

MELINDA: (*Suddenly throwing down her trowel and shears*): I'm just tired of staying home all day, day after day, doing nothing but tending the flowers and sweeping the floors and drying the dishes. I want to go away, to find something big to do. Mother, I want to go to seek my fortune!

Passage 2

Finn McCool, a giant in Irish legends, has his home high on a mountain so he can see his enemy, another giant named Cuhullin, if he ever comes toward the house.

from *Finn McCool* by May Lynch

Characters

FINN McCOOL; UNA, his wife; his children: OWEN, JOHN, JAMIE, MEG, CELIA

SETTING: *The interior of Finn McCool's cabin, on top of Knockmany Mountain, in Ireland.*

AT RISE: UNA *stands at a washtub, wringing out a piece of clothing. She places it on top of a basket of laundry at her feet. OWEN, JAMIE, and JOHN are sitting nearby.*

UNA: There! That's the last of my washing, and I must say it was a big one.

OWEN: I'll say it was. I carried six buckets of water up Knockmany Mountain this morning.

JOHN: And so did Jamie and I. We do it all the time.

OWEN: You didn't carry six buckets, John.

JAMIE (*Laughing*): No, Owen, but you spilled half of yours.

OWEN: I did not, Jamie McCool!

JAMIE: You did, too.

OWEN: (*Loudly*): I did not!

UNA: Children! Stop that brawling and squalling. My, I'll be glad when your father, Finn McCool, finds us a spring up here near the house.

JOHN: He says that there's water right out there under those two rocks.

JAMIE: Yes, and he's going to move them someday.

OWEN (*Interrupting*): Someday! Someday! he keeps saying *someday*, but *someday* never comes.

UNA: Owen McCool, don't speak that way of your father. After all, the dear man is very busy and tired—and—and busy. (MEG *and* CELIA *enter.*)

CELIA: Mother! Mother! Guess what!

MEG: Grannie Owen and Mrs. O'Malley and Mrs. Shane are coming up Knockmany Mountain right now.

Critical Reading

On the line, write the letter of the best answer.

_____ 1. What setting do both passages have in common?
a. They are both set at a family's home.
b. They are both set on a mountain top.
c. They are both set in the yard of a cottage.
d. They are both set in Ireland.
e. They are both set near a spring.

_____ 2. What action are the main characters performing in both passages?
a. They are washing clothes.
b. They are tending flowers.
c. They are doing household chores.
d. They are carrying water.
e. They are seeking their fortune.

_____ 3. Based on your reading of the two passages, what do Melinda and Owen have in common?
a. They both have to carry buckets of water.
b. They both argue with their siblings.
c. They both are good gardeners.
d. They both are dissatisfied with their lives at home.
e. They both want to leave home.

____ 4. How might the stage lighting be used in the two plays?
   I. Passage 1 would be lit to look like it takes place outside.
   II. Passage 2 would be lit to look like it takes place indoors.
   III. The stage lighting would be the same for both plays.
   IV. No lighting would be needed for either play.
   a. I   b. II   c. I and II   d. III   e. III and IV

____ 5. What is different about the two families in Passage 1 and Passage 2?
   I. The family in Passage 1 has no father, while the father in the family in Passage 2 is not at home.
   II. The family in Passage 2 has no father, while the father in the family in Passage 1 is not at home.
   III. The family in Passage 1 is smaller than the family in Passage 2.
   IV. The family in Passage 2 is smaller than the family in Passage 1.
   a. I and IV   b. II and III   c. I and III   d. II and IV   e. none of the above

____ 6. In Passage 2, what is the disadvantage the family faces because they live on top of Knockmany Mountain?
   a. The mother has to wash clothes by hand.
   b. The family has to live in a cabin.
   c. The brothers argue often.
   d. The father is away from home.
   e. The family has to carry water up the mountain.

____ 7. Based on the title of Passage 1, what do you predict will happen to Melinda?
   a. She may go away to seek her fortune.
   b. She may stay at home and her fortune will seek her.
   c. She may get a job as a gardener.
   d. She may convince her mother to give her different chores.
   e. She may take a trip with her mother.

____ 8. Based on what Meg says in Passage 2, what do you predict will happen next in the play?
   a. Owen and Jamie will continue to argue.
   b. Owen will run away from home.
   c. Finn McCool will find a spring near their home.
   d. Una will hang out the laundry.
   e. Three women will come into the cabin.

____ 9. In Passage 1, what do you learn about Melinda from what the Widow says?
   a. Melinda is usually talkative rather than quiet.
   b. Melinda needs to learn how to be more gentle with the flowers.
   c. Melinda has to sweep the floor and dry the dishes.
   d. Melinda wants to leave home.
   e. Melinda has a bad temper.

____ 10. In Passage 1, what do you learn about Melinda from her actions as revealed by the stage directions?
   a. She has a nice touch with flowers.
   b. She is usually talkative.
   c. She wants to go away to seek her fortune.
   d. She is frustrated at tending the flowers.
   e. She is polite to her mother.

_____ 11. In Passage 2, what do you learn about Una and Finn McCool from these words by Una?

> Owen McCool, don't speak that way of your father. After all, the dear man is very busy and tired—and—and busy.

    a. Una knows something about Finn that she is not telling the children.
    b. Una feels sorry for Finn because he is busy and tired.
    c. Una wishes her husband would come home and discipline Owen.
    d. Una thinks her husband is lazy not to find the spring near the cabin.
    e. Una wishes Finn would come home and do the laundry.

_____ 12. What props would you need if your class planned to put on both plays?

    I. washtub, basket of laundry   III. gardening tools, flowers, window boxes
    II. benches and stools or chairs   IV. buckets, broom, dish cloth

    a. I, II, III, IV   b. I, II, III   c. I and II only   d. I and III only   e. I and IV only

_____ 13. Which pair of events may set the plots of the plays in motion?
    a. In Passage 1, Melinda comes outside; in Passage 2, Una finishes her washing.
    b. In Passage 1, Melinda tends the flowers; in Passage 2, the boys argue about carrying the buckets.
    c. In Passage 1, the Widow gives Melinda a lecture; in Passage 2, Una tells the boys to stop arguing.
    d. In Passage 1, Melinda throws down her tools; in Passage 2, Meg and Celia bring news of visitors.
    e. In Passage 1, Melinda says she is tired of staying home; in Passage 2, Owen says "someday never comes."

_____ 14. What do the mothers have in common in Passage 1 and Passage 2?
    a. They both have large loads of laundry to do.
    b. They both lecture their children on being gentle with living things.
    c. They both ask the children to talk about their problems.
    d. They both are too busy to notice the children.
    e. They both have the children help with the household chores.

_____ 15. The phrase that best describes the group of characters in both passages is
    a. a family living alone on a mountain top
    b. a family that is experiencing a conflict
    c. a family that must do a lot of hard work
    d. a family that is expecting visitors
    e. a family that loves nature

Essay Questions

16. Write an essay describing the similarities and differences between the two families in Passage 1 and Passage 2.

17. Imagine that Melinda goes off to seek her fortune and comes to the McCool's cabin on Knockmany Mountain. In an essay, tell whether you think Melinda finds what she wants there. Explain why or why not.

18. Both Melinda and Owen have a complaint about life at home. In an essay, compare and contrast their complaints. Tell whether you think their feelings are justified, and explain why or why not. What advice would you give to each character?

Unit 8: Drama

"The Walrus and the Carpenter" by Lewis Carroll
"The Geese" by Richard Peck
"Jimmy Jet and His TV Set" by Shel Silverstein

Selection Test

Critical Reading

On the line, write the letter of the best answer.

____ 1. In "The Walrus and the Carpenter" the two main characters are first seen
    a. swimming in the ocean   c. lying in the sun
    b. walking on the beach   d. playing with the oysters

____ 2. The speaker in "The Walrus and the Carpenter" is
    a. someone watching the action   c. the carpenter
    b. the walrus   d. the eldest oyster

____ 3. One feature of "The Walrus and the Carpenter" that is characteristic of a narrative poem is
    a. poetic language   c. a story line
    b. lines that rhyme   d. a speaker

____ 4. In "The Walrus and the Carpenter," the walrus and the carpenter tell the oysters they must end their walk to
    a. take a nap   c. sweep the sand away
    b. tell a story   d. talk and eat

____ 5. What is the "trick" that the walrus and the carpenter play on the oysters?
    a. They tire them out.   c. They get them lost.
    b. They eat them.   d. They steal their shells.

____ 6. If you were to describe the tone of "The Walrus and the Carpenter" you might say it was
    a. silly   c. mysterious
    b. tragic   d. romantic

____ 7. In "The Walrus and the Carpenter," what does the moon call the sun?
    a. Your Highness   c. rude
    b. ready for an eclipse   d. dull

____ 8. At the beginning of "Jimmy Jet and His TV Set," the speaker states
    a. that he is a friendly neighbor of Jimmy's family
    b. that he knows a lot about fixing TV sets
    c. that he has been the host of several TV programs
    d. that he will tell a true tale

____ 9. In "Jimmy Jet and His TV Set" Jimmy eventually turns into a
    a. couch potato   c. ghost
    b. TV set   d. grown-up

____ 10. In "Jimmy Jet and His TV Set" the speaker's attitude toward Jimmy is
    a. humorous   c. fearful
    b. sympathetic   d. awestruck

_____ 11. "Jimmy Jet and His TV Set" is a narrative poem because it
  a. has characters and a plot
  b. is funny
  c. has strong images
  d. is short

_____ 12. If there is a serious message or moral to "Jimmy Jet and His TV Set" it is
  a. Television is educational and entertaining
  b. Some children don't watch enough television.
  c. Too much television is bad for children.
  d. Homework comes before television.

_____ 13. In the poem "The Geese" the geese are seen
  a. feeding on the speaker's lawn
  b. flying south for the winter
  c. nesting on a roof
  d. returning north in the spring

_____ 14. The speaker's father in "The Geese" wants to be like the geese because they
  a. are beautiful creatures
  b. need little to live
  c. are always happy
  d. represent freedom and escape

_____ 15. "The Geese" is a lyric poem because it
  a. expresses feelings and emotions
  b. tells a story
  c. contains dialogue
  d. has characters

Vocabulary, Spelling, and Grammar

_____ 16. The comparative form of _fast_ is
  a. most fast
  b. faster
  c. fastest
  d. most fastest

_____ 17. Which word or words are closest in meaning to _beseech_ in this excerpt from "The Walrus and the Carpenter"?

  "O Oysters, come and walk with us!" The Walrus did _beseech_.

  a. command
  b. beg for
  c. scream
  d. question

_____ 18. Which of the following sentences uses the comparative form of the adjective or adverb _incorrectly?_
  a. Jimmy Jet is a lot paler than his brother.
  b. The oysters grew more curious by the minute.
  c. My father heard the passage of the geese sooner than I did.
  d. Of all three poems, I thought "The Walrus and the Carpenter" was the more interesting.

_____ 19. Which of the following is spelled correctly?
  a. keen
  b. keene
  c. keane
  d. kean

_____ 20. What is the meaning of _lean_ in this passage from "Jimmy Jet and His TV Set"?

  He watched all day, he watched all night / Till he grew pale and _lean_.

  a. thin
  b. rest against
  c. fat
  d. colorless

Essay Questions

21. Write an essay showing why "The Walrus and the Carpenter" is an excellent example of nonsense verse. In your essay, cite examples of events and characters in the poem that would be impossible in the real world.

22. Choose one of the poems and, in an essay, describe the kind of character you think the speaker of the poem might be. Back up your ideas about the speaker with clues found in the poem. You might include which details you cannot know about the speaker, for example, whether the speaker is male or female.

23. In an essay, explain in your own words the personal thoughts and feelings expressed by the speaker in "The Geese." Use examples and quote passages from the poem to support your points.

"The Sidewalk Racer" by Lillian Morrison
Haiku by Matsuo Bashō
Limerick Anonymous

Selection Test

Critical Reading

On the line, write the letter of the best answer.

_____ 1. Which of the following best describes how the concrete form of "The Sidewalk Racer" relates to the subject of the poem?
   a. The words form a circle and reflect the fast rotation of a skateboard wheel.
   b. The words form a torpedo shape and reflect the aerodynamic quality of a skateboard.
   c. The form suggests an upside-down skateboarder.
   d. The diagonally arranged words look like a skateboarder in flight.

_____ 2. Which of the following statements best describes the speaker's feelings in this passage from "The Sidewalk Racer"?

   I'm the one and only / single engine / human auto / mobile.

   a. In his excitement, the speaker has a sense that he and his skateboard have become one.
   b. The speaker feels a sense of being both a car and a human being.
   c. The speaker sadly feels the limitations of being human.
   d. The speaker feels that only a fast auto ride could be as exciting as a skateboard ride.

_____ 3. Which of the following best summarizes "The Sidewalk Racer"?
   a. The poem uses uniquely arranged words to describe the thrill of riding a skateboard.
   b. The speaker is the skateboard itself.
   c. The speaker uses rhythm and rhyme to describe a fast skateboard ride.
   d. Each word is important in this short poem about skateboarding.

_____ 4. How would you describe the speaker's tone in "The Sidewalk Racer"?
   a. bored
   b. hesitant
   c. angry
   d. confident

_____ 5. From clues in "The Sidewalk Racer," you can conclude that the speaker probably
   a. enjoys being a skateboard salesperson
   b. likes exciting activities
   c. sails boats
   d. is often absent from school

_____ 6. How many lines does a haiku poem contain?
   a. three
   b. two
   c. five
   d. four

7. What is the number of syllables in each line of a haiku poem?
   a. seven, five, seven
   b. six, four, six
   c. seven, eleven, seven, eleven
   d. five, seven, five

8. If you were the frog in Bashō's haiku, which sense would you experience?
   a. the feeling of wetness
   b. the sound of voices
   c. the smell of smoke
   d. the taste of snowflakes

9. Which pair of words best describes the mood of Bashō's haiku?
   a. peace and warmth
   b. calmness and wonder
   c. power and desolation
   d. patience and humor

10. Which of the following best explains why haiku poems are enriched by their poetic form?
    a. Nature is best described by using words that do not rhyme.
    b. The fewer the words, the stronger the poem.
    c. The disciplined use of language calls forth deep thoughts and emotions.
    d. Poems that rhyme cannot be deeply expressive.

11. Which of the following statements comes closest to explaining this line from Bashō's haiku?

    splash! Silence again.

    a. Nature is violent.   c. Animals teach us wisdom.
    b. A pond is like life.   d. After a disturbance, peace again.

12. Which lines in a limerick usually rhyme?
    a. only the first and second
    b. the first, third, and fifth
    c. all the lines except the last
    d. the first, second, and fifth and the third and fourth

13. The limerick about insects is humorous because of
    a. the fact that a fire is about to be built.
    b. the fact that the limerick is anonymous.
    c. the sound effects and meanings of *flea, fly, flue, flee,* and *flaw.*
    d. the irregular rhythm of the third and fourth lines.

14. The limerick is
    a. a serious poem about a humorous event.
    b. a rhyming, rhythmical poem about love.
    c. a poem about nature.
    d. a short, funny poem of five lines.

15. Which of the following statements about the limerick form is true?
    a. Limericks are usually funny or silly.
    b. As long as they are funny, limericks do not have to rhyme.
    c. The limerick form uses rhythm but not rhyme.
    d. Limericks always include serious subjects and events.

Vocabulary, Spelling, and Grammar

____ 16. Which sentence uses the comparative form of *bad* correctly?
   a. Dying in the spring is more bad than dying in the fall.
   b. Dying in the fall is worst than dying in the spring.
   c. It is badder to die in the spring than to die in the fall.
   d. Dying in the spring is worse than dying in the fall.

____ 17. Which of the following comes closest to the meaning of *flue* in this sentence?

   The heating problem was caused by a blockage in the *flue*.

   a. radiator   c. tube for passage of smoke
   b. switch   d. wiring used in heating systems

____ 18. Which of the following words in italics is an incorrect homophone?
   a. I would love to *hear* your limerick, Tina.
   b. I can't decide which limerick I like best; *their* all funny.
   c. Penny is so talented that she can *write* a limerick in less than ten minutes.
   d. Roberto scribbled his limerick on a *piece* of notepaper.

____ 19. What is the meaning of the italicized word in this sentence?

   They had to *flee* from the coming hurricane.

   a. hide   c. seek shelter
   b. fly   d. escape from danger

____ 20. Which of the following best describes the word *most* in this sentence?

   Of all the poems, Fatima enjoyed the haiku by Bashō *most*.

   a. positive   c. superlative
   b. comparative   d. adjective

Essay Questions

21. In an essay, summarize either "Sidewalk Racer," the haiku, or one of the two limericks. Describe how you use your senses to experience the poem. Start by telling what the poem is about. Then explain its effect on your senses. Does the poem appeal to one sense more than others? Use details from the poem to support your explanation.

22. In an essay, compare and contrast any two of the following different forms of poetry: concrete, haiku, and limerick forms. Your essay should include a description of each of the two forms you've chosen. Be specific about the qualities that define each of these special forms. Next, explain what the two forms have in common and how they differ. Back up your opinions with quotes and paraphrases from the poems.

23. In an essay, explain how one of the poems in this grouping uses words that appeal directly and indirectly to one or more of your senses. For example, in "The Sidewalk Racer," the poet appeals to the sense of sight directly in the line "I swerve, I curve . . ." The poet appeals to the sense of touch indirectly by evoking images of the vibrations of the rough sidewalk as the skateboarder skims across the asphalt. Support your explanation with examples from the text.

"Wind and water and stone" by Octavio Paz
"February Twilight" by Sara Teasdale
"The Fairies' Lullaby" by William Shakespeare
"Cynthia in the Snow" by Gwendolyn Brooks
"Parade" by Rachel Field

Selection Test

Critical Reading

On the line, write the letter of the best answer.

____ 1. According to "Parade," what are some of the things to see at the circus procession?
   a. lions
   b. horses, camels, and elephants
   c. a ferris wheel
   d. a carousel

____ 2. In "Parade," which of the following best describes the speaker's attitude toward the circus procession?
   a. She is filled with excitement by what she sees and hears.
   b. She loves the circus music.
   c. She enjoys watching the horses and riders.
   d. She is curious about the camels and elephants.

____ 3. In "Parade," one of the features of the circus parade that the speaker enjoys most is
   a. a sense of danger caused by the wild animals
   b. feelings of friendliness when everyone comes out to watch
   c. the unusual excitement the circus brings to ordinary small-town life
   d. a chance to spend time out of doors

____ 4. Which of the following words or phrase can be described as a sound device in "Parade"?
   a. the day the circus comes
   b. blare, beating, clashing
   c. red or blue
   d. gilded, leisurely

____ 5. In the following lines of "Parade," after which words would you pause if you were reading the poem aloud?

   This is the day the circus comes / With blare of brass, with beating drums, /
   And clashing cymbals, and with roar / Of wild beasts never heard before /

   a. comes, roar
   b. day, and
   c. brass, drums, cymbals
   d. day, blare, clashing, beasts

_____ 6. In "Parade," the poet uses alliteration in the phrase
    a. clashing cymbals   c. cage and van
    b. beating drums   d roar of wild beasts

_____ 7. Who is the speaker in the poem "Cynthia in the Snow"?
    a. the poet   c. a stranger observing a child
    b. the child Cynthia   d. Cynthia's mother

_____ 8. What does the speaker in "Cynthia in the Snow" mean in these lines about the snow?

      It hushes / The loudness in the road.

    a. The snow tells the road to be quiet.
    b. The snow is like a lullaby.
    c. The snow muffles the sound of cars passing over the road.
    d. The noise of cars drowns out the tiny sound of snowflakes falling.

_____ 9. The words _sushes_ and _hushes_ in the poem "Cynthia in the Snow" are examples of
    a. onomatopoeia   b. alliteration   c. symbolism   d. structure

_____ 10. Which is the correct way to read this first line of the poem "Cynthia in the Snow"?

      It SUSHES.

    a. Pause slightly at the end of the line.
    b. Stop completely at the end of the line where the period is.
    c. Keep going at the end of the line without pausing.
    d. Pause between the word it and the word SUSHES.

_____ 11. In the poem "Cynthia in the Snow," which of the following phrases is an example of alliteration?
    a. the loudness in the road   c. still white as milk
    b. flitter-twitters   d. whitely whirs

_____ 12. In "The Fairies' Lullaby," what do the fairies ask the animals and insects _not_ to do?
    a. come near the Queen   c. eat too much
    b. sing a lullaby   d. fight each other

_____ 13. The phrase "beetles black" in "The Fairies' Lullaby" is an example of
    a. alliteration   c. rhyme
    b. symbolism   d. onomatopoeia

_____ 14. In "The Fairies' Lullaby," Philomel is
    a. a spider   c. the nightingale
    c. the King   d. a blindworm

_____ 15. In the following lines of "The Fairies' Lullaby," after which words would you _not_ pause if you were reading the poem aloud?

      Philomel, with melody / Sing in our sweet lullaby; /

      Lulla, lulla, lullaby, lulla, lulla, lullaby./

      Never harm / Nor spell nor charm.

    a. Philomel, lullaby
    b. lulla, lullaby, charm
    c. melody, harm
    d. lullaby, charm

Vocabulary, Grammar, and Spelling

____ 16. Which of the following sentences is punctuated incorrectly?
   a. We arrived early at the parade, so we bought some cotton candy.
   b. The floats were wonderful, and the band played well.
   c. The camels were impressive; the elephants were stately.
   d. After an hour Dad wanted to leave; but we persuaded him to stay till the end.

____ 17. Which of the following words is spelled incorrectly?
   a. ceiling   b. liesurely   c. neighbor   d. weird

____ 18. In which sentence is the comma used correctly?
   a. We watched the clowns, and we saw lots of animals.
   b. We watched the clowns and we saw, lots of animals.
   c. We watched the clowns and, we saw lots of animals.
   d. We watched, the clowns and we saw lots of animals.

____ 19. Which of the following phrases is closest in meaning to *leisurely*?
   a. in a rushed way
   b. in an unhurried way
   c. in a startled way
   d. in a nervous way

____ 20. What is the meaning of the word *gilded* in this line from from "Parade"?

   each gilded cage and van

   a. covered with gold paint
   b. painted silver
   c. made of sturdy metal
   d. shining brightly

Essay Questions

21. "Parade," "Cynthia in the Snow," and "The Fairies' Lullaby" use sound devices such as rhyme, alliteration, and onomatopoeia. In an essay, compare and contrast the use of sound devices in two of these poems. Which poem depends more on rhyme, alliteration, or onomatopoeia for its musical effect? Which sound device or devices are used in more original ways in one of the poems? Support your ideas with examples from both poems.

22. "Parade" tells of an extraordinary event in a small, quiet town. Write an essay in which you explain how the poet conveys the excitement the circus brings to the town. In your explanation, include details about the sound devices and images used in the poem.

23. Choose one of the poems, and, in an essay, explain why it is important to read the poem according to punctuation. In your essay, show examples of how the meaning of specific lines could be lost or distorted by a reader who ignores punctuation or who pauses or stops at the ends of lines where no punctuation appears.

"Simile: Willow and Ginkgo" by Eve Merriam
"Fame Is a Bee" by Emily Dickinson
"April Rain Song" by Langston Hughes

Selection Test

Critical Reading

On the line, write the letter of the best answer.

____ 1. Which of the following is the best papaphrase of these lines from "Simile: Willow and Ginkgo"?

> The willow's music is like a soprano, / delicate and thin.

   a. When the wind blows through a willow it makes a high-pitched sound, like a soprano.
   b. The branches of the willow tree are skinny.
   c. The willow is dainty and refined.
   d. The willow is weak and sickly.

____ 2. Which of the following lines from "Simile: Willow and Ginkgo" contains a simile?
   a. Wherever it grows, there is green and gold and fair.
   b. The willow dips to the water,
   c. The ginkgo forces its way through gray concrete;
   d. Like a city child, it grows up in the street.

____ 3. Which of the following best explains the comparison being made in these lines from "Simile: Willow and Ginkgo"?

> The willow is like an etching, / Fine-lined against the sky. / The ginkgo is like a crude sketch, / Hardly worthy to be signed.

   a. The willow is much taller than the ginkgo.
   b. The willow is more difficult to draw than the ginkgo.
   c. The poet compares a picture of the willow with a picture of the ginkgo.
   d. The poet compares the willow's elegant qualities to the ginkgo's more ordinary appearance.

____ 4. Which of the following statements best describes the trees in "Simile: Willow and Ginkgo"?
   a. The willow is delicate and beautiful, while the ginkgo is tough and strong.
   b. The willow is rough and robust, while the ginkgo is fragile and dainty.
   c. The willow and the ginkgo are very much alike.
   d. The willow is shorter than the ginkgo.

____ 5. Which of the following statements about "Fame Is a Bee" is correct?
   a. Each line is a metaphor.
   b. Only the first line is a metaphor.
   c. The whole poem is an example of personification.
   d. The last line is a simile.

Unit 9: Poetry

6. Which of the following would be an appropriate response to "Fame Is a Bee"?
   a. I understand this poem, because I've been stung by a bee.
   b. I can think of famous people who would have been better off if they'd never achieved fame.
   c. I agree that fame always brings happiness.
   d. I disagree that all famous people are really unhappy.

7. Which of the following best paraphrases "Fame Is a Bee"?
   a. People who are famous become wealthy and live glamorous lives.
   b. Although fame can be glorious, it can also wound, and it can disappear as quickly as it comes.
   c. It is best not to desire fame, but instead, live simply and busily, as a bee.
   d. A person who tries to become famous will experience nothing but disappointment.

8. Which of the following best states what the poet means by fame's "sting" in "Fame Is a Bee"?
   a. If you're famous, it doesn't hurt to be stung.
   b. Famous people often are often thoughtless about the feelings of others.
   c. Fame can cause unhappiness.
   d. It's better to be famous, even if you get stung.

9. Which of the following lines from "April Rain Song" uses personification?
   a. The rain makes still pools on the sidewalk.
   b. The rain makes running pools in the gutter.
   c. Let the rain kiss you.
   d. I love the rain.

10. Which of the following would be an appropriate response to "April Rain Song"?
    a. I have been lulled to sleep by a gentle rain on the roof over my bed.
    b. I agree that rain is a nuisance, but we need water to drink.
    c. It never rains in the desert.
    d. Rain is necessary to make plants grow.

11. Which of the following statements best paraphrases this line from "April Rain Song"?

    The rain plays a little sleep-song on your roof at night—

    a. People feel tired when it rains.
    b. Rain can make a calming, comforting sound.
    c. Storms at night are frightening.
    d. The storm will be over in the morning.

12. Which of the following lines from "April Rain Song" contains an example of personification?
    a. The rain makes still pools on the side walk.
    b. Let the rain sing you a lullaby.
    c. The rain makes running pools in the gutter.
    d. And I love the rain.

13. Which of the following best describes the speaker's feelings for rain in "April Rain Song"?
    a. The speaker finds the rain inconvenient.
    b. The speaker feels the rain is powerful and awesome.
    c. The speaker has affectionate feelings for rain.
    d. The speaker hates the rain's wetness.

14. Which of the following is a reason the speaker of "April Rain Song" loves the rain?
    a. Rain makes plants and flowers grow.   c. Rain makes mud puddles to play in.
    b. Rain provides us with water to drink.   d. Rain sounds nice on the roof at night.

Vocabulary, Spelling, and Grammar

____ 15. Which of the following words in italics is spelled incorrectly?
   a. The *portfolios* had beautiful covers.
   b. The dancers' *adagios* were beautifully performed.
   c. She knew the *altoes* would sing in the second section.
   d. We took *photos* of all the singers.

____ 16. What is the meaning of the italicized word in this sentence?

   The children sang in *soprano* voices.

   a. soft   b. loud   c. low   d. high

____ 17. For which purpose listed below is a colon used?
   a. to form a compound sentence by joining two simple sentences
   b. to separate the items in a list
   c. to set off a parenthetical statement
   d. to introduce a list of items following an independent clause

____ 18. What is the meaning of the italicized word in this sentence?

   The ginkgo's tune is like a *chorus*.

   a. the back of a stage
   b. the last line of a song
   c. the part of a song sung by many voices at once
   d. a large group of people singing together

____ 19. Which of the following words in italics is spelled incorrectly?
   a. I love *tomatoes*.
   b. The *sopranoes* sounded incredible.
   c. None of the *radios* worked.
   d. We loved hearing all the *oratorios* at the concert.

____ 20. In which of the following sentences is the colon used incorrectly?
   a. Parades usually include: the following, clowns, bands, and balloons.
   b. People like to skateboard for many reasons: excitement, speed, and danger.
   c. The bus leaves at 12:30 sharp.
   d. I found three coins: a nickel, a dime, and a quarter.

Essay Questions

21. Which poem did you like the best? How did you respond to it? In an essay, explain if you responded by bringing your own thoughts and feelings to the poem, by enjoying its rhythms and language, by agreeing or disagreeing with its ideas, or by having the poem remind you of an experience or something you've read or heard about. Support your response by citing or paraphrasing lines from the poems.

22. In an essay, explain the speaker's thoughts and feelings for the willow tree and the ginkgo tree in "Simile: Willow and Ginkgo." Explain to what two different kinds of people the trees are compared in the poem. In your own words, tell why the speaker says, "My eyes feast upon the willow, / But my heart goes to the ginkgo." Use specific passages and words from the poem to support your explanation.

23. Choose one of the poems and, in an essay, analyze the poet's use of figurative language. Cite examples of simile, metaphor, and/or personification in the poem you choose. Conclude your essay by explaining how the figurative language contributes to the poem's main feeling or idea.

Unit 9: Poetry

Unit Test

Critical Reading

On the line, write the letter of the best answer.

_____ 1. In "The Walrus and the Carpenter," after which word or words should you pause when reading these lines?

       The moon was shining sulkily,

       Because she thought the sun

       Had got no business to be there

       After the day was done—

    a. sulkily, done   c. sun, done

    b. sulkily, there   d. there, done

_____ 2. "The Walrus and the Carpenter" is an example of

    a. a lyric poem   c. a narrative poem

    b. a concrete poem   d. a limerick

_____ 3. In "The Walrus and the Carpenter," Walrus and the Carpenter trick the oysters in order to

    a. eat them   c. sell them

    b. play with them   d. teach them about life

_____ 4. In "The Walrus and the Carpenter," why doesn't the eldest Oyster agree to walk with the Walrus and the Carpenter?

    a. The eldest oyster is too old.

    b. The eldest oyster is too suspicious.

    c. The eldest oyster knows it isn't welcome.

    d. The eldest oyster doesn't hear the invitation.

_____ 5. In "Jimmy Jet and His TV Set," Jimmy's brains turned into

    a. antennae   c. a turning dial

    b. a plug   d. TV tubes

_____ 6. In "Jimmy Jet and His TV Set," how does Jimmy feel about being turned into a television?

    a. There is no way to tell.   c. Jimmy feels happy.

    b. Jimmy feels sad.   d. Jimmy feels proud.

_____ 7. In "The Geese," the speaker's father is fascinated by the migrating geese because

    a. he finds them beautiful   c. he loves their cry

    b. he is amazed they could fly so far   d. they make him think of distant places

_____ 8. In "The Sidewalk Racer," the speaker says that he or she is "the sailor and the sail" because

    a. he uses a sail to catch the wind and go faster

    b. he is both the one who rides the board and the one who makes it move

    c. the skateboard is shaped like a boat

    d. the wind is at the speaker's back

_____ 9. "The Sidewalk Racer" is an example of
     a. a haiku   c. a limerick
     b. a concrete poem   d. a simile

_____ 10. The haiku by Bashō uses images that affect which sense or senses?
     a. sight only   c. sight and sound
     b. sight and smell   d sound and smell

_____ 11. In "Cynthia in the Snow," which is an example of onomatopoeia?
     a. "It SUSHES"   c. "the loudness in the road"
     b. "it laughs a lovely whiteness"   d. "Still white as milk or shirts"

_____ 12. In "Cynthia in the Snow," who is Cynthia?
     a. the author
     b. someone the speaker is describing
     c. someone the author is describing
     d. the speaker

_____ 13. In "Parade," which of the following lines uses no alliteration?
     a. With blare of brass, with beating drums.
     b. Within town limits. Spick and span
     c. And clashing cymbals, and with roar
     d. Till leisurely and last of all,

_____ 14. Which of the following would be an appropriate response to "Simile: Willow and Ginkgo"?
     a. I agree that willows are beautiful trees.
     b. We don't have any ginkgos in our yard.
     c. Willows are good shade trees.
     d. "Ginkgo" is a funny name.

_____ 15. The speaker of "Fame Is a Bee" sees fame as
     a. a wonderful thing that all people should seek
     b. something that has both good and bad points
     c. a terrible fate that everyone should try to avoid
     d. something nobody has any control over

_____ 16. Which line from "April Rain Song" uses personification?
     a. The rain makes still pools on the sidewalk.
     b. The rain makes running pools in the gutter.
     c. Let the rain sing you a lullaby.
     d. Let the rain beat upon your head with silver liquid drops.

_____ 17. In "Simile: Willow and Ginkgo," the speaker's "heart goes to the ginkgo" because
     a. unlike most people, the speaker thinks the ginkgo is a prettier tree
     b. the speaker has grown up among ginkgos
     c. the speaker thinks that the willow is too delicate
     d. the speaker admires and cherishes many of the ginkgo's qualities

_____ 18. In "Simile: Willow and Ginkgo," which line uses a simile?
     a. The willow dips to the water,
     b. My eyes feast upon the willow,
     c. The willow is like an etching,
     d. Thrust against the metal sky,

_____ 19. Which of the following statements about metaphor is true?
      a. A metaphor compares two apparently unlike things by describing one as if it were the other.
      b. The words *like* or *as* usually introduce a metaphor.
      c. In a metaphor, the words sound exactly like what they mean.
      d. In a metaphor, sounds are repeated at the beginning of the words or in stressed syllables.

Vocabulary, Spelling, and Grammar

_____ 20. Which of the following sentences uses an adjective with an ending signifying *the most*?
      a. The cheetah is a faster runner than the lion.
      b. The blue whale is the heaviest creature that ever lived.
      c. It is better to get there too early than to get there too late.
      d. My father has very good handwriting.

_____ 21. A *leisurely* pace is one that is
      a. lazy   c. determined
      b. hesitant   d. unhurried

_____ 22. Which of the following words is misspelled?
      a. ceiling   c. wierd
      b. height   d. retrieve

_____ 23. Which of these sentences uses a superlative adjective incorrectly?
      a. The sloth is one of the slowest animals.
      b. That was the goodest movie I ever saw.
      c. The hardest part of arithmetic for me is fractions.
      d. Yesterday our team had its worst loss of the year.

_____ 24. Which is the closest word in meaning to *beseech* in the following sentence?

      We beseech you to come and see our play next week.

      a. beg   b. invite   c. want   d. command

_____ 25. Which of the following sentences contains an incorrectly used homophone?
      a. We wanted to see *their* new skateboards.
      b. *There* are several reasons why you should enjoy these haiku.
      c. Concrete poetry is constructed according to certain *principals.*
      d. The *principal* of our school will speak at the assembly.

_____ 26. Which of the following sentences uses *well* or *good* incorrectly?
      a. She is a very good swimmer.
      b. She writes very well.
      c. I didn't do very good in the quiz.
      d. If we schedule our time well, we will probably get more done.

_____ 27. If something is described as having a *flaw*, then
      a. it does not smell good
      b. it is very slippery
      c. it has a handle
      d. it is not perfect

_____ 28. For which of the following is a semicolon used?
      a. to separate two independent clauses in a compound sentence
      b. to introduce a coordinating conjunction
      c. to set off an introductory phrase
      d. to introduce a list following an independent clause

___ 29. Which of the following items is punctuated incorrectly?

    a. The school bus arrived at 7:30 A.M.

    b. We bought three items; a newspaper, a magazine, and a book.

    c. Willow trees have many features: long branches, strong trunks, and small leaves.

    d. The sign states this warning: Trespassers will be prosecuted.

___ 30. Which of the following would a *soprano* be most likely to do?

    a. sing loudly

    b. sing low notes

    c. sing middle notes

    d. sing high notes

Essay Questions

31. In lyric poetry, a writer focuses on thoughts and feelings about some experience or idea, rather than a story or plot. Choose two of the following lyric poems from this unit: "April Rain Song," "Cynthia in the Snow," and "The Geese." Write an essay in which you analyze the thoughts and feelings suggested by the poets, and describe your personal response to these poems. Say whether your reactions were similar to, or different from, those of the poet, and suggest reasons for your conclusions. Support your analysis with details from the texts.

32. Like prose, poetry can be funny. Write an essay analyzing two of the following poems: "The Walrus and the Carpenter," "Jimmy Jet and His TV Set," and the two limericks. Explain what techniques the writers use to make these poems humorous, and the ways in which they are alike and different. Support your analysis with details from the text.

33. Sometimes, poems reveal a good deal about their speakers, even though the information may come through in an indirect way. Choose two of these poems: "The Geese," "The Sidewalk Racer," and "Simile: Willow and Gingko." In an essay, analyze what the poems say about the speaker, in terms of personality and other qualities. Compare and contrast the two speakers, indicating ways in which they are similar and in which they are different. Use details from the texts to support your analysis.

34. Poetry often uses language in ways that emphasize the sounds and musical qualities of words. It can do so by using devices such as onomatopoeia, alliteration, the use of regular rhythms, and the use of punctuation. Write an essay in which you analyze how the authors of two of the following poems use language in this fashion: "The Fairies' Lullaby," "Cynthia in the Snow," "Fame Is a Bee," and "Parade." Use details from the texts to support your analysis.

35. Images are one of the most effective devices in poetry. Poets use sensory language to create images that appeal to the reader's sense of sight, or to any of the other senses. Choose two of the following poems: "The Sidewalk Racer," "Cynthia in the Snow," "Simile: Willow and Ginkgo," "April Rain Song," and "The Fairies' Lullaby." Write an essay in which you analyze the sensory language the authors use and the images they create. State which sense or senses the poem is designed to appeal to. Conclude by indicating whether the imagery is designed to give the reader a sense of what the poem's speaker is thinking or feeling, or to provide the reader with imagery to make the poem more effective for him or her. Support your conclusions with details from the texts.

Unit 9: Poetry

Alternative Unit Test:

The two passages below are followed by questions based on their content and on the relationship between the two passages.

Passage 1

"Music Mother" by Naomi Feigelson Chase

I am twelve years old, my hair in braids,
my pedal feet in Oxfords.
I practice my scales, stepping up ivory.
Only the music, the metronome's heart-beat,
and my teacher's voice are real, as I sit at the piano.
Playing Mozart, in Pittsburgh, Pennsylvania.

I love Mrs. Karenyi, my piano teacher.
My mother calls her a "blue-stocking," but she wears
ordinary nylons on her bony knees.
Great paintings cut from magazines
fill her staircase wall.
They are even in the bathroom.

Alone as I practice, I think of her, alone,
in her crisp, gray skirt and silky blouse.
She sits by a brass bed with a white cover, lilacs
in a vase by the table. She reads.

Sometimes she invites me to dinner,
chicken paprikash and dumplings her mother
made in Hungary, so perfect in silver bowls
at first I am afraid to eat.
Then she opens her phonograph, takes out a record,
tells me the great Landowska, just for me,
will now play Mozart on the clavichord.

"Involuntary Music" by D. Nurkse

I practiced the piano all afternoon
while the others played ball.
As I memorized the notes
stepping out of my mind
in time, each harmony
abolishing the one before,
I could hear the crack of wood,
the bench applauding,
the batter squealing with delight:
then I resumed climbing
the ladder of the minor scale
broken at the third and seventh rung.
I tucked my thumb under my middle finger
and rose to the top, and once, my hand
traveled off the keys and paced
mechanically over the black walnut casing
and dropped, and I'd come to silence:
very far away, I heard
the triplewound metronome
and the scuff of bases being dragged home.

Critical Reading

On the line, write the letter of the best answer.

____ 1. Both passages use images of climbing to describe
      a. practicing the piano
      b. the sound of the metronome
      c. playing scales
      d. becoming a better pianist
      e. daydreaming while practicing the piano

____ 2. Which statement is true of the speakers of both passages?
      a. They hate playing the piano.
      b. They dislike their piano teachers.
      c. They would love to play baseball.
      d. They love playing the piano.
      e. They take piano lessons.

____ 3. Which of the following excerpts from Passage 2 uses onomatopoeia?
      a. I practiced the piano all afternoon
      b. I could hear the crack of wood
      c. the triplewound metronome
      d. the bench applauding
      e. traveled off the keys and paced

_____ 4. In contrast to the speaker of Passage 1, the speaker of Passage 2
a. does not directly express his or her feelings about music
b. practices the piano very little
c. is an adult
d. is happy to be playing the piano
e. is just beginning to learn to play the piano

_____ 5. In Passage 1, the speaker
a. is constantly being distracted when she practices the piano
b. finds practicing boring
c. practices hard because she is frightened of her piano teacher
d. does not admire her piano teacher as much as her mother does
e. disregards all distractions while playing the piano

_____ 6. If you read the following line from passage 1 aloud, after which word would you pause?

        She sits by a brass bed with a white cover, lilacs

a. bed
b. sits
c. with
d. cover
e. She

_____ 7. Which adjective best describes the speakers of both passages?
a. happy
b. resentful
c. obedient
d. bored
e. stubborn

_____ 8. In Passage 2,
a. the ball game ends before the speaker finishes practicing
b. the speaker finishes practicing and joins the ball game
c. the speaker had been playing ball before practicing
d. the speaker is annoyed by the distracting noises from the ball game
e. the speaker would like to learn how to play ball

_____ 9. In Passage 1, which line contains a personification?
a. I practice my scales, stepping up ivory.
b. Alone as I practice, I think of her, alone
c. Sometimes she invites me to dinner
d. Only the music, the metronome's heart-beat
e. at first I am afraid to eat

_____ 10. For which sense do both passages have images?
a. sight
b. hearing
c. smell
d. touch
e. taste

_____ 11. The speaker of Passage 2 is shown to be
a. more aware of his or her surroundings than the speaker of Passage 1
b. less aware of his or her surroundings than the speaker of Passage 1
c. a better-trained pianist than the speaker of Passage 1
d. not as well-trained a pianist as the speaker of Passage 1
e. more dedicated to music than the speaker of Passage 1

_____ 12. What do both of the following lines from Passage 1 and Passage 2, respectively, have in common?

> Playing Mozart in Pittsburgh, Pennsylvania.
> I practiced the piano all afternoon

   a. Both lines use personification.
   b. Both lines use onomatopoeia.
   c. Both lines have sensory images.
   d. Both lines use metaphors.
   e. Both lines use alliteration.

_____ 13. Which of the following statements most accurately reflects the attitudes of the speakers of the two passages?
   a. Both speakers would like to be professional pianists when they grow up.
   b. The speaker of Passage 1 plays by her own choice, while the speaker of Passage 2 has been made to play.
   c. Neither speaker cares much about music.
   d. Both speakers find their teachers interesting.
   e. The speaker of Passage 1 likes classical music and the speaker of Passage 2 does not.

_____ 14. In Passage 2, what does the speaker realize when he or she stops playing?
   a. that he or she doesn't mind playing after all
   b. that his metronome is broken
   c. that the ball game is over
   d. that his metronome is going too fast
   e. that the ball game was all in his or her imagination

_____ 15. Which statement is true about the rhythms of both passages?
   a. They both use regular rhythm.
   b. Passage 1 uses regular rhythm and Passage 2 does not.
   c. Passage 1 does not use regular rhythm and Passage 2 does.
   d. Neither passage uses regular rhythm.
   e. Parts of both passages have regular rhythm.

Essay Questions

16. While the speakers of the two passages practice their piano lessons, they think about other things. Write an essay in which you describe the thoughts that occupy the minds of the speakers, and compare and contrast the ways in which their thoughts relate to the music they are playing. Indicate which of the speakers, if either, is more involved in his or her piano playing, and why this is so. Use details from the passages to support your conclusions.

17. Although the speakers of the two passages do not say much about themselves, readers can still learn something about their personalities and interests. In an essay, write a brief description of each speaker based on what the passage reveals about him or her. Compare and contrast the two. Are there any interests or feelings that they share? In what ways are they different from each other? Support your conclusions with details from the passages.

18. A narrative poem is one that tells a story, and a lyric poem is one in which the speaker expresses his or her thoughts and feelings. Into which of these categories do the two passages fit? Write an essay in which you place them into one or the other category, and give your reasons. You may conclude that both passages fit into the same category. You may also find that one or both passages have elements of both. Use details from the passages to support your conclusions.

Name _____ Date _____

"The Ant and the Dove" by Leo Tolstoy
"He Lion, Bruh Bear, and Bruh Rabbit" by Virginia Hamilton
"Señor Coyote and the Tricked Trickster" by I. G. Edmonds

Selection Test

Critical Reading

On the line, write the letter of the best answer.

_____ 1. "The Ant and the Dove" focuses on the importance of
   a. fairness
   b. kindness
   c. cleverness
   d. beauty

_____ 2. In "The Ant and the Dove," why did the ant bite the hunter's foot?
   a. The ant was angry because the hunter had almost stepped on it.
   b. The ant wanted to drive the hunter out of the forest.
   c. The ant wanted to startle the hunter so that he would shoot at the dove.
   d. The ant wanted to startle the hunter so that he would drop the net in which he
      was trying to catch the dove.

_____ 3. The storyteller's main purpose in "The Ant and the Dove" is to
   a. entertain
   b. explain something in nature
   c. teach a lesson
   d. surprise and amaze

_____ 4. Which of the following statements best expresses the message conveyed in "The Ant
   and the Dove"?
   a. Good deeds inspire other good deeds.
   b. Virtue is its own reward.
   c. It sometimes takes great courage to stand up for what's right.
   d. Kindness is not always repaid.

_____ 5. Which word best describes how the dove feels toward the ant at the end of "The Ant
   and the Dove"?
   a. jealous   c. embarrassed
   b. grateful   d. indifferent

_____ 6. Which word best describes the overall mood of "He Lion, Bruh Bear, and Bruh
   Rabbit"?
   a. sad
   b. amusing
   c. mysterious
   d. realistic

_____ 7. In "He Lion, Bruh Bear, and Bruh Rabbit," he Lion is causing a problem by
   a. fighting with any animal that disagrees with him or displeases him
   b. grabbing all the land, food, and water in the forest for himself
   c. refusing to fulfill his duties as king or the forest
   d. scaring the little animals of the forest with his roaring

_____ 8. In "He Lion, Bruh Bear, and Bruh Rabbit," he Lion learns to be more
      a. modest   b. cautious   c. thrifty   d. generous

_____ 9. In "He Lion, Bruh Bear, and Bruh Rabbit," why does Bruh Rabbit think that Man is the real king of the forest?
      a. because Man is more powerful than he Lion
      b. because Man is smarter than he Lion
      c. because Man is bigger than he Lion
      d. because Man is more kind-hearted than he Lion

_____ 10. Which of the following best describes the storyteller's purpose in "He Lion, Bruh Bear, and Bruh Rabbit"?

        I.   to entertain
       II.   to explain something in nature
      III.   to teach a lesson in life
      IV.   to teach a skill or technique

      a. I only   b. II only   c. I and III   d. I and IV

_____ 11. Which of the following statements best describes the animal characters in "Señor Coyote and the Tricked Trickster"?
      a. They behave like real animals.
      b. They behave like people.
      c. They are models of proper behavior.
      d. They behave in wild and unpredictable ways.

_____ 12. Which of the following passages from "Señor Coyote and the Tricked Trickster" provides a detail about Mexican culture?
      a. "I fear my memory of yesterday is too dim," Mouse said, "but I could remember very well what you could do for me tomorrow."
      b. A life is worth a life. If a save your life, you should work for me for a lifetime. That is the only fair thing to do.
      c. "Why, how can you suggest such a thing!" Coyote cried indignantly. And then to himself he added, "This mouse is getting too smart."
      d. "But it is like the story Mamacita tells her children at bedtime," Mouse said quickly. "Once there was a poor burro who had a load of hay just as large as he could carry."

_____ 13. In "Señor Coyote and the Tricked Trickster," who is the tricked trickster?
      a. Señor Mouse   b. Baby Mouse   c. Rattlesnake   d. Owl

_____ 14. What is the storyteller's purpose in including the following conversation in "Señor Coyote and the Tricked Trickster?"

      "I'd like to gnaw you free, but I am old and my teeth tire easily."

      "Really, Señor Mouse, you are ungrateful," said Señor Coyote reproachfully. "Remember all the nice things I have done for you?"

      "What were they?"

      "Why—" Coyote began and stopped. He was unable to think of a single thing.

      a. to explain something in nature
      b. to teach a lesson about the importance of always telling the truth
      c. to teach a lesson about friendship
      d. to amuse readers and listeners

Vocabulary, Spelling, and Grammar

____ 15. Which of the following would be most likely to *startle* someone?
   a. the sound of a cat purring
   b. the sound of a favorite song on the radio
   c. the sound of leaves rustling in the wind
   d. the sound of a telephone ringing

____ 16. Which of the following words contains the *j* sound spelled with *di*?
   a. encyclopedia
   b. different
   c. engine
   d. soldier

____ 17. Titles showing a family relationship are capitalized
   a. only when the title appears with a person's name
   b. when the title is used before a person's name, in place of the person's name, or in direct address
   c. only when the title appears in a direct address
   d. when the title follows a possessive noun or pronoun

____ 18. Which word is closest in meaning to *cordially*?
   a. indignantly
   b. reproachfully
   c. pleasantly
   d. apologetically

____ 19. An animal's *lair* is its
   a. enemy
   b. offspring
   c. food
   d. den

____ 20. Which of the following sentences contains incorrect capitalization?
   a. Brother, you must speak to He Lion and make him stop scaring the animals.
   b. Can you tell me, Father, who can help you?
   c. Excuse me, Señor, my Father is stuck in a trap.
   d. Bruh Rabbit's brother doesn't like He Lion, either.

Essay Questions

21. Choose "The Ant and the Dove," "He Lion, Bruh Bear, and Bruh Rabbit," or "Señor Coyote and the Tricked Trickster" and write an essay in which you explain the purpose of the tale. Does the tale entertain, teach, or both entertain and teach? Support your answer with details from the text.

22. Choose "The Ant and the Dove," "He Lion, Bruh Bear, and Bruh Rabbit," or "Señor Coyote and the Tricked Trickster" and explain in an essay why the work is a good example of a folk tale. In your explanation, discuss what a folk tale is and identify the main characteristics of this type of story. Also discuss how the work that you chose fits these characteristics, citing details from the text where appropriate.

23. Write an essay in which you compare and contrast "The Ant and the Dove" with one of the other folk tales in this group. In your discussion, point out at least two similarities and at least two differences. Cite specific details and examples from the works to support your points.

"Why Monkeys Live in Trees" by Julius Lester
"Arachne" by Olivia E. Coolidge
"A Crippled Boy" by My-Van Tran
"The Three Wishes" by Ricardo E. Alegría

Critical Reading

On the line, write the letter of the best answer.

_____ 1. In "Why Monkeys Live in Trees," the animals have a contest to see who can
    a. move a mound of black dust
    b. beat King Gorilla in a fight
    c. chase Monkey to the top of a tree
    d. eat a mound of black dust

_____ 2. The best morale or message of "Why Monkeys Live in Trees" might be
    a. Don't try eating black pepper.
    b. Animals aren't as smart as humans.
    c. Trickery may win the contest, but in the end, you'll be found out.
    d. Monkeys didn't always live in trees.

_____ 3. In "Why Monkeys Live in Trees," the monkeys tricked the other animals by
    a. helping Monkey eat the pepper
    b. hiding the pepper in the tall grasses
    c. hiding the gold in the trees
    d. burying the gold in the mound of pepper

_____ 4. The most predictable part of "Why Monkeys Live in Trees" is that
    a. no one can eat the mound of pepper
    b. gorillas aren't as smart as monkeys
    c. the monkeys end up in the trees
    d. Leopard discovers the monkeys' trick

_____ 5. In "Arachne," the goddess Athene appeared to Arachne as
    a. a spider
    b. an old woman
    c. another spinner
    d. a spinning wheel

_____ 6. Athene slapped Arachne because she had
    a. beaten her in the contest
    b. refused to take back her angry words
    c. insulted her with scenes she designed
    d. stepped on a spider

_____ 7. What about the ending of "Arachne" is most predictable?
    a. The gods are defeated by humans.
    b. A person is turned into an animal.
    c. Arachne has her revenge.
    d. A proud and willful person is punished.

_____ 8. One purpose of the myth about Arachne is to explain how
    a. weaving developed
    b. spiders came into the world
    c. contests started
    d. human justice was established

9. In "The Crippled Boy," the King had Theo sit behind a curtain because he
   a. didn't want the mandarins to see him
   b. was ashamed of Theo
   c. knew Theo was shy
   d. wanted him to surprise the mandarins

10. In "The Crippled Boy," Theo threw a pebble into each mandarin's mouth so the person would
   a. speak up
   b. talk louder
   c. leave the King's presence
   d. shut up

11. The people who passed down the folk tale "The Crippled Boy" probably believed strongly that
   a. silence is golden
   b. throwing pebbles is fun
   c. kings should be respected and listened to
   d. talking is more important than listening

12. By the end of "The Three Wishes," we realize that the old man granted the couple the wishes in order to
   a. reward them
   b. test them
   c. trick them
   d. make them rich

13. The woodsman in "The Three Wishes" was angry with his wife because she
   a. hadn't let him make a wish
   b. had given the old man their food
   c. had wasted the first wish
   d. had wished for donkey ears

14. Based on other folk tales, you should be able to predict that, at the end of "The Three Wishes," the wishes will
   a. not bring happiness
   b. not be appreciated
   c. ruin the couple's marriage
   d. bring great wealth

15. In "The Three Wishes," the last wish the woodsman made showed that he
   a. was as foolish as his wife
   b. was still angry at his wife
   c. wanted more and more things
   d. loved his wife more than riches

Vocabulary, Spelling, and Grammar

16. The word root *mort*, as in the word *mortal*, means
   a. life
   b. god-like
   c. death
   d. human-like

_____ 17. The sentence "Suddenly he leaped straight into the air and screamed" from "Why Monkeys Live in Trees" begins with
   a. a subject
   b. an adverb
   c. a prepositional phrase
   d. a verb

_____ 18. Which is the correct spelling?
   a. obstinacy
   b. obstinasy
   c. obstinacey
   d. obstinatsy

_____ 19. Which sentence converts the declarative sentence below into an exclamatory sentence?

   It is wrong for humans to claim equality with the gods.

   a. When humans claim equality with the gods, humans are wrong.
   b. Is it wrong for humans to claim equality with the gods?
   c. How wrong it is for humans to claim equality with the gods!
   d. Humans, do not dare to claim equality with the gods.

_____ 20. Which word best defines _foliage_ in this excerpt from "A Crippled Boy":

   He aimed stones at the thick _foliage_ and managed to cut it into the outlines of animal forms.

   a. trees
   b. leaves
   c. bark
   d. flowers

Essay Questions

21. Even though "Why Monkeys Live in Trees" is about animals, it reveals truths about human nature. Write an essay citing specific examples of human greed, pride, and trickery as the animals respond to King Gorilla's challenge.

22. In each of these tales people or animals are rewarded or punished for their deeds. Choose one tale and explain why you think the main character or characters deserve the fate they receive. Give details from the story to support your argument.

23. One main theme running through all four stories is that people should be respectful of others and be content with what they have. Choose one tale and, in an essay, show how these values are illustrated in it.

Unit 10: The Oral Tradition

Unit Test

Critical Reading

On the line, write the letter of the best answer.

_____ 1. In "The Ant and the Dove," the ant's troubles begin when it
a. gets caught in a whirlpool
b. gets lost in the forest
c. sees other ants being eaten by a dove
d. sees a hunter

_____ 2. "The Ant and the Dove" is an example of a
a. limerick
b. parable
c. folk tale
d. ballad

_____ 3. Which statement below best expresses the lesson of "The Ant and the Dove"?
a. Animals must struggle to survive.
b. Hunters must watch out for clever animals.
c. You can never tell how or when a kindness may be repaid.
d. It is foolish to do good deeds for others.

_____ 4. In "The Ant and the Dove" why does the dove drop the twig from its beak?
a. The dove wants to hit the ant and crush it.
b. The dove wants to strike the hunter and make him drop his net.
c. The dove wants to give the ant something to grab hold of so it won't drown.
d. The dove wants to watch the twig swirl in a whirlpool.

_____ 5. In "He Lion, Bruh Bear, and Bruh Rabbit," the Lion's repeating of "Me and Myself" is a sign of his
a. sense of humor   c. strength
b. modesty   d. conceitedness

_____ 6. You can tell "He Lion, Bruh Bear, and Bruh Rabbit" is a folk tale because it
a. contains only one human character
b. has spoken dialogue
c. is written in black dialect
d. teaches a lesson while entertaining readers

_____ 7. In "Señor Coyote and the Tricked Trickster," who saves Señor Coyote from the trap?
a. Señor Rattlesnake   c. Baby Mouse
b. Señor Mouse   d. Owl

_____ 8. In "Señor Coyote and the Tricked Trickster," Señor Mouse persuades Señor Coyote to save him from Señor Rattlesnake by appealing to his
a. sympathy   c. sense of pride
b. sense of justice   d. thirst for revenge

_____ 9. Why does Señor Mouse decide at the end of "Señor Coyote and the Tricked Trickster" that he and Señor Coyote are even?
   a. He doesn't want Señor Rattlesnake to eat him.
   b. He agrees that this is the fair thing to do.
   c. He is grateful to Señor Coyote.
   d. Señor Coyote will eat him if he argues with him.

_____ 10. Many details in "Señor Coyote and the Tricked Trickster" reflect the tale's origins in
   a. Vietnamese culture
   b. Mexican culture
   c. Russian culture
   d. African American culture

_____ 11. In "Señor Coyote and the Tricked Trickster," to what story told by *Mamacita* does Señor Mouse refer when he wants to convince Snake and Coyote that a little mouse could have the strength to roll away a big rock?
   a. a tale about a burro and a load of hay
   b. a tale about an eagle's nest
   c. a tale about a prairie dog
   d. a tale about a tortoise and a hare

_____ 12. In "Señor Coyote and the Tricked Trickster," how does one of the characters save Coyote?
   a. by running to tell snake about Coyote's problem
   b. by gnawing the leather strap of the trap in two
   c. by biting a hunter on the foot
   d. by showing Coyote how to gnaw the strap in two

_____ 13. In "Why Monkeys Live in Trees," Monkey's trick depends on
   a. some advice given by Hippopotamus
   b. the nearsightedness of Leopard
   c. the carelessness of King Gorilla
   d. the assistance of many monkeys that look exactly alike

_____ 14. The monkey's trickery in "Why Monkeys Live in Trees" is first discovered by
   a. King Gorilla   c. Hippopotamus
   b. Leopard   d. Lion

_____ 15. "Why Monkeys Live in Trees" was probably passed down from generation to generation because of the appeal of its
   a. unique characters
   b. heartfelt emotions
   c. realistic plot
   d. wisdom and humor

_____ 16. Based on what you know of Arachne's character in "Arachne," you can predict that when Athene beats her in the contest she will
   a. become humble and repentant
   b. give up weaving forever
   c. become angry and want revenge
   d. becomes best friends with Athene

___ 17. In "A Crippled Boy," Theo develops skill in throwing pebbles because he
   a. wants to get a job with the king
   b. can't play games with the other children
   c. likes to hit things
   d. needs to defend himself from other children

___ 18. In "The Three Wishes," the first two wishes the woman and her husband make are
   a. foolish   c. mean-spirited
   b. thoughtful   d. accidental

___ 19. The lesson taught in "The Three Wishes" focuses on the nature of true
   a. speech   c. justice
   b. happiness   d. honesty

Vocabulary, Spelling, and Grammar

___ 20. Which of the following is closest in meaning to the word *cordial* in this sentence: Even though Bruh Rabbit and He Lion didn't like each other, they were *cordial* when they met.
   a. surface   c. warm and friendly
   b. lengthy   d. brief

___ 21. Which sentence contains an error in capitalization?
   a. Señor Mouse helped Señor Coyote out of a trap.
   b. My Brother wouldn't have helped you.
   c. Please trick the snake, Señor.
   d. Excuse me, Señor, but your leg is stuck in a trap.

___ 22. If you do something *indignantly* you do it
   a. angrily   c. recklessly
   b. cautiously   d. happily

___ 23. Which of the following is *not* capitalized?
   a. a title used in place of a person's name
   b. a title used before a person's name
   c. a title that follows a possessive noun or pronoun
   d. a title showing a family relationship when it refers to a specific person

___ 24. Which of the following sentences is interrogative?
   a. Bruh Bear asked Lion to stop roaring.
   b. How loud Lion's roars were!
   c. Stop roaring, Lion.
   d. Why do you roar so loudly, Lion?

___ 25. Which word is spelled incorrectly?
   a. candidacy   c. bankruptcy
   b. courtesy   d. obstinansy

___ 26. Which sentence begins with a prepositional phrase?
   a. In the middle, between King Gorilla and the animals, was a huge mound of what looked like black dust.
   b. King Gorilla sat at one end of the clearing on his throne.
   c. Finally, only Monkey remained.
   d. Soon the pile was about gone.

_____ 27. If a being is *immortal* he or she will
   a. shortly die
   b. remain unfinished
   c. be well remembered
   d. live forever

_____ 28. The sentence "A miracle had happened" from "A Crippled Boy" begins with
   a. the verb
   b. the subject
   c. the direct object
   d. a prepositional phrase

_____ 29. Which sentence begins with a subordinate clause?
   a. Suddenly the woodsmen's wife sound herself making a wish.
   b. When the woman put her hand to her head, she knew what had happened and began to cry.
   c. Remember, you have only one wish left.
   d. Living in their little forest house, the poor woodsman and his wife were very happy.

_____ 30. Which word is closest to the meaning to the word *obstinacy* in the following sentence?

   Arachne would not give in; she pressed her pale lips together in *obstinacy* and pride.

   a. silliness
   b. misunderstanding
   c. stubbornness
   d. disgust

Essay Questions

31. One purpose of myths and folk tales is to explain how something in nature came to be. Choose either "Why Monkeys Live in Trees" "Arachne," and write an essay telling about one or more things in nature that are explained by the story. How does the story use character traits and plot to make these explanations believable or logical?

32. Tricksters are often the heroes of folk tales and are frequently portrayed as animals. Write an essay comparing the trickster characters in "Señor Coyote and the Tricked Trickster". How are Coyote, Mouse, and Snake alike in displaying their cleverness? How are they different: Use details from the story to support your ideas. Then tell which character you admire more and why.

33. Many folk tales have two purposes— to entertain, and also to teach some important truth about life. Choose "He Lion, Bruh Bear, and Bruh Rabbit," "Why Monkeys Live in Trees," or "The Three Wishes," and write an essay explaining how the story achieves both these purposes. Do you think humor is a good way to get a message across? Why or why not?

34. Myths and folk tales often blend realistic characters and actions with fantastic events. Choose two of the following stories: "Arachne," "A Crippled Boy," or "The Three Wishes." In an essay, compare and contrast the ways in which the stories you have chosen combine realism with fantasy.

35. Cultural values are expressed in myths and folk literature and often give you clues about what was (or still is) important to a people or a civilization. Choose "The Ant and the Dove," "Arachne," "A Crippled Boy." Write an essay explaining the values expressed in the tale and how character and plot contribute to the lesson that is taught.

Unit 10: The Oral Tradition

Alternative Unit Test:

The two passages below are followed by questions based on their content and on the relationship between the two passages.

Passage 1

This story is a Native American legend as supposedly told by a Native American grandfather, Grandpa Iron, to his family.

from "The Moose" by Eagle Walking Turtle

Long ago, a band of our people was camped in a spot with lots of hot-water springs and natural fountains called geysers. Today that land is called Yellowstone National Park.

The chief of the band was a woman called White Wolf. White Wolf was good and kind at heart but given to fits of bad temper and loud yelling for even the slightest wrong. The people were beginning to wonder if they'd chosen the right person to be their leader. Some of the council began to meet secretly without her to talk about choosing a new chief.

The head of the council was a man called Small Bear. He had been struck by lightning some years before and had strong medicine powers as a result.

One day Small Bear was out alone, walking by a big lake that stretched halfway across the valley. He saw a bull moose in the crystal-clear water, grazing on the lake's bottom. A cow moose and her calf were standing on the shore watching the bull. Small Bear stopped behind a tree to observe. The big bull would graze on the lake's bottom for a few minutes, then wade out to stand by the cow and calf, then wade back in again to graze on the water plants. The bull was teaching the young calf how to obtain food.

Small Bear could not but admire the graceful, intelligent moose family and the gentle, patient way they communicated as they searched for food.

When Small Bear returned to his village, he called a special council meeting with White Wolf present. There he told the story of the three moose and what he had learned from them. White Wolf listened without her usual bad manners. Small Bear's medicine powers worked within him, and White Wolf realized the moose story was directed at her. She apologized to the council for her past rudeness, and her apology was accepted.

After that meeting, White Wolf was a different person. She was polite and considerate and always set a good example for her people. She remained chief until she died, an old woman.

Passage 2

This story is another Native American legend as supposedly told by a Native American grandfather, Grandpa Iron, to his family.

from "The Bear" by Eagle Walking Turtle

A long time ago, when our people still lived in caves and walked everywhere, there was a medicine man called Moves Walking. Moves Walking had bear medicine power.

At that time, food was getting hard to find, so our people split into smaller bands, each band going in a different direction. Moves Walking was the leader of one band. He went into the wilderness to meditate and seek wisdom so he could take his people in the right direction. While seeking his vision, he saw a family of bears gather in a grove of trees below the hill he was on. Moves Walking watched them for days. He watched the cubs play with each other and with their mother and father. He saw the mother bear discipline her young by cuffing their ears, and the father bear ignore them when he was tired or had other things on his mind. Moves Walking saw the roots, plants, and insects that the bears ate, many of which his people had thought inedible. He learned the roots and plants they ate when they were ill. After the bears left, Moves Walking went down the hill into their camp and found the remains of their food and medicine.

When Moves Walking went back to his people, he had a vision for the direction they should go, and he had the wisdom that the bears had taught him.

From that time on, his name was Medicine Bear.

Critical Reading

On the line, write the letter of the best answer.

_____ 1. Which statement best describes the narrator of Passages 1 and 2?
   a. He has a good sense of humor.
   b. He thinks everyone should pay attention to his stories.
   c. He misses the good old days.
   d. He sees wisdom in the behavior of animals.
   e. He is hungry.

_____ 2. Which important quality do you think Small Bear in Passage 1 shares with Moves Walking in Passage 2?
   a. Both have families.
   b. Both share their visions to help their tribes.
   c. Both like to walk in the woods every day.
   d. Both enjoy hunting.
   e. Both are good horseback riders.

_____ 3. Which of the following best states the lesson the storyteller of the two passages wants to teach his listeners?
   a. Nature teaches valuable lessons to those who are willing to listen.
   b. You will become wealthy and wise if you respect animals.
   c. Animals and humans should live together in harmony.
   d. If you meditate, all things will be shown to you.
   e. Never argue with the chief.

_____ 4. In Passage 1, White Wolf is a typical folk tale character because
   a. she is powerful and wise
   b. everyone loves her
   c. she is foolish at the beginning of the tale, but wise at the end
   d. she represents a type of character rather than an individual
   e. she has a unique personality all her own

_____ 5. Which statement is true of both Small Bear in Passage 1 and Moves Walking in Passage 2?
   a. Both make wishes that came true.
   b. Both have medicine power.
   c. Both are tricksters.
   d. Both have been struck by lightning.
   e. Both are chiefs.

_____ 6. Which statement best describes how both Passage 1 and Passage 2 are typical of the oral tradition?
   a. Both are filled with action.
   b. Both include detailed descriptions of settings.
   c. Both leave listeners in suspense.
   d. Both make use of humor to teach a lesson.
   e. They are both related to the history of a tribe.

_____ 7. In Passage 1, what can you infer about Small Bear's experience watching the moose family?
   a. Animals are more intelligent than humans.
   b. Small Bear has not been able to think clearly ever since he was struck by lightning.
   c. Small Bear wishes that people could treat each other with the kindness and patience of the moose family.
   d. Small Bear wishes that the members of his tribe could learn to gather food more efficiently.
   e. Yellowstone National Park is a good place to hunt.

_____ 8. Which element common to both passages most certainly reflects the Native American culture?
   a. a character with medicine powers
   b. animals living freely in the wilderness
   c. a character with a bad temper
   d. plants eaten by animals
   e. a place with hot-water springs and geysers

_____ 9. Based on your reading of Passage 2, what can you predict for the future of the people of Moves Walking?
   a. They will always be kind to bears.
   b. They will get along together and find enough food.
   c. They will become more powerful than the other bands.
   d. The will always live in peace with other tribes.
   e. They will always remain healthy.

_____ 10. In Passage 2, why is Moves Walking called Medicine Bear?
   a. He learned wisdom from the bears and used it to help his people.
   b. He helped his people by learning how to cure illness.
   c. He once saved a bear's life.
   d. His life was once saved by a bear.
   e. It was the name of his father and grandfather before him.

_____ 11. In Passage 1 and Passage 2, details that reflect a respect for strong family relationships are
   a. the behavior of the chief in Passage 1 and the leader in Passage 2
   b. the behavior of the moose family in Passage 1 and the bear family in Passage 2
   c. the importance of patience in Passage 1 and food in Passage 2
   d. the female leader in Passage 1 and the male leader in Passage 2
   e. the respectful behavior of the children in both passages

_____ 12. Based on your reading of Passage 1, what can you predict for the future of the people of White Wolf?
   a. They will communicate politely with each other but be treated by White Wolf with cruelty.
   b. They will choose a new chief and be treated with respect.
   c. They will find edible water plants and share all food with each other.
   d. They will be as angry as White Wolf and be disrespectful at council meetings.
   e. They will communicate politely with each other and be treated by White Wolf with respect.

_____ 13. Which statement best describes the motives of Small Bear and Moves Walking?
   a. Both want to become great leaders.
   b. Both think the leader of a tribe should be a woman.
   c. Both want better lives for their people.
   d. Both know how to communicate with wild animals.
   e. Both are good storytellers.

_____ 14. What useful knowledge does Moves Walking learn from the bears in Passage 2?
   a. He becomes a better hunter.
   b. He learns that it is not good to go swimming right after eating.
   c. He learns that food is not the most important thing in the world
   d. He learns which roots and plants are edible.
   e. He learns how to keep from getting lost in the woods.

_____ 15. Which of the following can be inferred from Passage 1?
   a. If you are struck by lightning, you will gain special powers.
   b. There are no longer hot springs or geysers in Yellowstone National Park.
   c. Politeness and consideration were valued by the tribe.
   d. All chiefs were women in those days.
   c. All the people of the tribe lived to be very old.

Essay Questions

16. Both passages teach that important lessons can be learned by observing how animals live. Write an essay in which you explain how these passages demonstrate this truth. Explain the lessons that Small Bear and Moves Walking learned and how they learned those lessons. End your essay by explaining why each lesson is important.

17. In an essay, identify aspects of the history and culture of Eagle Walking Turtle's people that are revealed in the two passages. What events that occurred long ago are still remembered in these stories? What values are considered important by the people? Identify the specific details from which you learned or inferred this information.

18. The characters in each passage are typical folk-literature characters because they represent qualities or types rather than individuals. In an essay, explain what each character represents. Then explain why neither Small Bear nor Moves Walking can be considered an individualized, fully drawn character. To prove your point, suggest details about each character's life and personality that would have to be added to the story in order to make each one an individual rather than a type or a representation. Finally, tell what might be lost from each passage if the characters were represented as true individuals.

ANSWERS
Unit 1: Growing and Changing

"The Sound of Summer Running"
by Ray Bradbury

Selection Test (p.1)

Critical Reading/Vocabulary, Spelling, and Grammar

1. b 2. c 3. b 4. c 5. d 6. a 7. d 8. c
9. d 10. d 11. a 12. a 13. c. 14. b
15. d 16. b 17. c 18. b 19. c 20. a

Questions are classified in these categories:
Comprehension 2(E), 3(A), 13(A), 14(E)
Interpretation 5(C), 6(E), 10(C), 12(C)
Literary Analysis 1(E), 4(C), 7(A), 8(C)
Reading Strategy 9(A), 11(A)
Vocabulary 16(A)
Spelling 17(A), 20(C)
Grammar 15(A), 18(A), 19(A)
E = Easy, A = Average, C = Challenging

Essay Questions

21. (Easy) *Guidelines for student response:* Students should explain how two different reading strategies helped them comprehend Bradbury's story. They should offer at least one example related to each strategy. For instance, students might say that they found it helpful to break down long sentences and give an example of a sentence that they approached in this way.

22. (Average) *Guidelines for student response:* Douglas's main motive is his desire for a new pair of sneakers. This desire motivates him to offer to run errands for Mr. Sanderson and to encourage Mr. Sanderson to try on the sneakers while he lays out his proposal. Mr. Sanderson is motivated by his admiration for Douglas's spunk as well as memories brought on by wearing the sneakers. These motives lead him to accept Douglas's offer.

23. (Challenging) *Guidelines for student response:* Students may cite Bradbury's colorful and exuberant descriptions of summer and how it feels to wear a brand new pair of sneakers. They may note that these descriptions resemble the "rush of words" in which Douglas tends to speak and think. This aspect of the story's style is appropriate because it reflects Douglas's character and state of mind.

"Stray" by Cynthia Rylant

Selection Test (p. 4)

Critical Reading/Vocabulary, Spelling, and Grammar

1. b 2. d 3. d 4. c 5. c 6. d 7. a 8. a
9. b 10. c 11. b 12. b 13. d 14. c 15. a
16. b 17. b 18. a 19. c 20. d

Questions are classified in these categories:
Comprehension 1(E), 2(C), 3(E), 6(A). 8(A)
Interpretation 4(C), 7(A), 9(A), 14(C)
Literary Analysis 5(E), 10(C), 13(A)
Reading Strategy 11(A), 12(E)
Vocabulary 16(A), 19(E)
Spelling 17(E), 20)E)
Grammar 15(E), 18(A)
E = Easy, A = Average, C = Challenging

Essay Questions

21. (Easy) *Guidelines for student response:* Students may write that Mr. and Mrs. Lacey are alike in that neither is in the habit of expressing feelings openly, and they both believe in being firm parents. As an example of the former, they may cite both parents' refusal to discuss the dog with Doris; as an example of the latter, they may cite that neither parent shows any sign of giving in to Doris's wishes throughout most of the story. Students should note that Mr. Lacey is the more softhearted of Doris's two parents, as he is the one who relents, in the end, and allows the puppy to stay.

22. (Average) *Guidelines for student response:* Students may say that Doris learns that people are not always as they seem. Later in life, Doris may be more optimistic and positive about her relationships with people as a result of having seen how much her father cared about her, even though he did not always show it. Some students may respond that remembering how her experience had turned out happily in the end, in spite of her earlier despair, could

"Stray" by Cynthia Rylant
(continued)

make Doris a more optimistic person in general.

23. (Challenging) *Guidelines for student response:* Students may answer that Doris seems to be a lonely child, as during the nine days during which the story takes place, she never sees any friends or other children.

"Dust of Snow" by Robert Frost
"My Picture-Gallery" by Walt Whitman
"Saying Yes" by Diana Chang

Selection Test (p. 7)

Critical Reading/Vocabulary, Spelling, and Grammar

1. d 2. a 3. c 4. a 5. a 6. d 7. d 8. c
9. d 10. c 11. c 12. b 13. b 14. d 15. b
16. c 17. a 18. d 19. b 20. c

Questions are classified in these categories:
Comprehension 1(A), 5(E), 10(E)
Interpretation 2(E), 3(C), 7(C), 8(A), 11(C)
Literary Analysis 6(A), 13(E), 14(A)
Reading Strategy 4(C), 9(C), 12(E)
Vocabulary 15(E), 18(D)
Spelling 17(A), 20(E)
Grammar 16(A), 19(A)
E = Easy, A = Average, C = Challenging

Essay Questions

21. (Easy) *Guidelines for student response:* Students should recount an experience that they have had and explain how it resembles the one described in either "Saying Yes" or "Dust of Snow." They should briefly discuss what they learned from or concluded about the experience.

22. (Average) *Guidelines for student response:* Students should identify an image such as the picture gallery in Whitman's poem or the crow in the snowy tree in Frost's poem. They should point out that the image helps bring to life the scene that the poet is depicting. They should also explain the image's significance within the overall message of the poem.

23. (Challenging) *Guidelines for student response:* Students who choose "Saying Yes" should point out that Diana Chang helps readers see a person who is Chinese American in a new way; she does this through a series of short, direct questions followed by thoughts in which the speaker sorts out who she really is. Students who choose "My Picture-Gallery" should point out that Whitman helps readers see a person's head in a new way; he does this in a poem that unfolds like a riddle and by comparing the head to a gallery full of pictures and shows. Students who choose "Dust of Snow" should point out that Frost helps readers see a small event in a new way; he does so by describing in clear and simple terms how a crow shook some snow onto him and in this way dispelled the gloomy mood he had been in.

"Jeremiah's Song"
by Walter Dean Myers

Selection Test (p. 10)

Critical Reading/Vocabulary, Spelling, and Grammar

1. b 2. c 3. b 4. d 5. a 6. a 7. a 8. d
9. d 10. c 11. c 12. a 13. a 14. b 15. d
16. a 17. d 18. c 19. a 20. b

Questions are classified in these categories:
Comprehension 3(A), 5(E), 11(A),
Interpretation 1(A), 6(E), 7(A), 9(C)
Literary Analysis 2(E), 4(A), 12(C)
Reading Strategy 8(C), 10(A), 13(C)
Vocabulary 16(C), 18(A)
Spelling 15(E), 20(A)
Grammar 14(A), 17(E), 19(C)
E = Easy, A = Average, C = Challenging

Essay Questions

21. (Easy) *Guidelines for student response:* Students should comprehend that Sister Todd means that young people, with their education and exposure to modern technology, have no use for the past, exemplified by Grandpa Jeremiah's stories. They should recognize, however, that an important message of the story is that older people do have valuable lessons and

advice to pass on to the young. To support this position, they may mention that Jeremiah says that his stories serve as "a bridge" to link the people of the past with those of the present. Those stories can show younger people how to cope with adversity and inspire them to develop strength of character. Students may also cite valuable advice or information that they have received from older people in their own lives.

22. *Guidelines for student response:* Students should note how the narrator's young age affects his perspective; for example, the narrator wants Ellie to sleep in the same bed, is afraid of Jeremiah's stories sometimes, and does not understand Macon's tears. Students might comment that the young narrator's perspective is similar to that of the readers: We are all learning about the changes in Ellie, Macon, and Grandpa Jeremiah.

23. *Guidelines for student response:* Students' responses will vary, but they should address Ellie's feelings about education, friends, music, and storytelling. For example, some students might suggest that Ellie chooses not to go back to college at all because she wants to stay home and learn more about her ancestors. Others might suggest that she goes back to school but becomes involved in activities that help her understand her past.

"The King of Mazy May"
by Jack London

Selection Test (p. 13)

Critical Reading/Vocabulary, Spelling, and Grammar

1. a   2. d   3. c   4. c   5. d   6. b   7. d   8. c
9. b   10. a   11. a   12. d   13. a   14. b   15. c
16. a   17. d   18. b   19. b   20. d

Questions are classified in these categories:
Comprehension 4(E), 5(E), 6(C), 8(A)
Interpretation 1(A), 2(C), 10(A), 12(E), 14(A)
Literary Analysis 3(A), 9(E), 13(C)
Reading Strategy 7(E), 11(A)
Vocabulary 15(E), 18(A)
Spelling 16 (E)
Grammar 17(A), 19(C), 20(E)

E = Easy, A = Average, C = Challenging

Essay Questions

21. (Easy) *Guidelines for student response:* Students may point out Walt's "good heart," the strength and bravery he inherited from his father, his refusal to tolerate injustice and several examples of his courage. Students should note that the claim-jumpers steal what others have worked hard to earn and they are willing to shoot Walt if necessary in order to keep him from ruining their plans.

22. (Average) *Guidelines for student response:* Students may say that Walt has developed the following skills because of the harsh and demanding environment in which he has grown up: his knowledge of sleds and dogs, and his ability to take care of himself without an adult for long stretches of time. Students may say that Walt was born with senses of justice and bravery. Students may say that Walt's ability to react quickly in a crisis and to keep functioning through a long, difficult night are qualities which may be inborn and which are brought out in such an environment.

23. (Challenging) *Guidelines for student response:* Students should be aware of the extreme nature of the climate: the bitter cold and constant presence of snow and ice. They should note that there are no people around, no law enforcement, and no modern communication. Prospectors have to make a long trek to Dawson to register a claim, the cold and ice make the pursuit of Walt by the claim-jumpers especially exciting; the lack of any surrounding community makes the threat posed by the claim-jumpers much more menacing.

"The Circuit" by Francisco Jiménez
"Hard as Nails" by Russell Baker

Selection Test (p. 16)

Critical Reading/Vocabulary, Spelling, and Grammar

1. a   2. b   3. a   4. b   5. d   6. c   7. c   8. d
9. b   10. d   11. c   12. a   13. d   14. b   15. a
16. b   17. c   18. b   19. d   20. d

"The Circuit" by Francisco Jiménez
"Hard as Nails" by Russell Baker
(continued)

Questions are classified in these categories:
Comprehension: 2(A), 3(E), 12 (C), 14(A)
Interpretation: 8(A), 4(A), 6(C), 10(E), 11(A)
Literary Analysis: 1(E), 5(A), 13(C)
Reading Strategy: 7(A), 9(E), 15(C)
Vocabulary: 17(C), 20(A)
Spelling: 18(A)
Grammar: 16(A), 19(E):
E = Easy, A = Average, C = Challenging

21 (Easy) *Guidelines for student response:*
Students should be aware of sensory images, such as the heat in the field, Panchito's mouth feeling "as though I had been chewing on a handkerchief," getting sick to his stomach after drinking too much water, dizziness, how his muscles ache after work, and so forth. Students should point out how sad Panchito feels at the prospect of moving to Fresno, and how relieved he feels at the prospect of going to school rather than working on a farm for a while. They may also mention details such as working seven days a week, twelve hours a day.

22 (Average) *Guidelines for student response:*
Students should note the following similarities between Panchito and Russell: both boys have to work at a young age in order to contribute to their families' incomes; both boys come from close, loving families who are struggling together to get by under difficult conditions. They should note some of the following differences between the two boys: Panchito and his family have come to the United States from Mexico and have only a limited command of English. They do not have a home, but travel to wherever they can find work. Russell Baker and his family are United States citizens, but the Depression, at its height in the 1930s, has forced the boy to get a job to supplement the family income. The Bakers have a place to live, and, unlike Panchito and his brothers and sisters, the Baker children go to school regularly. Panchito sees the work he does as endless, tedious, and exhausting, with only occasional breaks. Russell regards his job as rewarding and chal-

lenging, and believes he is doing something that is important.

23 (Challenging) *Guidelines for student response:* Students may use words such serious, solemn, heavy, or pessimistic to describe Jiménez's tone. They should support their choice of words with examples, such as descriptions of the family's preparations for moving, the living conditions in Mr. Sullivan's garage, and Panchito's disappointing discovery that the family is moving again, just when he thought he would be going to school. To describe Baker's tone, students may use words such as humorous, amusing, or light. They may cite as examples the way Baker pokes fun at himself as a boy, imagining that others are watching him admiringly as he delivers his newspapers, and the way he describes his nervousness at the banquet. The quote from William Randolph Hearst, and Baker's comments on it, are amusing well.

Unit Test (p. 19)

Critical Reading/Vocabulary, Spelling, and Grammar

1. b   2. a   3. a   4. c   5. b   6. d   7. b   8. a
9. d   10. a   11. c   12. b   13. b   14. a   15. d
16. c   17. d   18. b   19. d   20. b   21. a
22. d   23. c   24. b   25. c   26. a   27. d
28. a   29. b   30. a

Questions are classified in these categories:
Comprehension: 2(A), 4(E), 15(A)
Interpretation: 5(A), 8(E), 10(A), 12(C), 14(A), 16(A), 19(C)
Literary Analysis: 1(A), 6(E), 9(A), 11(C), 18(A)
Reading Strategy: 3(A), 7(E), 13(C), 17(E)
Vocabulary: 22(E), 24(A), 28(C)
Spelling: 21(A), 26(E), 29(A)
Grammar: 20(A), 23(A), 25(A), 27(E), 30(C)
E = Easy, A = Average, C = Challenging

Essay Questions

31. (Easy) *Guidelines for student response:*
Students should note that Russell Baker in "Hard as Nails" develops his ability to work hard and meet challenges; these changes result from his awareness of his family's need for money and the difficult financial times throughout the country during the Great Depression. Douglas in

"The Sound of Summer Running" is motivated by his desire for new tennis shoes. He shows his persuasive power and determination. Panchito in "The Circuit" is desperate to escape his situation but is so trapped in it that he changes least of these characters. In "Jeremiah's Song," Macon matures and becomes more responsible, partly because he grows older and partly because of the influence of Jeremiah.

32. *Guidelines for student response:* Students should be able to define the point of view of the selection chosen and be able to give examples to show the effect of the point of view. In "Stray" the narration is third person, which helps to keep the reader in suspense about what will happen. "Saying Yes" and "My Picture Gallery" are told from the first-person point of view, revealing the personal nature of the poems. (Both deal with personal identity.) "Jeremiah's Song" is told by a young first-person narrator, which enables the reader to learn about the situation as the narrator does.

33. (Average) *Guidelines for student response:* Students may recognize "O To Be Up and Doing" as not only a description of the speaker's wish to fill his life with worthwhile activity, but also as a call to readers to do the same. In "Saying Yes," the speaker is expressing her wish that people accept both parts of her heritage as positive aspects of who she is. Students should note that the author is urging readers to be equally accepting and positive of themselves. In "Dust of Snow," the author shows how an unexpected event, like being hit with an icy shower of powdery snow, can suddenly brighten a gloomy mood. There is also a suggestion that readers can experience the same unexpected lift. "My Picture-Gallery" describes how the poet stores memories for future recall and enjoyment. The poet suggests that the reader has the same ability.

34. (Average) *Guidelines for student response:* Students should note powerful and unpleasant images in "The Circuit"—images of heat, bodily aches, thirst, and dust, among others, that contribute to the bleakness of the story. The images in "The King of Mazy May" heighten the dramatic nature of the setting: gleaming ice, rugged terrain, and drifted snow. Some images add to the excitement of the climactic chase: the sound of ricocheting bullets, the careening of the speeding dogsled, and the extreme cold and fatigue that plague Walt as he struggles to stay ahead of his pursuers. The sensory images in this story reinforce its effectiveness in positive and negative ways, unlike the imagery in "The Circuit," which is almost exclusively negative. "Stray" uses less dramatic images, although visual ones help to make the puppy appealing and explain Doris's love for it. Also, the early images of winter help to establish that Doris's family, while loving and supportive, is burdened by some financial need.

35. (Challenging) *Guidelines for student response:* Students should recognize "Stray" as using a totally unexpected surprise ending to make readers as happy as Doris herself. The author takes care to make readers believe that Doris will not get to keep the puppy, making the story's final resolution especially happy. "The King of Mazy May" builds suspense through most of its length. The author makes it clear that Walt, though resourceful, is very young, while his enemies are grown up and capable of terrible things, including murder. London heightens the suspense by having Walt nearly caught at one point, and not until almost the end of the story does the author give readers a chance to relax. "The Circuit" offers neither surprises nor suspense—pointing out the hopelessness of Panchito's situation. Each type of plot serves to enhance the kind of story its author had in mind.

Alternative Unit Test (p. 23)

Critical Reading

1. b   2. c   3. e   4. a   5. c   6. b   7. e   8. e
9. d   10. a   11. c   12. b   13. a   14. d   15. b

Questions are classified in these categories:
Comprehension 6(A), 12(E)
Interpretation 2(A), 4(C), 8(A), 11(E), 13(A)
Literary Analysis 1(C), 3(C), 5(A), 9(A),
10(A), 14(E)
Reading Strategy 7(A), 15(E)
E = Easy, A = Average, C = Challenging

Essay Questions

16. (Easy) *Guidelines for student response*: Students should note that the author of passage 1 uses vivid sensory images, while passage 2 uses first-hand direct quotations. As examples of vivid visual images in passage 1, students might cite the following: ". . . red or yellow running gear and green paint with fancy scrollwork . . .," "Over the years the paint weathered and peeled, leaving bare wood that was never repainted," "In summer the sun bleached the wood; winter snow drifted over it." As examples of first-hand direct quotations in passage 2, students might cite the following: "That tractor cost $18,000 when I bought it in '77," "There's lots of equipment being auctioned off these days by fellows going out of business," or almost any statements Frank makes. Students should realize that, while imagery is an appropriate technique for describing times gone by, directly quoting a subject is more appropriate for an interview.

17. (Average) *Guidelines for student response:* Students' essays should demonstrate that they understand sentimental to mean "having to do with emotions or feelings" and practical to mean "having to do with what is sensible or useful." Students should note that the author of Passage 1 is more sentimental than practical because he looks back fondly on the time of the Studebaker wagon, even though an automobile is a much more efficient means of transportation. Students should note that Frank, in Passage 2, is more practical than sentimental because, while he values his father's tractor for sentimental reasons, his main reason for wanting to keep his old equipment is to save money. Examples of sentimentality in Passage 1 might include the description of the colorful and "fancy scrollwork" of the Studebaker wagon and the personification of the wagon as "the faithful Studebaker"; examples of practicality in Passage 2 might include the statements "He keeps it running because it saves him the price of a new one," and "I don't need the smell of new paint."

18. (Challenging) *Guidelines for student response:* Students might infer that the author of Passage 1 is a sentimental, nostalgic dreamer because he looks back at the past as a simpler, happier time than the modern age of fast transportation and mass production. He does so without considering the hardships people of the past had to endure because they lacked the advantages of modern technology. As examples that lead to this inference, students might cite quotations such as "Homesteaders and farmers in that era were given to fits of wanderlust," and ". . . the Studebaker would be loaded to overflowing with his family's belongings and the team of faithful horses would pull it to the next land of promise." Students might infer that Frank, in Passage 2, is a down-to-earth, practical, "no-nonsense" kind of person because his main concern is running his farm as economically as possible. He looks back fondly at the past only because equipment was not so expensive then. As examples, students might cite quotations such as "Now it's about $50,000. You can't keep up with that," and "Now we're reverting to our old ways because we can't afford all the equipment we need."

Unit 2: Reaching Out

"How to Write a Letter" by Garrison Keillor
"How to Write a Poem About the Sky" by Leslie Marmon Silko

Selection Test (p. 27)

Critical Reading/Vocabulary, Spelling, and Grammar

1. a 2. b 3. d 4. b 5. c 6. c 7. d 8. b
9. b 10. c 11. d 12. c 13. d. 14. c
15. a 16. c 17. d 18. d 19. d 20. b

Questions are classified in these categories:
  Comprehension 2(E), 3(A), 8(C), 13(C)
  Interpretation 6(A), 7(C), 10(E), 14(A)
  Literary Analysis 1(E), 4(A), 5(A), 9(C)
  Reading Strategy 11(E), 12(E)
  Vocabulary 15(A), 17(C)
  Spelling 18(A), 20(E)
  Grammar 16(A), 19(C)

Essay Questions

21. (Easy) *Guidelines for student response:* Students should summarize Keillor's reasons for stating that letters are a gift. For example, they might point out that letters allow people to express themselves, to stay close to friends and loved ones, and to leave a legacy for future generations. Students should also clearly state whether they agree or disagree with Keillor, citing examples from their own experience for support.

22. (Average) *Guidelines for student response:* Students should clearly state their opinions as to whether the informal essay is an interesting and enjoyable form of writing as well as briefly define the informal essay. They should develop their opinions with citations from the text and conclude by restating their opinion in a slightly different way.

23. (Challenging) *Guidelines for student response:* Students should analyze Keillor's use of humor in the essay, citing and briefly discussing specific examples. They should use appropriate words, such as *gentle* and *low-key*, to describe the style of the author's humor. They should conclude by explaining how the touches of humor

are appropriate; for example, they might say that the gentle humor fits in well with the essay's casual and informal style and its emphasis on the importance of friendship and tenderness.

"Aaron's Gift" by Myron Levoy
"Water" by Helen Keller

Selection Test (p. 30)

Critical Reading/Vocabulary, Spelling, and Grammar

1. a 2. c 3. c 4. c 5. a 6. c 7. a 8. b
9. d 10. d 11. c 12. d 13. a 14. a 15. a
16. d 17. c 18. b 19. a 20. c

Questions are classified in these categories:
  Comprehension 1(A), 3(E), 9(C), 13(A)
  Interpretation 2(E), 4(C), 6(C), 7(E), 10(A), 15(A)
  Literary Analysis 5(A), 8(E), 11(C)
  Reading Strategy 12(A), 14(E)
  Vocabulary 16(E), 19(A)
  Spelling 17(A)
  Grammar 18(A), 20(C)

Essay Questions

21. (Easy) *Guidelines for student response:* In their essays, students should demonstrate understanding of the importance Miss Sullivan played in Helen's life. They should bring out that, had Helen's parents chosen another teacher, Helen Keller may have remained as she was before the episode in "Water" takes place, i.e., not only blind, deaf, and unable to speak, but without the ability to reason or think. To support their ideas, students should cite Miss Sullivan's patience with Helen and her determination to teach the child to connect words with objects.

22. *Guidelines for student responses:* Students should list at least three examples of rising action; for example: the pigeon first appears, Aaron catches the pigeon, Aaron trains the pigeon, the gang leader asks for Pidge as a mascot, and so on. The climax of the story is when Aaron takes Pidge to the shack and the boys are lighting a fire to throw Pidge in. Students should

"Aaron's Gift" by Myron Levoy
"Water" by Helen Keller
(continued)

comment that the rising action is important because the readers become attached to Aaron and Pidge. They can also understand how much Aaron loves the bird.

23. (Challenging) *Guidelines for student response:* In their essays, students should show that they understand the story's main idea: that Aaron's gift to his grandmother is Pidge's freedom, which helps the grandmother get over her hurt from long ago when the Cossacks cruelly killed her beloved pet goat. The title expresses this idea by including the word *gift*. The irony of the title makes the reader think about the story's idea, because Aaron actually has no physical gift to give his grandmother.

"Zlateh the Goat"
by Isaac Bashevis Singer

Selection Test (p. 33)

Critical Reading/Vocabulary, Spelling, and Grammar

1. a 2. a 3. c 4. d 5. c 6. a 7. c 8. b
9. c 10. a 11. d 12. b 13. b 14. a 15. d
16. b 17. a 18. c 19. c 20. b

Questions are classified in these categories:
Comprehension 1(C), 4(E), 7(A)
Interpretation 2(E), 5(E), 10(A), 13(C)
Literary Analysis 3(E), 8(A), 11(C)
Reading Strategy 6(C), 9(A), 12(E)
Vocabulary 14(A), 19(A)
Spelling 15(A), 20(E)
Grammar 16(A), 17(E), 18(C)

Essay Questions

21. *Guidelines for student response:* Students' summaries should include the following events: Aaron's father says Zlateh the goat must be sold to Feivel the butcher; Aaron sets off for Feivel's house with Zlateh; Aaron and Zlateh are caught in a blizzard; Aaron finds a haystack where he and Zlateh can take shelter; Zlateh eats hay from the haystack, and Aaron drinks Zlateh's milk; the blizzard ends; Aaron decides to take Zlateh home, not to the butcher's; Aaron and Zlateh return home; the family rejoices and, from then on, treats Zlateh as a beloved household pet.

22. *Guidelines for student response:* Students' explanations should stress that Aaron and Zlateh not only save each others' lives, but also bond as friends as they take shelter in the haystack during the blizzard. Students should cite examples of how Aaron and Zlateh take care of each other: Aaron provides a shelter where Zlateh can have warmth and food, while Zlateh gives Aaron her milk to drink; Aaron comforts Zlateh by talking to her, while Zlateh comforts Aaron by keeping him company.

23. *Guidelines for student response:* Students should mention that the snowstorm begins as a dark cloud. The cloud spreads, as a cold wind begins to blow. It begins to hail, then to snow harder and harder until Aaron cannot see where he is. He is lost, his hands and feet become numb, and he can hardly breathe. Aaron and Zlateh are both frightened. It seems that the snowstorm will defeat Aaron, until he finds the haystack. Students should note that Aaron's cleverness, or resourcefulness, lead him to recognize immediately that the haystack is just what he and Zlateh need to survive. He further proves his resourcefulness by using his stick to make a hole in the haystack, allowing air to come in.

"Door Number Four"
by Charlotte Pomerantz

"Count That Day Lost"
by George Eliot

"The World Is Not a Pleasant Place to Be" by Nikki Giovanni

Selection Test (p. 36)

Critical Reading/Vocabulary, Spelling, and Grammar

1. b 2. c 3. b 4. d 5. a 6. c 7. c 8. b
9. d 10. b 11. b 12. a 13. d 14. b 15. d

Questions are classified in these categories:
Comprehension 9(A)
Interpretation 3(A), 6(A), 10(C)
Literary Analysis 1(C), 4(A), 7(E)
Reading Strategy 2(A), 5(E), 8(A)

Vocabulary 12(A), 14(A)
Spelling 15(E)
Grammar 11(A), 13(C)

Essay Questions

16. (Easy) *Guidelines for student response:* Students should summarize the message about friendship in one of the poems. For example, students who choose "Count That Day Lost" might say that the poem stresses the importance of being kind and considerate to everyone we meet. Students should also include citations or paraphrases to support their points.

17. (Average) *Guidelines for student response:* Students should clearly identify the speakers of two of the poems and then go on to compare and contrast them. For example, students who choose "Door Number Four" and "The World Is not a Pleasant Place to Be" should identify the speaker of the first poem as a person— probably a child—who knows Indonesian and whose uncle has a store, and the speaker of the second poem as a voice of wisdom. Among the differences they might point out is that the speaker of "Door Number Four" seems playful, while the speaker of "The World Is Not . . ." seems thoughtful and serious. Among the similarities they might point out is the fact that both speakers are concerned with friendship and caring.

18. (Challenging) *Guidelines for student response:* Students should clearly express their opinion as to whether each poem seems mainly relevant or mainly old-fashioned. They should cite phrases or passages from the poem to support their points.

"Old Ben" by Jesse Stuart
"Feathered Friend"
by Arthur C. Clarke

Selection Test (p. 39)

Critical Reading/Vocabulary, Spelling, and Grammar

1. d   2. d   3. a   4. d   5. c   6. a   7. a   8. c
9. d   10. b   11. b   12. a   13. b   14. d   15. a
16. c   17. d   18. b   19. b   20. b

Questions are classified in these categories:
Comprehension: 2(E), 11(A), 12(E)
Interpretation: 3(E), 5(C), 7(A), 9(A)
Literary Analysis: 4(A), 8(C)
Reading Strategy: 1(E), 6(E), 10(C)
Vocabulary: 15(A), 17(E)
Spelling: 14(E), 19(A)
Grammar: 13(E), 16(A), 18(C), 20(A)

Essay Questions

21. (Easy) *Guidelines for student response:* Students' essays should demonstrate awareness that the narrator feels affection for animals, rather than simply considering them useful. Students should point out that the narrator's other pets—groundhogs, crows, and hawks—are not usually considered useful animals; they should cite the narrator's lack of fear, even of snakes; and quote examples of the friendly manner in which he talks to Ben. They should also point out that his concern when Ben is missing is more than he would feel if Ben could simply be replaced by another snake.

22. (Average) *Guidelines for student responses:* Students should focus on the canary's rescue of the people on the space station. For the space station crew, the word "friend" shows how they feel about Claribel. (Students may agree or disagree about whether the title expresses the main idea.)

23. (Average) Guidelines for student response: Students should point out that both animals are important to the people around them: Ben because he keeps mice out of the corncrib, and Claribel because she saves the spacers' lives. They should see that, in both stories, humans feel affection for the animals; however, Ben's owners seem to relate more emotionally to the snake than the spacers do to Claribel. Students might mention that the narrator's father in "Old Ben" says that the snake looked at him "as if he understood,"

"Old Ben" by Jesse Stuart
"Feathered Friend" by Arthur C. Clarke
(continued)

while the spacers simply acknowledge Claribel as a source of pleasure and entertainment. In addition, students should mention that, while Claribel saves the spacers' lives, she does so unintentionally, while Ben seems to have true affection for his owners, demonstrated by the fact that he returns to the corncrib voluntarily.

Unit Test (p. 42)

Critical Reading/Vocabulary, Spelling, and Grammar

1. a 2. d 3. b 4. c 5. a 6. a 7. c.
8. b. 9. c. 10. b 11. d 12. c 13. b
14. b 15. c 16. a 17. a 18. c 19. a
20. a 21. d 22. c 23. d 24. b 25. a
26. b 27. c 28. a 29. d 30. b

Questions are classified in these categories:
  Comprehension: 3(A), 5(C), 10(E),
    12(A), 16(A)
  Interpretation: 1(E), 6(A), 9(A), 13(C),
    15(A), 19(C)
  Literary Analysis: 2(C), 8(E), 18(A)
  Reading Strategy: 4(A), 11(C), 14(E), 17(A)
  Vocabulary: 22(A), 24(E), 28(C)
  Spelling: 21(E), 26(A), 29(C)
  Grammar: 20(A), 23(C), 25(E), 27(A),
    28(A) 30(E)

Essay Questions

31. (Easy) *Guidelines for student response:*
Students should recall that the narrator of "Old Ben" finds the snake and recognizes it as friendly. Ben is affectionate to the narrator's family, and also keeps the corncrib free of mice. When he dies, the family members feel a sense of loss. The canary in "Feathered Friend" is smuggled onto a space station, where its songs provide a bright note in the drab world of the station. The canary saves the lives of the crew by alerting them to a potentially fatal air supply problem. In both stories, the animal is both useful and a source of companionship. Zlateh the goat has always been friendly toward Reuven's family, which does not deter Reuven from resolving to sell Zlateh to the butcher during hard times. But Zlateh and Aaron save each

other's lives in a blizzard, after which selling the goat is a family pet. Here, as in "Feathered Friend," a friendly animal and a human being save each other's lives—a powerful illustration of rewarding ties between animals and people. In "Aaron's Gift," Aaron heals a pigeon with a broken wing and, when he inadvertently sets it free, provides his grandmother with an especially precious gift. The pigeon, while it saves no lives, liberates the grandmother from a life-long nightmare that has haunted her memory.

32. (Average) *Guidelines to student response:*
Students may say that the author of "How to Write a Letter" believes that friends should acknowledge their appreciation of each other, and that letters are an ideal means of doing it. No occasion is necessary, in his view. "Aaron's Gift" presents a narrower view; the friendship here is between a boy and his grandmother, and Aaron wants to give her a gift for a specific occasion, her birthday. He does feel protective of the pigeon, even risking the anger of a group of older boys to save it. So Aaron observes ties between himself and both his grandmother and the pigeon. In "Zlateh the Goat," Zlateh is saved from death at the hands of the butcher because of his role in saving Aaron's life. But Aaron reaches out to create a closer tie with Zlateh when they are trapped during the blizzard and the goat becomes his source of food and sole companion.

33. (Average) *Guidelines for student response:*
Students should note that one of these poems, "Count That Day Lost," is one in which the poet openly speaks to the reader, urging him or her to behave in a certain way. "Door Number Four" is similar in that its author also speaks to the reader, issuing an invitation for him or her to make the acquaintance of child who is the poem's speaker. The writers of the other poems seem to want to share experiences with readers. "How to Write a Poem About the Sky" captures a vivid cold-climate scene: a gray sky, indistinguishable from land and sea, that suddenly lets some blue show through a break in the clouds.

34. (Average) *Guidelines for student response:*
Students may note that the author of

"How to Write a Letter" identifies himself as a shy person, one for whom the act of reaching out socially is not easy, although he considers it an important act. Even shy people, he feels, must see to it that their friends know how much he appreciates them, which is one reason that letters are so vital as a means of expression. The narrator of "Water" has a special need to reach out, and also the greatest difficulty in doing so, because she cannot see, hear, or speak. She must depend on the determined efforts of others, especially her teacher, to break through her isolation and establish connections with the rest of the world. To the speaker of "The World Is Not a Pleasant Place," reaching out is necessary, too. She feels that it is only connections to other people that give life its pleasures, and that nothing can be enjoyed while a person feels alone.

35. (Challenging) *Guidelines for student response:* For "Aaron's Gift," students should notice that the rising action begins with Aaron's discovery of the pigeon and continues to grow as the gang becomes interested in Pidge. The climax of the story comes when Aaron takes the bird to the shed and discovers that the boys want to throw her in the fire. Students should comment that in "Zlateh the Goat" the rising action begins with Aaron taking the goat away to be sold. As the weather changes, the tension rises about Aaron's safety. When the weather finally changes, they are able to return home. For "Old Ben," students should talk about the way the author pulls the reader into the growing friendship between the snake and the narrator and his family. When the snake is missing, the tension rises until they find the path to the hog pen and realize that he has been killed. (Students will have different opinions about which author does the better job.)

Alternative Unit Test (p. 46)

Critical Reading

1. a 2. b 3. c 4. d 5. a 6. b 7. d 8. a
9. c 10. d 11. e 12. c 13. b 14. a 15. b

Questions are classified in these categories:
Comprehension 1(A), 8(C)
Interpretation 3(A), 15(C), 2(A), 13(C)
Literary Analysis 4(A), 5(E), 6(C), 9(C)
Reading Strategy 7(E), 10(E), 11(A), 12(A), 14(A)
E = Easy, A = Average, C = Challenging

Essay Questions

16. (Easy) *Guidelines for student response:* Students should note that the sensory language in Passage 1 appeals to the senses of sight, hearing, smell, and touch; whereas the sensory language in Passage 2 appeals only to the sense of sight. They should quote examples of language appealing to each sense they mention. Students' descriptions of the scene they envision in Passage 1 should include Miyak, the sleeping wolves, and the fog. Descriptions of the scene students envision in Passage 2 should include the man standing on the trail; the gently rolling, snowy landscape; the dark, gloomy sky; and the long trail stretching in either direction, interrupted at intervals by groups of trees.

17. (Average) *Guidelines for student response:* Students' summaries of Passage 1 should include the following: Miyak wakes up feeling uneasy, but then relaxes; she comforts the wolf sleeping by her side; she wonders why the wolves aren't hunting; she notices the fog rolling in; she thinks about the fog and its meaning. Summaries of Passage 2 should include: a man leaves the trail and climbs a steep bank. His watch says 9:00 A.M., but the sky is dark and gloomy because there is little sunlight during the Arctic winter. From the top of the bank, he gazes at the long trail ahead, then at the long length of trail behind him, which he has already traveled. Students may say either passage captures their interest, so long as they give appropriate reasons. For example, some may say that Passage 1 makes them curious about how Miyak's relationship with the wolves will grow and change; others will be more interested in knowing what adventures might lie on the trail ahead for the man in Passage 2. Conversely, students may have varied reasons why one passage interests them less. For

example, some may say that the relationship between Miyak and the wolves in Passage 1 seems friendly and therefore will not lead to interesting conflicts; others may say that a solitary person walking along in a vast empty landscape is far from exciting.

18. (Challenging) *Guidelines for student response:* Students may predict any conflicts that are reasonable. For example, Miyak, in Passage 1, may have to battle hunger, hostile wolves, or humans who wish to harm her wolf friends; the man in Passage 2 may have to battle fatigue, freezing weather, attack by wild animals or other humans. Students should note that the personal qualities most likely to help Miyax, in Passage 1, are her ability to calm herself down when she feels uneasy; her interest in comforting others, even when she herself is feeling worried; and her ability to size up a situation, as she does when she uses what she knows about fog to answer her own question about why the wolves aren't hunting. The quality most likely to help the man in Passage 2 survive is his ability to remain completely calm and untroubled in the face of difficult circumstances. Students might cite as an example that he doesn't mind the lack of sun and shows no emotional reaction to the long trail either behind or ahead of him. Students should give an example of each personal quality they mention.

Unit 3: Proving Yourself

from *The Pigman & Me*
by Paul Zindel

Selection Test (p. 50)

Critical Reading/Vocabulary, Spelling, and Grammar

1. b 2. a 3. d 4. a 5. c 6. d 7. d 8. b
9. d 10. c 11. a 12. b 13. a 14. b 15. a
16. d 17. b 18. b 19. a 20. b

Questions are classified in these categories:
    Comprehension 1(E), 3(A), 10(C), 13(A)
    Interpretation 2(E), 5(C), 8(A), 12(A)
    Literary Analysis 4(A), 6(C), 9(E)
    Reading Strategy 7(A), 11(E)
    Vocabulary 15(C), 18(A), 20(A)
    Spelling 16(A)
    Grammar 14(C), 17(A), 19(E)
    E = Easy, A = Average, C = Challenging

Essay Questions

21. (Easy) *Guidelines for student response:* Students should include in their arguments that John should have thought of a better way of asking for the paddle. They should cite the passage in which John tells Paul to give him the paddle, rather than asks him: "Look, you *have* to give it to me." Students should also recognize that Paul should have exercised more self-control, even though he was nervous and frightened about his first days in a new school.

22. (Average) *Guidelines for student response:* Students might offer examples such as the following: getting a traffic ticket in a foreign country where one doesn't know the traffic regulations; appearing to have bad table manners at a home of a friend whose culture is different; getting detention for breaking a school rule of which a new student is unaware. Their examples should support the main idea of the essay: It is important to find out the rules and laws that apply to any new situation.

23. (Challenging) *Guidelines for student response:* Students might suggest alternatives such as the following: Paul publicly apologizes to John; Paul offers to do John an important favor; Paul offers to accept an official punishment, such as detention after school or loss of a privilege for a set amount of time. Students should reflect an awareness that there is always an alternative to physical violence.

"Thunder Butte"
by Virginia Driving Hawk Sneve

Selection Test (p. 53)

Critical Reading/Vocabulary, Spelling, and Grammar

1. a   2. d   3. c   4. c   5. c   6. d   7. b   8. b
9. b   10. a   11. c   12. a   13. a.   14. a
15. d   16. b   17. c   18. b   19. a   20. c

Questions are classified in these categories:
    Comprehension 2(A), 7(C), 13(E)
    Interpretation 4(A), 5(C), 8(A), 10(C), 14(E)
    Literary Analysis 1(A), 6(E), 9(A), 11(E)
    Reading Strategy 3(C), 12(E), 15(A)
    Vocabulary 16(A), 19(E)
    Spelling 17(A)
    Grammar 18(E), 20(A)
    E = Easy, A = Average, C = Challenging

Essay Questions

21. (Easy) *Guidelines for student response:* Students should show that Norman feels two ways about the ancient customs of his people. On the one hand, Norman obeys his grandfather's wishes, he feels uneasy every time he hears the thunder rumble, and he laughs nervously when he thinks his grandfather is suggesting that the coup stick is *Wakan,* or haunted. On the other hand, Norman says that the only message from the thunder is that a storm is coming, he scoffs at the coup stick, and points out to his grandfather that he would be thrown in jail if he used it.

22. (Average) *Guidelines for student response:* Students may express either opinion in their essays. They should back up their ideas with concrete examples, such as, "Traditions make people feel connected to others in their group" or "Keeping traditions may cause people to mistrust or dislike people in other cultures with different traditions."

23. (Challenging) *Guidelines for student response:* Students should point out Norman's father's respect for the old ways of his people. They should also point out that Sarah feels two ways. On the one hand, she thinks the old traditions are superstitious and "heathen." On the other hand, she seems to acknowledge some sort of power in the coup stick by her apparent fear of the object.

"Mowgli's Brothers"
by Rudyard Kipling

Selection Test (p. 56)

Critical Reading/Vocabulary, Spelling, and Grammar

1. d   2. c   3. c   4. a   5. d   6. a   7. c   8. b
9. d   10. a   11. b   12. a   13. c   14. b   15. b
16. a   17. a   18. c   19. d   20. b

Questions are classified in these categories:
    Comprehension 2(C), 6(A), 15(E)
    Interpretation 1(C), 4(E), 7(A), 11(C)
    Literary Analysis 5(A), 8(E), 10(C), 13(A)
    Reading Strategy 3(C), 9(A), 12(E), 14(E)
    Vocabulary 17(E), 20(A)
    Spelling 18(A)
    Grammar 16(A), 19(E)
    E = Easy, A = Average, C = Challenging

Essay Questions

21. (Easy) *Guidelines for student response:* Students might predict that a conflict will arise between Mowgli and Shere Khan, based on Mother Wolf's words to Shere Khan, ". . . he shall hunt thee"; that Mowgli will never harm any of the jungle animals, based on Baloo's words, "There is no harm in a man's cub"; that Mowgli will help the Pack, based on Akela's words, "He may be a help in time"; or that Akela will eventually be killed, based on the words, "He was thinking of the time that comes to every leader of every pack when . . . he is killed by the wolves and a new leader comes up . . . ."

22. (Average) *Guidelines for student response:* Students comparing Mother Wolf and Father Wolf might write that both characters are good parents, based on descriptions in the story of how they take care of their cubs; they might say that Mother Wolf is more fierce than Father Wolf, based on Mother Wolf's words to Shere Khan regarding Mowgli. Students comparing Bagheera and Baloo might suggest that Baloo speaks for Mowgli out of kindness and compassion, based on his words at the Pack Council, whereas Bagheera is clever, as he buys Mowgli's life hoping that Mowgli will grow up to kill Shere Khan. They might quote the author's descriptions of each character to show that Baloo is harmless, while

"Mowgli's Brothers" by Rudyard Kipling
(continued)

Bagheera is dangerous. Students comparing Shere Khan and Tabaqui might use plot events to show that both characters are greedy and will disobey the Law of the Jungle to get what they want; they might show that Tabaqui is willing to act humble and self-abasing in order to get scraps of food, whereas Shere Khan is aggressive and wants the most dangerous prey of all, Man.

23. (Challenging) *Guidelines for student response:* As pros, students may write that, because Mowgli is human, he may be able to help defend the Pack against humans when he grows up; that he may be able to defend the Pack against other animals when he grows up; that he may be able to teach the animals some of Man's wisdom. As cons, students may write that Mowgli might go back to the world of humans when he grows up and become a skilled hunter since he will know the ways of the animals, or that the Pack is endangering Mowgli's life by exposing him to the fury of Shere Khan. Depending on the number and strength of their pros and cons, students may decide either that the Pack should or should not accept Mowgli.

"Names/Nombres" by Julia Alvarez
"The Southpaw" by Judith Viorst
"Alone in the Nets" by Arnold Adoff

Selection Test (p. 59)

Critical Reading/Vocabulary, Spelling, and Grammar

1. d 2. c 3. c 4. b 5. c 6. b 7. c 8. c
9. a 10. a 11. d 12. c 13. b 14. d 15. d
16. b 17. c 18. c 19. a 20. a

Questions are classified in these categories:
Comprehension 6(A), 10(C), 12(E)
Interpretation 1(A), 2(E), 5(A), 9(C)
Literary Analysis 3(C), 4(A), 8(A), 14(E)
Reading Strategy 7(A), 11(E), 13(C)
Vocabulary 15(E), 19(A)
Spelling 16(A), 18(A)
Grammar 17(C), 20(A)

Essay Questions

21. (Easy) *Guidelines for student response:* Students who choose "Names/Nombres" might describe the friendly nicknames that Julia adopts and her preference at one point for the name Judy because it helped her blend in with her friends. Students who choose "The Southpaw" should describe Janet's efforts to join a baseball team that doesn't include girls. In their descriptions, they might cite such details as her remarks that the team is having a bad season and her explanation of her own skills.

22. (Average) *Guidelines for student response:* Students who choose "Names/Nombres" should explain how the account helped them see an event such as the family's arrival in the United States or Julia's high-school graduation from Julia's point of view. They also should discuss their own reactions to the event that they cite. Students who choose "The Southpaw" should point out that we see the disagreement about whether Janet should play on the team from both Janet and Richard's point of view. They should reconstruct the argument that prompts the exchange of letters as well as offer their own reactions. Students who choose "Alone in the Nets" should point out that we see a soccer game from the perspective of a player who wrestles with her self-doubts but who rises above them to do well in a critical moment. They should summarize the situation and react to the thoughts and feelings that the speaker shares.

23. (Challenging) *Guidelines for student response:* Students should point out that in "Names/Nombres" Julia Alvarez experiences several changes in her perspective on the way that people react to her, her Dominican family, and their names. For example, for the first few years after her arrival in the United States, she feels a desire to be known by her correct Dominican name. By the time she is in high school she finds this desire fading; instead, she wants to be known as Judy so that she will fit in with the "Sallys" and "Janes" in her class.

In "The Southpaw," both Richard and Janet experience changes in their perspectives. Each softens his or her position somewhere around the middle of the correspondence; this change makes it possible for them to be friends again by the end of the story. In "Alone in the Nets," the unnamed goalie is uncertain, even self-doubting, as she watches the action on the field. She is detached from it. A turning point comes, however, when we read, "But Frozen Moments Can Unfreeze . . ." The goalie realizes that she does have a part to play in the game; and as the action rushes toward her in the critical moment, she confidently takes action and gets the save.

"Adventures of Isabel" by Ogden Nash
"I'll Stay" by Gwendolyn Brooks
"Wilbur Wright and Orville Wright" by Rosemary and Stephen Vincent Benét
"Dream Dust" by Langston Hughes

Selection Test (p. 62)

Critical Reading/Vocabulary, Spelling, and Grammar

1. d 2. a 3. d 4. a 5. c 6. b 7. a 8. d
9. c 10. b 11. c 12. d 13. b 14. d 15. a
16. a 17. b 18. c 19. c 20. d

Questions are classified in these categories:
  Comprehension 2(E), 9(A), 10(A)
  Interpretation 1(A), 3(A), 4(C), 7(E)
  Literary Analysis 5(C), 12(A), 13(E)
  Reading Strategy 6(A), 8(E), 11(C)
  Vocabulary 14(A), 16(E), 18(C)
  Spelling 20(A)
  Grammar 15(C), 17(A), 19(E)

Essay Questions

21. (Easy) *Guidelines for student response:* Students should show awareness that each poem is a model for success based on confidence and self-esteem. Isabel's secret of success is her fearlessness, shown by the way she defeats each challenger in the poem; the speaker's in "I'll Stay" is her confidence that there is always "something/to be done about everything," and her efficiency in getting things done; the speaker in "Dream Dust" is the empowerment that comes from cherishing one's

dreams; the Wright brothers' is their perseverance and their devotion and loyalty to each other.

22. (Average) *Guidelines for student response:* Students' essays should show that they appreciate the "Adventures of Isabel" as a "take-off" on the traditional fairy tale. Each of the first three stanzas begins with Isabel's conflict with an evil magical character, as happens in many fairy tales. Each stanza, however, ends with Isabel calmly and efficiently defeating her enemy with no drama, no fuss, no bother. In most fairy tales, the main character triumphs in the end, but usually after much difficulty, clever planning, or outside assistance.

23. (Challenging) *Guidelines for student response:* In their essays, students should include that Hughes considers dreams among a person's most precious possessions, citing as support that dream-dust, as opposed to "star-dust, earth-dust, cloud-dust, storm-dust, and splinters of hail," is "Not for sale." Whether students agree or disagree with Hughes's assessment of dreams, they should support their opinions with well-reasoned arguments and/or examples from experience or literature.

Unit Test (p. 65)

Critical Reading/Vocabulary, Spelling, and Grammar

1. c 2. a 3. d 4. a 5. b 6. c 7. a 8. c
9. d 10. c 11. b 12. a 13. d 14. d 15. a
16. b 17. c 18. a 19. b 20. d 21. b
22. c 23. a 24. d 25. c 26. a 27. b
28. d 29. b 30. a

Questions are classified in these categories:
  Comprehension 2(E), 6(A), 8(C), 12(A), 15(A)
  Interpretation 3(A), 5(C), 9(E), 11(C), 16(A), 17(E), 19(A)
  Literary Analysis 1(A), 7(E), 14(C)
  Reading Strategy 4(A), 10(A), 13(E), 18(C)
  Vocabulary 21(C), 24(E), 28(C)
  Spelling 22(A), 26(E), 29(C)
  Grammar 20(A), 23(C), 25(E), 27(C), 30(A)

Essay Questions

31. (Easy) *Guidelines for student response:* Students might observe that Paul in *The Pigman & Me* feels that he must prove

himself by not looking like a coward, despite his reluctance to fight. He manages to overcome his fear and have a fight of sorts, and, when John, his opponent, declares himself satisfied, he seems to have proven himself. The fact that his big sister is willing to defend him suggests that it is unlikely that anyone will pick on Paul in the future, another sign of his acceptance into his new school. In "Thunder Butte," Norman must prove himself by making a frightening climb because his grandfather has dreamed that he would do so. Despite some nervousness, he overcomes his fears and succeeds. Julia in "Names/Nombres" feels herself caught between two cultures and not quite accepted by the one in which she lives, that of the United States. Unlike Paul and Norman, she does not face a single test in order to gain acceptance. Instead, over a period she finds a way to honor both the heritage of her ancestry and the culture into which she has been brought. She is able both to cherish and love her family and its traditions and to live happily within her larger community.

32. (Average) *Guidelines for student response:* Students may say that the speaker of "Alone in the Nets"shows that people have inner resources that they may call upon to overcome a problem or threat. The speaker of "I'll Stay" exemplifies a quality that is essential to taking on whatever obstacles and challenges we meet: that of total self-confidence. Such an attitude tends to give people more of what it takes to accomplish their goals. The speaker in "Dream Dust" suggests that we need dreams, and students may see that message as a hope in times of challenge. "Wilbur Wright and Orville Wright" is a tribute to another valuable trait when we need to prove ourselves: determination. We are most likely to achieve that which we set out to do if, like the Wright Brothers, we do not let temporary setbacks and unexpected snags discourage us.

33. (Average) *Guidelines for student response:* Students might write that Paul in *The Pigman & Me* wants to be accepted by the other students at his new school. Failure to do so would lead to a sense of isolation and vulnerability to bullying. Students should grasp the importance any new arrival would place on being accepted by schoolmates. Mowgli in "Mowgli and His Brothers" does not really understand the importance of being accepted into the wolf pack because he is too young. But the issue of acceptance is, for him, a matter of life and death; if he is not accepted, he has no protectors and will certainly be the prey of a tiger, panther, or other predator. While he cannot be said to have done anything to be accepted by the pack, the issue of acceptance for Mowgli is the most vital one in all of these selections. In "Thunder Butte," Norman wants to be accepted as an authentic heir of the culture from which he comes by meeting the expectations of this grandfather, who represents that heritage. While acceptance is not a life-and-death matter, it has great enough significance for Norman to put himself at risk to gain it.

34. (Average) *Guildelines for student response:* Students may say that Paul in *The Pigman & Me* shows very little confidence. The prospect of either fighting or appearing cowardly makes him a nervous wreck. But he does demonstrate sufficient self-reliance; he wills himself to show up for the fight and has the wit to stay down once he has been hit. Mowgli is certainly the most self-confident of these characters because he is too little to understand the dangers he faces. He neither feels nor shows fear at any time. However, he is also the least self-reliant of all the characters, since he is little more than a baby, completely unequipped at this point to exist on his own. Janet in "The Southpaw" shows herself to be confident of her ability to play ball with Richard's team and angry that ability will not be the criterion by which she is to be judged. Also, she ex-

habits self-reliance in the way in which she bargains with Richard (and yields on one small point as a concession). She shows herself more confident and self-reliant than Paul and more self-aware than Mowgli.

35. (Challenging) *Guidelines for student response:* Students should point out that, since *The Pigman & Me* is a first-person narrative, the author can write vividly about Paul's thoughts and feelings. The author takes pains to describe that nervousness and the agony Paul suffers at the thought of taking part in a fight in public. "Thunder Butte," a third-person narrative, also describes the emotions of the central character, pointing out times when Norman is tempted to play it safe and not follow his grandfather's explicit (and sometimes risky) instructions. This author also makes use of vivid description, such as the sheer drop that Norman must make at one point. By stressing the difficulty and danger involved in Norman's climb, the author emphasizes the importance Norman places on passing this test. This is the only story in the grouping in which a character takes physical risks. "Names/Nombres," another first-person narrative, focuses, like *The Pigman & Me,* on the thoughts and feelings of the central character. But unlike *The Pigman & Me,* which deals with a single incident, "Names/Nombres" is about a long-term challenge: that of finding a balance between Julia's family heritage and her desire to be accepted in the world in which she now lives.

Alternative Unit Test (p. 69)

Critical Reading

1. a   2. d   3. b   4. e   5. c   6. a   7. c   8. b
9. d   10. e   11. a   12. b   13. c   14. e   15. d

Questions are classified in these categories:
  Comprehension 13(C), 15(A)
  Interpretation 7(A), 9(A), 10(C), 12(E)
  Literary Analysis 1(A), 3(E), 5(C), 11(E), 14(A)

Reading Strategy 2(A), 4(C), 6(A), 8(E)
E=Easy, A=Average, C=Challenging

Essay Questions

16. (Easy) *Guidelines for student response:* Students should relate an experience with an animal in detail. Their explanations of how the experience enriches their understanding of Passage 1 might mention learning of an animal's shyness, trying to gain the trust of an animal, observing an animal in the wild; explanations with regard to Passage 2 might mention knowledge of pet-training techniques, observing birds, or being patient with a pet. Accept all explanations that make sense.

17. (Average) *Guidelines for student response:*   Students should conclude that the author of Passage 1 includes details of a more isolated and natural area than does the author of Passage 2, who includes allusions to a more populated place. Examples of the natural atmosphere in Passage 1 might include the following: "Red foxes also live on the island...," "...to find a fox pup sitting in the middle of my strawberries,..." "...dazzling February snow..." "...a hanging birch log studded with suet for the woodpeckers," "a wild animal out in the open...," "steel-jaw leghold traps," "...limped off into the woods." Examples of the domestic atmosphere in Passage 2 might include: "...the suitcases were unpacked and the fresh sheets spread on all the sun-aired beds...," "She would bring a pillow and sit in the yard...," "voices laughing at the creek's edge...."

18. (Challenging) *Guidelines for student response:* Students' descriptions of the relationship between the narrator and the fox in Passage 1 should include that the narrator is trying to earn the trust of an animal; their descriptions of the relationship between June and Zander in Passage 2 should include that June is trying to teach the falcon how to do something, or that she is trying to gain control over the falcon. Broader meanings for Passage 1 should include that it takes patience, kindness, and gentleness to deserve a person's trust; for Passage 2, that it takes patience and determination to be a good teacher or to convince someone to do as you wish.

Unit 4: Seeing It Through

"Lob's Girl" by Joan Aiken
"The Tiger Who Would Be King"
by James Thurber
"The Lion and the Bulls" by Aesop

Selection Test (p. 73)

Critical Reading/Vocabulary, Spelling, and Grammar

1. d 2. b 3. d 4. a 5. d 6. c 7. a 8. c
9. a 10. d 11. d 12. b 13. d 14. a 15. d
16. c 17. a 18. b 19. c 20. b

Questions are classified in these categories:
Comprehension 1(C), 6(E), 7 (E), 10(A)
Interpretation 2(A), 4(E), 6(C), 12(C), 13(A)
Literary Analysis 3(A), 5(E), 9(C), 14(E)
Reading Strategy 8(C), 11(E), 15(A)
Vocabulary 18(A), 20(E)
Spelling 17(A)
Grammar 16(A), 19(C)
E = Easy, A = Average, C = Challenging

Essay Questions

21. (Easy) *Guidelines for student response:* Students should include in their descriptions that Lob is a young, lively, friendly German shepherd with topaz eyes, black-tipped pointy ears, thick, soft fur, and a bushy black-tipped tail. They should recognize loyalty as Lob's most important quality and cite the way he keeps coming back to Sandy—even after death.

22. (Average) *Guidelines for student response:* Students may observe that, from the moment Lob first sees Sandy, he overcomes all obstacles to be with her. The obstacles grow greater through the story: he first goes from one end of the town to the other; he walks 400 miles from Liverpool to the Pengelly home twice, suffering a few injuries the second time; he finally overcomes death itself for a final visit.

23. (Challenging) *Guidelines for student response:* Students should note that, in addition to having his animal characters speak, Thurber takes a humorous approach, while Aesop is more serious. While both writers teach moral lessons, Thurber encourages readers to laugh at

his animals and the human weaknesses they illustrate.

"Greyling" by Jane Yolen

Selection Test (p. 76)

Critical Reading/Vocabulary, Spelling, and Grammar

1. d 2. b 3. d 4. b 5. c 6. d 7. d 8. d
9. b 10. b 11. b 12. c 13. a 14. a 15. c
16. c 17. b 18. a 19. b 20. c

Questions are classified in these categories:
Comprehension 3(C), 7(A), 11(E)
Interpretation 1(A), 2(E), 5(A), 9(C)
Literary Analysis 4(C), 6(E), 10(A), 13(A)
Reading Strategy 8(C), 12(A)
Vocabulary 15(E), 18(E), 20(A)
Spelling 17(C), 19(E)
Grammar Skill 14(C), 16(A)

Essay Questions

21. (Easy) *Guidelines for student response:* Students may note that they didn't predict the fisherman's wife would want to keep a seal, because she really wanted a child. Finding out that the seal takes the form of a human child might make them change this prediction. They might write that knowing how much Greyling longs for the sea made them predict that he would eventually become a seal again. Students might explain that making predictions made them want to keep on reading to find out if their predictions were correct.

22. (Average) *Guidelines for student response:* Students may answer that the fisherman's wife expresses her grief, crying and complaining, while the fisherman keeps his feelings to himself. When faced with the conflict of deciding to keep Greyling or not, the fisherman's wife decides right away that Greyling will never go back to the sea. The fisherman agrees with her decision but inside he feels bad. In the end they are more alike than unalike because they both learn to accept Greyling's return to the sea.

23. (Challenging) *Guidelines for student response:* Students may note that Greyling feels torn between returning to the sea and staying with his parents. The storm increases his conflict because he wants to save the fisherman but knows that if he goes into the sea, he will never come back. When he decides to rescue the fisherman, he resolves this conflict. He will no longer miss the sea. Students may predict that Greyling will later have conflicting feelings about leaving his parents, or that he will find himself in other situations in which he can't decide whether he prefers being a human or a seal.

"Abuelito Who" by Sandra Cisneros
"The Open Road" by Walt Whitman
"Life Doesn't Frighten Me"
by Maya Angelou
"who knows if the moon's"
by E. E. Cummings

Selection Test (p. 79)

Critical Reading/Vocabulary, Spelling, and Grammar

1. c 2. d 3. c 4. b 5. a 6. b 7. a 8. c
9. c 10. d 11. b 12. a 13. d 14. a 15. c
16. b 17. d 18. c 19. c 20. b

Questions are classified in these categories:
- Comprehension 7(A), 12(A)
- Interpretation 3(C), 5(E), 8(A), 9(A), 13(C), 14(A)
- Literary Analysis 1(A), 2(E), 6(C)
- Reading Strategy 4(A), 10(E), 11(C)
- Vocabulary 15(E), 20(A)
- Spelling 17(A)
- Grammar 16(C), 18(A), 19(E)

Essay Questions

21. (Easy) *Guidelines for student response:* Students who choose "Abuelito Who" might say that the image "throws coins like rain" leads to the inference that Abuelito was generous and that the image "talks to me inside my head" leads to the inference that Abuelito lives on in the speaker's mind. Students who choose "who knows if the moon's" might write that the image "flowers pick themselves" leads to the inference that everything is perfect in the "keen city"; students who choose "The Open Road" might say that the line "Done with indoor complaints, libraries, querulous criticisms" leads to the inference that the speaker intends to become independent of other people's ideas and values. Students who choose "Life Doesn't Frighten Me" might cite images such as "mean old Mother Goose" and "(Kissy little girls/With their hair in curls)" as leading to the inference that even seemingly wholesome things may have their frightening side—but it's a side that doesn't frighten the speaker.

22. (Average) *Guidelines for student response:* Students should note the following ideas: "Abuelito Who" relates to the theme "New Roads to Follow" by considering how the speaker's life will be changed by the loss of Abuelito; "who knows if the moon's" relates to the theme by presenting an imagined voyage out of ordinary, everyday experience; "The Open Road" relates to the theme by sharing with the readers the speaker's feelings about liberating oneself from concerns, such as other people's criticisms and complaints, and becoming more confident and self-directed. "Life Doesn't Frighten Me" expresses the idea that one can walk the road of life without fear of any of the things that traditionally might inspire fear.

23. (Challenging) *Guidelines for student response:* Students who choose "Abuelito Who" might say that the repetition of the words "rain" and "coins" at the beginning and end of the poem emphasizes Abuelito's generosity and the fact that he will always be part of the speaker's life, since at the end, he is "the rain on the roof that falls like coins." The repetition of the words "who loves him" emphasizes the speaker's love for Abuelito. Students who choose "who knows if the moon's" might say that the repetition of the words "pretty people" and "keen city" emphasizes the idea that the place in the speaker's imagination is better and different than reality. Students who choose "The Open Road" might say that the repeated words "no more" emphasize that the speaker is making an important change in life. Students who choose

"Abuelito Who" by Sandra Cisneros

"The Open Road" by Walt Whitman

"Life Doesn't Frighten Me" by Maya Angelou

"who knows if the moon's"
by E. E. Cummings
(continued)

"Life Doesn't Frighten Me" should discuss how the title of the poem is repeated throughout to emphasize the speaker's determination.

"A Backwoods Boy"
by Russell Freedman
"Jackie Robinson: Justice at Last"
by Geoffrey C. Ward and Ken Burns

Selection Test (p. 82)

Critical Reading/Vocabulary, Spelling, and Grammar

1. b 2. d 3. a 4. d 5. c 6. a 7. b 8. a
9. d 10. c 11. a 12. b 13. b 14. d 15. a
16. d 17. c 18. b 19. a 20. d

Questions are classified in these categories:
Comprehension 1(C), 7(A), 10(E), 13(A)
Interpretation 3(E), 5(A), 9(C), 12(E), 15(A)
Literary Analysis 4(E), 8(A), 14(C)
Reading Strategy 2(A), 6(E), 11(A)
Vocabulary 17(E), 20(A)
Spelling 18(E)
Grammar 16(A), 19(C)
E = Easy, A = Average, C = Challenging

Essay Questions

21. (Easy) *Guidelines for student response:* Students should name such people as Lincoln's father, mother, and stepmother or Jackie Robinson's boss, Branch Rickey. For "A Backwoods Boy," they should cite examples that show Thomas Lincoln's ability to get along with people, his mother's and stepmother's love and support, and friends who gave him advice and loaned him books. For "Justice at Last," they might point to Rickey's advice and support, as well as his faith in Robinson; the fans' love and loyalty; and the Dodgers' acceptance of Robinson and respect for him as a teammate.

22. (Average) *Guidelines for student response:* Students may note that Lincoln faced such obstacles as poverty, rootlessness, a poor education, failure, and a way of life that put little value on learning or self-improvement. Examples they might cite to show how Lincoln overcame these obstacles include the many jobs he took to earn money, his settling in New Salem and becoming an important member of the community, and his constant pursuit of reading and learning to better himself and eventually become a lawyer.

23. (Challenging) *Guidelines for student response:* Students may express both the opinion that Robinson would have won respect more quickly or found it harder to be accepted as a black in the major leagues. The second part of the question should be based on their opinions and should be backed by serious thinking and possibly personal experience.

Unit Test (p. 85)

Critical Reading/Vocabulary, Spelling, and Grammar

1. d 2. c 3. a 4. c 5. b 6. d 7. c 8. b
9. a 10. c 11. c 12. b 13. a 14. d 15. d
16. c 17. c 18. d 19. b 20. b 21. a
22. d 23. c 24. b 25. d 26. a 27. b
28. c 29. b 30. d

Questions are classified in these categories:
Comprehension: 5(A), 6(A), 11(C), 18(A)
Interpretation 2(E), 4(C), 9(A), 13(A), 15(A), 17(E)
Literary Analysis 1(E), 7(A), 12(C), 16(E), 19(C)
Reading Strategy 3(A), 8(E), 10(C), 14(C)
Vocabulary 21(A), 24(E), 27(A), 29(A)
Spelling 22(A), 26(E)
Grammar 20(A), 23(A), 25(E), 28(C), 30(C)
E = Easy, A = Average, C = Challenging

Essay Questions

31. (Easy) *Guidelines for student response:* Students may note that Lob originally overcomes physical and geographical challenges when he twice walks "the length of England" to be with Sandy. Ultimately, it seems that he overcomes death itself to be with her one more time. Students should see that Lincoln has to overcome poverty and a lack of formal education. They may point to his determination, willingness to work hard, and strong moral values as

virtues that help him succeed. Jackie Robinson must deal with deeply rooted racial prejudice, expressed in baseball's ban on African Americans in the major leagues and in the hostility of many players and fans. The qualities that are most important to him are determination to break the race barrier, iron self-control to avoid responding inappropriately to the hostility he faces, and the exceptional athletic ability that, along with his strength of character, eventually brings players and fans around to his side. In all three cases, determination is an important factor in overcoming hardships.

32. (Average) *Guidelines for student response:* The speaker of "Life Doesn't Frighten Me," says that nothing in real life is frightening; only sometimes, in dreams, does he or she get scared. The character trait that helps the speaker stay unafraid is self-confidence; the speaker *knows* that he or she has the inner strength to face up to any scary encounter. That confidence is shown by the repeated insistence that "life doesn't frighten me at all." The speaker of "who knows if the moon's" maintains a positive attitude toward life by focusing on a lovely fantasy instead of reality. While the speaker may conceivably have moments of worry, there is no indication of it in the poem. In "The Open Road," the speaker is also positive; the open road to the future seems to contain nothing but hope and excitement. These poems stress that self-confidence and a positive approach to life are qualities that help people maintain an optimistic attitude.

33. (Average) *Guidelines for student response:* In "The Lion and the Bulls," fear is the weapon that the lion uses. By spreading lies, he encourages the bulls to fear and mistrust each other; and when that fear drives them apart, they become easy prey. The lesson in the fable could be "Do not let fear drive you apart from those who can help you." The title character in "Greyling" has an inexplicable longing for the sea, but he has been warned to keep away from it. He probably must overcome some amount of fear to rescue the fisherman. The story's lesson about fear might

be "Sometimes the only way to solve a problem is to set one's fears aside." The speaker in "The Open Road" rejoices that he has set aside his fears of people who do not agree with him and looks forward to traveling the road ahead with a light heart. The poem's lesson might be "The best way to travel through life is to reject one's fear of other people." A similar lesson can be taken from "Life Doesn't Frighten Me," in which the speaker has learned that the best way for her to live is not to be afraid—even of the things that often do frighten people. The title character in "Jackie Robinson: Justice at Last" chooses to act in spite of his fear of prejudice when he agrees to integrate the Major Leagues; his lesson might be "You can achieve great things for others if you do not let your own fears hold you back."

34. (Average) *Guidelines for student response:* Students should recognize that Greyling undergoes a physical metamorphosis. He takes up a life in which he changes to a seal when he is in the water, and back into a human being when on land. As a human being, he loves and cares about his human parents, but he never loses his love of the sea. Greyling retains elements of both land and sea creature at all times. Lincoln's metamorphosis is from an unschooled, poverty-stricken boy into an educated lawyer and successful politician. Students may realize that Lincoln had inner qualities that made his transformation possible: the will to work hard and long and a determination to better himself.

35 (Challenging) *Guidelines for student response:* The challenge faced by Lob in "Lob's Girl" is that of being with Sandy, the person he loves most in the world. The author shows Lob's strength of will by describing increasingly difficult hardships Lob faces to join Sandy—from walking a few miles, to walking 400 miles, to overcoming death itself. Greyling has to resist an increasingly powerful urge that attracts him to the sea in order to remain with his parents. He succeeds in doing so until he is forced back into the sea to rescue his father, but by that point his parents are able to let him follow his instincts. The author of "Abuelito

Who" suggests that the speaker is having difficulty coming to terms with her grandfather's death. Everything she says about him is in present tense, as if he were still alive. Much of the poem is a list of details of his life that are dear to her. Even when she mentions the details that indicate his death, she talks about it in a roundabout way: "too sad to come downstairs," "can't come out to play," "doesn't live here anymore," and so on. In "Jackie Robinson: Justice at Last," the author uses historical background to show the challenge that Robinson faces in breaking the racial barrier in major league baseball. He also goes into some detail about the abuse Robinson is subjected to during his first year with the Brooklyn Dodgers.

Alternative Unit Test (p. 89)

Critical Reading

1.a 2. d 3. b 4. c 5. a 6. e 7. a 8. d
9. b 10. c 11. e 12. b 13. c 14. e 15. d

Questions are classified in these categories:
Comprehension 2(A), 7(A), 15(C)
Interpretation 1(A), 5(C), 9(C), 13(E)
Literary Analysis 3(C), 6(E), 10(A), 12(A)
Reading Strategy 4(A), 8(C), 11(E), 14(A)
E = Easy, A = Average, C = Challenging

Essay Questions

16. (Easy) *Guidelines for student response:* Students should recognize that, in Passage 1, Joseph starts to play because he and Martine have a long night ahead of them and are too concerned about Rousa to sleep. He plays to help them relax during their vigil. Joseph has been playing for at least fifty years, so it is likely that his music is an essential part of their lives. Students may be able to see that the detail about music being about survival is a clue that music may help them get through a difficult time. In Passage 2, Papa's fiddle playing seems to be something he does often, if not every evening. Dog is clearly his constant companion in these sessions, and, as in Passage 1, music is

seen as central to the life of the character. In both instances, music is more than a pastime—it is an important means of expressing and influencing feelings.

17. (Average) *Guidelines for student response:* Students should note that, in Passage 1, Martine and Joseph are faced with a crisis that they must deal with: their cow has fallen and appears to be seriously, perhaps fatally, injured. This is a source of distress for them, in part because cows are valuable animals, for milk, meat, or both, and in part because Martine, and possibly Joseph, feels badly for Rousa's being in pain. For these two, "seeing it through" means getting through a long, cold, unpleasant night. No such crisis occurs in Passage 2. Papa plays his fiddle, and the reader gets the impression that he does this every night, or on many nights. His only companion—or the only one in the passage—is Dog. For Papa, then, "seeing it through" would apply in a more general sense, to making his way through life as best he can, with the help of his music and his pet. Unlike Passage 1, which involves a specific and painful situation, Passage 2 deals with the way in which this particular man spends much, perhaps all, of his leisure time.

18. (Challenging) *Guidelines for student response:* Students may point out that music can be a way of expressing emotions, and also of affecting emotions, often for the better. In Passage 1, Joseph's playing might be a way of helping Martene and himself to lift their spirits to get through a crisis. To play a mouth-organ (students may know that this is another word for "harmonica"), the player must move his hands with precision and delicacy. The image of "smoothing and ruffling" might apply to Joseph's hand movements—most likely quite refined after fifty years of playing—and to the piping sound of the mouth-organ, which could be compared to the music of a songbird. In Passage 2, "music of melting sky" might suggest the slurred sounds of a country fiddle. While Papa plays, the moon is rising, and he is probably outdoors. "Melting sky" is an image not based on reality, but

one which suggests that Papa's music has a haunting and mysterious quality. The language in both passages is designed to show that music involves depths of feeling and can conjure up complex feelings. The language used in either passage could easily have been applied to the musician in the other passage.

Unit 5: Mysterious Worlds

"The Fun They Had"
by Isaac Asimov

Selection Test (p. 93)

Critical Reading/Vocabulary, Spelling, and Grammar

1. d 2. b 3. b 4. d 5. c 6. d 7. a 8. a
9. c 10. b 11. c 12. b 13. a 14. a 15. b
16. a 17. b 18. a 19. c 20. b

Questions are classified in these categories:
Comprehension 1(E), 11(A), 13(C)
Interpretation 3(E) 7(A), 8(A), 10(E), 15(C)
Literary Analysis 2(E), 4(C), 12(A)
Reading Strategy 5(C), 6(A), 9(E), 14(A)
Vocabulary 16(A), 17(E)
Spelling 18(A)
Grammar 19(A), 20(A)
E = Easy, A = Average, C = Challenging

Essay Questions

21. (Easy) *Guidelines for student response:* Students' essays should indicate awareness of such personality traits in the character of Margie as curiosity, sociability, and sensitivity to others. Appropriate responses to the cue questions about Margie's likes and dislikes include that she enjoys: being with other people (sociable), reading, history (intellectual curiosity); that she dislikes: being alone for much of the time, being taught by a computer, too much emphasis on grades. Responses to the question about her study and free time should reflect students' awareness that Margie would prefer learning in group situations and participating in social activities with peers.

22. (Average) *Guidelines for student response:* Students should choose a definite side of this issue and offer well-reasoned points in support of their views. Essays should include clearly stated topic sentences such as "Students learn best when they are in tradi-tional classrooms because they learn from each other as well as from the teacher" and "Students learn more by using computer programs because these programs can be repeated until the student has mastered all the necessary information."

23. (Challenging) *Guidelines for student response:* Students' essays should show awareness that by using the science fiction form, the author can strengthen his points by giving actual examples of the dangers of going too far in embracing technology. Essays should include appropriate details that back up this message, such as Margie's dislike and anxiety in her learning environment, the insensitivity of the computer to the needs of a child, and the isolation imposed by this sort of learning situation. Students' essays should use quotations and details from the story to support their ideas.

"A Dream Within a Dream"
by Edgar Allan Poe
"The Spring and the Fall"
by Edna St. Vincent Millay
"Ankylosaurus"
by Jack Prelutsky

Selection Test (p. 96)

Critical Reading/Vocabulary, Spelling, and Grammar

1. c 2. a 3. d 4. d 5. a 6. d 7. d 8. a
9. a 10. c 11. c 12. a 13. b 14. d 15. a
16. b 17. b 18. c 19. d 20. c

Questions are classified in these categories:
Comprehension 3(C), 9(A), 11(E)
Interpretation 1(C), 5(A), 8(C), 13(A)
Literary Analysis 2(A), 6(E), 7(E), 10(E)
Reading Strategy 4(A), 12(A)
Vocabulary 18(C), 19(A), 20(A)
Spelling 15(E), 17(A)
Grammar 14(C), 16(C)

"A Dream Within a Dream"
by Edgar Allan Poe
"The Spring and the Fall"
by Edna St. Vincent Millay

"Ankylosaurus" by Jack Prelutsky
(continued)

Essay Questions

21. (Easy) *Guidelines for student response:* Students who choose "A Dream Within a Dream" should include in their summaries that the speaker is crying about how nothing he loves in life lasts. Students might quote the lines "How few! yet how they creep / Through my fingers to the deep" to explain that the poet is comparing the grains of sand to the precious things in life. Students who choose "The Spring and the Fall" should include in their summaries that the speaker is sad, not only that love faded, but that it faded in such trivial ways. Students might support this with the line "He laughed at all I dared to praise," explaining that the speaker's beloved deliberately hurt the speaker's feelings. Students who choose "Ankylosaurus" should include in their summaries that the poet describes a dinosaur in an amusing way. They might quote the lines, "Clankity Clankity Clankity Clank! / Ankylosaurus was built like a tank," pointing out the humor in the repeated nonsense word "Clankity."

22. (Average) *Guidelines for student response:* Students who choose "A Dream Within a Dream" might cite the image "I stand amid the roar / Of a surf-tormented shore," explaining that, to the speaker, life is dangerous and threatening because it takes away all that is precious and lovely, just as the surf pounds the shore and drags the grains of sand out to sea. Those who choose "The Spring and the Fall" might cite the image "He broke me a bough of the blossoming peach / That was out of the way and hard to reach," explaining that, at that time, the beloved wanted to show how much he loved the speaker. Those who choose "Ankylosaurus" might cite the image "It waddled about on its four stubby legs / nibbling on plants with a mouthful of pegs," explaining that these lines are examples of the poet's

humorous view of Ankylosaurus. The image of a huge animal "built like a tank," walking around on "stubby" legs, and having teeth like "a mouthful of pegs" is entertaining and funny.

23. (Challenging) *Guidelines for student response:* Students might respond by writing that, in "The Spring and the Fall," the speaker is grieving over the loss of love. She focuses on the way in which love "went in little ways." They might say that in "A Dream Within a Dream," the speaker also grieves over parting from a loved one, but he is really expressing a pessimistic view of life: that none of the most precious things last but slip away like grains of sand.

from *Exploring the* Titanic
by Robert Ballard

Selection Test (p. 99)

1. a 2. d 3. c 4. a 5. b 6. c 7. c 8. b
9. c 10. a 11. d 12. a 13. b 14. c 15. a
16. b 17. d 18. d 19. b 20. a

Questions are classified in these categories:
  Comprehension 3(A), 6(A), 9(E), 13(A)
  Interpretation 11(E), 14(A)
  Literary Analysis 1(C), 4(C), 5(A), 8(A), 12(A)
  Reading Strategy 2(E), 7(E), 10(E)
  Vocabulary 15(C), 19(E)
  Spelling 17(A)
  Grammar 16(A), 18(E), 20(A)

Essay Questions

21. (Easy) *Guidelines for student response:* Students who choose Harold Bride might describe him as a young man who is glad to have his job on board. He is a hard worker and eager to please. Bride is aware of all the warnings and he delivers one to the captain himself. Bride remembers that the captain seemed unconcerned. Bride is asleep when the collision occurs. Students who choose to write about Captain Smith might note that the captain is the commander of the ship. The captain does not receive all the warnings and he does not seem concerned about the ones he does receive. He is in bed when the collision occurs, and he gets up and inspects the ship with the ship's builder.

22. (Average) *Guidelines for student response:* Students might write that when the first warning is received, the radio room is in confusion. The operators receive even more warnings: Some they deliver, some they don't. The captain seems unconcerned with the warnings. The passengers have no idea that the warnings are coming in. If the radio operators had been more persistent in reporting the warnings, and if the captain had taken them more seriously, perhaps the *Titanic* would not have had its fatal collision.

23. (Challenging) *Guidelines for student response:* Students might write that the author creates an atmosphere of suspense in many ways, such as the *Titanic*'s near-collision at the beginning of the story, the numerous iceberg warnings, and the passengers' ignorance of the seriousness of the collision. The warnings might have made students want to know if someone would respond or react in any way other than ignoring the warnings. Students might note that the passengers' ignorance made the scene more terrifying.

"Breaker's Bridge" by Laurence Yep

Selection Test (p. 102)

Critical Reading/Vocabulary, Spelling, and Grammar

1. c 2. a 3. b 4. d 5. c 6. a 7. d 8. b
9. b 10. a 11. a 12. b 13. c 14. d 15. d
16. b 17. a 18. c 19. d 20. c

Questions are classified in these categories:
Comprehension 1(A), 6(C), 12(E)
Interpretation 2(C), 4(C), 9(E), 13(A), 14(A)
Literary Analysis 3(A), 5(C), 8(E), 15(A)
Reading Strategy 7(A), 10(E), 11(A)
Vocabulary 17(E), 20(A)
Spelling 18(A)
Grammar 16(C), 19(E)
E = Easy, A = Average, C = Challenging

Essay Questions

21. (Easy) *Guidelines for student response:* Students' essays should point out times when Breaker showed his determination to build the bridge, such as when he built the two piers, tried to think of another plan when they were washed away, and threw

the pellets into the river, despite not believing in the old man's powers.

22. (Average) *Guidelines for student response:* Students should note that the emperor spares Breaker's life and seems to have become generous and understanding. They may either agree or disagree that he will be a better ruler. Students should back up their opinion with logical thinking and concrete examples from the story. For example, the old man tells the emperor, "We are all bound by the same laws." This insight may make the emperor more humble, more forgiving, and less inflexible.

23. (Challenging) *Guidelines for student response:* Students might point out that the river cannot be controlled by humans, as when the dam breaks, destroying the bridge's piers, and that human error, such as when Breaker crushes the pellet, must be allowed for. Students are free to agree or disagree with the statement. Those who agree may use the illustration of the changing of the seasons and the cyclical dying and rebirth of nature.

"The Loch Ness Monster" by George Laycock
"Why the Tortoise's Shell Is Not Smooth" by Chinua Achebe

Selection Test (p. 105)

Critical Reading/Vocabulary, Spelling, and Grammar

1. a 2. b 3. c 4. d 5. b 6. b 7. c 8. c
9. b 10. d 11. b 12. b 13. a 14. d 15. d
16. c 17. b 18. c 19. a 20. b

Questions are classified in these categories:
Comprehension 1(A), 3(A), 5(C), 9(E)
Interpretation 4(E), 6(C), 10(A), 13(A)
Literary Analysis 2(A), 8(C), 11(E)
Reading Strategy 7(C), 12(C), 14(A)
Vocabulary 15(A), 19(E)
Spelling 18(A)
Grammar 16(A), 17(A), 20(E)

Essay Questions

21. (Easy) *Guidelines for student response:* Students should explain one of the works in the selection that reflects the oral tradition; they should briefly define the oral

"The Loch Ness Monster" by George Laycock

"Why the Tortoise's Shell Is Not Smooth"

by Chinua Achebe

(continued)

tradition and cite specific passages and details to support their points. Students who choose "The Loch Ness Monster" should point out that the author mentions various tales of sightings that have been told over the years and that these belong to the oral tradition. Students who choose "Why the Tortoise's Shell Is Not Smooth" should point out that this and other folk tales are part of the oral tradition; in fact, the opening of the tale describes how it was passed along among family members.

22. (Average) *Guidelines for student response:* Students should identify the author's purpose in one of the works as well as cite details that helped them identify the purpose. Students who choose "The Loch Ness Monster" should recognize that the author's purpose it to inform readers about the scientific side of the search for the Loch Ness Monster and to explain the scientists' methods. Students who choose "Why the Tortoise's Shell Is Not Smooth" should recognize that the author's purpose is to entertain readers and to teach a lesson in life.

23. (Challenging) *Guidelines for student response:* Students should explain why it is important that traditional tales such as "Why the Tortoise's Shell Is Not Smooth" be preserved, clearly stating their reasons. For example, students might say that the tales should be preserved because they continue to entertain, continue to teach valuable lessons in life, and help us learn about and appreciate ancient and traditional cultures. Where appropriate, students should offer examples from the story to support or illustrate their reasons.

Unit Test (p. 108)

Critical Reading/Vocabulary, Spelling, and Grammar

1. d   2. c   3. b   4. d   5. a   6. d   7. b   8. a
9. a   10. b   11. c   12. b   13. c   14. a   15. d
16. d   17. a   18. c   19. b   20. d   21. a
22. b   23. a   24. c   25. a   26. d   27. b
28. d   29. c   30. a

Questions are classified in these categories:
Comprehension 4(C), 6(E), 11(A), 14(A), 17(E)
Interpretation 3(E), 5(A), 8(A), 10(C), 15(A), 19(A)
Literary Analysis 2(C), 12(A), 13(E), 18(A)
Reading Strategy 1(A), 7(A), 9(A), 16(C)
Vocabulary 21(A), 24(C), 27(A)
Spelling 22(E), 25(A), 29(C)
Grammar 20(A), 23(C), 26(E), 28(A), 30(A)
E = Easy, A = Average, C = Challenging

Essay Questions

31. (Easy) *Guidelines for student response:* In "The Loch Ness Monster," the mystery is the unsolved question of whether Nessie really exists, and, if so, what it is. It is an unsolved riddle that has fascinated people for a long time. *Exploring the* Titanic, however, gets its mystery from the use of suspense. Most readers know that the ship did sink; but as they read this selection, they eagerly look for the details of the event. They want to know what will happen next.

32. (Average) *Guidelines for student response:* Students may say that "A Dream Within a Dream" focuses on whether what we experience in the "real world" is actually real, or an illusion. Poe does not deal with what is usually thought of as the imaginary world in this poem; instead, he creates an atmosphere of uncertainty and questions whether *everything* that seems real to us is nothing more than a mirage.

33. (Average) *Guidelines for student response:* In "The Fun They Had," the students behave realistically and seem natural. The imaginary part is the author's picture of life as it might be in the future. Asimov takes technical advances of his own day and guesses what the world might be like if that technology progresses in a certain direction. His imaginary details make readers think about possible effects of progress on the way people live and think. "Breaker's Bridge" presents realistic characters in a realistic situation: Breaker will be executed unless he builds the emperor a bridge, despite huge obstacles. It is the old man who helps him who is the imaginary part of the story; it is through his magical powers that Breaker succeeds.

The author uses the old man to give the story a moral that both Breaker and the emperor need to hear—it is the nature of some things to remain as they are, while other things are meant to undergo change. "Why the Tortoise's Shell Is Not Smooth" starts with one realistic fact—that tortoise's shells are made of plates—rather than being one continuous piece. The story then offers an imaginary explanation for this fact involving talking animals and birds. It is like most traditional folktales in that it gives an imaginative explanation for facts that people could not explain otherwise.

34. (Average) *Guidelines for student response:* In "Ankylosaurus," the repetition of "Clankity Clankity Clankity Clank" at the beginning and end of the poem help create an amusing picture of a lumbering, stupid dinosaur, a cartoonish image that effectively adds to the poem's humor.

35. (Challenging) *Guidelines for student response:* Students who choose "The Fun They Had" should focus on the loss of a way of life—in this case, the personal enrichment that comes from being educated in a classroom, with its many opportunities for personal interaction. For "A Dream Within a Dream" or "The Spring and the Fall," students can explore the idea of lost love. Exploring the *Titanic* deals with a lost ship and lost people; students may review the selection's coverage of how both came to be lost. For "The Loch Ness Monster" (and perhaps for "Ankylosaurus"), students may consider the attempt to portray a creature that is lost to (or hiding from) modern eyes. Students who choose "Why the Tortoise's Shell Is Not Smooth" may focus on the loss of prestige that Tortoise suffers when his deception is discovered.

Alternative Unit Test (p. 112)

Critical Reading

1. b   2. d   3. c   4. e   5. a   6. d   7. c   8. b
9. b   10. a   11. d   12. a   13. c   14. b   15. d

Questions are classified in these categories:
Comprehension: 1(A), 3(E), 4(A), 13(A)
Interpretation: 9(E), 10(A) 12(C),
Literary Analysis: 5(C), 6(E), 8(A), 11(A), 14(A)
Reading Strategy: 2(E), 7(E), 15(C)
E = Easy, A = Average, C = Challenging

Essay Questions

16. (Easy) *Guidelines for student response:* Suspenseful details students might cite in Passage 1 include the following: "I had hidden my clothes and pack..." lets the reader know the narrator is about to do something in secret; "keyed up as I was" lets the reader know that the narrator is probably about to do something scary or dangerous; referring to a mysterious journey to strange lands, and mentioning unusual creatures ("the Tripods and the Caps") makes the reader nervous about what might happen during the journey and at the destination; the quiet house and the creaking of the stairs also create suspense, while the repetition of the word *carefully*, in "Carefully I opened the bedroom door, and carefully closed it after me," creates a feeling of stealth. Details students might cite in Passage 2 include the following: "When I do something that's pretty terrific" makes the reader wonder what is about to happen; Max's refusing to believe that the time machine will work makes the reader wonder who is right; the subject of time machines makes the reader wonder about what adventures the two characters might possibly have. Some students might find Passage 1 more suspenseful because of the suggestion of danger. Others might find the suggestion of a time-travel adventure in Passage 2 more suspenseful.

17. (Average) *Guidelines for student response:* Students should mention that both

characters have adventurous and coura-geous traits. The narrator of Passage 1 says of the journey that "the idea was exciting," and he is willing to take risks in order to gain his freedom. Steve, the narrator of Pas-sage 2, has purchased a time machine and seems, through the excitement implicit in his statement that he has done "something that's pretty terrific," to be willing to take the risk of trying out the machine in the hope of having a thrilling adventure. The characters differ in that the narrator of Passage 1 is more serious-minded, while Steve has a more humorous and light-hearted attitude toward life, evidenced by his speech, as in "Bravo! Fantastic! Way to go!" and "When have I ever lied to you?"

18. (Challenging) *Guidelines for student response:* Students should indicate that the anticipated adventure of Passage 1 is the journey to "the strange lands be-yond," and what will happen at the end of the journey. There are numerous clues that the adventure will include a journey to a place seemingly exotic to the narrator because it is unknown. For example, the narrator speaks of "the strange lands beyond, the Great Lake, and the mountains on which snow lay all summer through." There are also clues that the adventure will be danger-ous, as when the narrator speaks with reservation of "the Tripods and the Caps." Passage 2 presents just a hint of the anticipated adventure of time travel. Students should note that the

Unit 6: Short Stories

"Dragon, Dragon" by John Gardner

Selection Test (p. 116)

Critical Reading/Vocabulary, Spelling, and Grammar

1. b 2. d 3. b 4. c 5. b 6. d 7. c 8. c
9. d 10. d 11. a 12. d 13. c 14. a 15. a
16. a 17. d 18. b 19. a 20. b

Questions are classified in these categories:
Comprehension 1(A), 8(A), 13(E)
Interpretation 3(E), 5(C), 9(C), 14(A)
Literary Analysis 4(A), 7(E), 10(E), 12(A)
Reading Strategy 2(A), 6(C), 11(A)
Vocabulary 17(E), 19(A)
Spelling 15(A), 18(E)
Grammar 16(A), 20(C)

Essay Questions

21. (Easy) *Guidelines for student response:* Students should explain that a story's plot is the sequence of events that take place in it. The main elements of a plot are a problem that the characters face; a series of events in which the characters try to solve the problem; a climax, or turning point; and a resolution, or conclusion. Students should also offer examples from

"Dragon, Dragon" to support their expla-nation. For example, the problem that the characters face is that a dragon is causing trouble in the kingdom; the climax of the story occurs when the youngest son slays the dragon.

22. (Average) *Guidelines for student response:* Students should compare and contrast "Dragon, Dragon" with traditional fairy tales that they know, citing examples in support. For example, students might point out that the story is similar to "Jack and the Beanstalk"—in both, an ordinary person becomes a hero by defeating a powerful and dangerous enemy. Comical and modern touches such as the detail that the dragon "stole spark plugs out of people's cars," however, make Gardner's story different from traditional tales.

23. (Challenging) *Guidelines for student response:* Students should name two read-ing strategies that helped them under-stand the story, using examples from the story to support their answers. For exam-ple, students might say that the fact that the youngest son followed his father's ad-vice when confronting the dragon helped them predict that he would succeed in his

quest and become the hero of the story; the fact that the wizard forgot his spells and accidentally turned the queen into a rosebush helped them infer that he is a bumbling and comical character.

"Becky and the Wheels-and-Brake Boys"
by James Berry

Selection Test (p. 119)

Critical Reading/Vocabulary, Spelling, and Grammar

1. c   2. b   3. d   4. a   5. c   6. d   7. b   8. a
9. c   10. a   11. c   12. d   13. d   14. c   15. b
16. c   17. b   18. b   19. c   20. a

Questions are classified in these categories:
    Comprehension 2(A), 6(A), 1(E), 15(E)
    Interpretation 4(A), 5(C), 7(A), 12(E)
    Literary Analysis 1(E), 3(C), 9(A), 10(A)
    Reading Strategy 8(A), 11(C), 13(E) 14(C)
    Vocabulary 16(A), 17(E)
    Spelling 19(A)
    Grammar 18(A), 20(E)

Essay Questions

21. (Easy) *Guidelines for student response:* Students' essays should take one side of the issue and clearly state an opinion. Students who think Becky is wrong to persist in her efforts to get a bike may cite the family's lack of money, her mother's hard work to support a large family, and the fact that most girls in the community do not own bicycles. Students who argue that Becky is right may cite her desire to be an individual with personal goals and wishes, her cleverness in hunting for solutions to her problem, and the position that girls and boys have many of the same needs, in this case, for physical activity and recreation.

22. (Average) *Guidelines for student response:* Students should begin their essays by analyzing these different ideas, and then show how these differences cause the conflict. They should show an understanding of the two positions on either side of the conflict, such as the mother's feeling that girls should be domestic rather than athletic and should adhere to group values rather than individualistic ones; essays should reflect Becky's indi-

vidualistic stance and her belief that girls can and should share activities that may be regarded as proper to boys, and that one should not be limited by either social or financial concerns.

23. (Challenging) *Guidelines for student response:* Students' essays should show sensitivity to multiple points of view in the story. As they picture events as seen through the mother's eyes, students should note this character's concern with real economic problems, social norms, and keeping up standards (not behaving or looking like a "field laborer" or riding with reckless neighborhood boys).

"Overdoing It" by Anton Chekhov
"Eleven" by Sandra Cisneros

Selection Test (p.122)

Critical Reading/Vocabulary, Spelling, and Grammar

1. c   2. c   3. c   4. d   5. b   6. d   7. c   8. c
9. d   10. b   11. b   12. a   13. c   14. b   15. d
16. b   17. a   18. d   19. c   20. b

Questions are classified in these categories:
    Comprehension 1(A), 8(A), 9(E), 12(A), 13(E)
    Interpretation 2(E), 6(C), 10(A), 11(C), 14(A)
    Literary Analysis 3(C), 4(A), 7(E)
    Reading Strategy 5(C)
    Vocabulary 15(A), 20(A)
    Spelling 17(A)
    Grammar 16(A), 18(A), 19(E)

Essay Questions

21. (Easy) *Guidelines for student response:* Students who choose Gleb Smirnov may say that they would have been nervous in the lonely railroad station; frightened by Klim, the driver; and jumpy and scared on the deserted road. Students who choose Rachel may say that they would feel angry when Felice says the sweater belongs to her, embarrassed that the other students think the sweater is hers, angry and outraged at Miss Price's unfairness, and disgusted with Phyllis for waiting so long to admit she owns the sweater.

22. (Average) *Guidelines for student response:* Students who choose Gleb Smirnov in "Overdoing It" should point out his sense

"Overdoing It" by Anton Chekhov
"Eleven" by Sandra Cisneros
(continued)

of isolation and fear of the driver and how he hides that fear with lying and empty bragging. If students choose Rachel of "Eleven," they should point out her inability to speak out about the red sweater and her excruciating embarrassment at the teacher's forcing her to put on the sweater.

23. (Challenging) *Guidelines for student response:* Students should recognize that Chekhov uses indirect characterization almost exclusively, rarely directly telling the reader anything about either character's personality. They should cite examples of indirect characterization through dialogue, thoughts, or another character's reaction. They should grasp that Cisneros uses direct characterization because the story is told in the first person by the main character, who tells the reader directly how she is feeling at each point in the story. They should cite examples such as, "I wish I was invisible, but I'm not." Students should also recognize that Cisneros uses indirect characterization as well, citing examples such as "That's not, I don't, you're not...not mine."

"The Lawyer and the Ghost"
by Charles Dickens
"The Wounded Wolf"
by Jean Craighead George

Selection Test (p. 125)

Critical Reading/Vocabulary, Spelling, and Grammar

1. b   2. d   3. d   4. a   5. c   6. b   7. a   8. c
9. d   10. a   11. c   12. b   13. a   14. d   15. b
16. a   17. c   18. a   19. d   20. b

Questions are classified in these categories:
   Comprehension 2(E), 6(A), 12(C)
   Interpretation 1(A), 4(A), 7(C), 10(E), 13(A)
   Literary Analysis 5(C), 9(E), 14(A)
   Reading Strategy 3(A), 8(A), 11(C), 15(A)
   Vocabulary 16(A), 19(E)
   Spelling 18(A)
   Grammar 17(E), 20(C)
   E = Easy, A = Average, C = Challenging

Essay Questions

21. (Easy) *Guidelines for student response:* Students' essays should point out that, in "The Lawyer and the Ghost," readers expect the ghost to frighten the lawyer, but instead the lawyer talks the ghost into leaving. What starts as a scary story ends up as a humorous one. In "The Wounded Wolf," students might expect Roko to die, but instead he is saved by the wolf pack. Most students will probably be pleasantly surprised by these unexpected endings.

22. (Average) *Guidelines for student response:* Students' essays should reflect an understanding that setting is an important element in a story. The miserable and depressing chambers in "The Lawyer and the Ghost" reflect the sad life of the lawyer who lived and died there. In "The Wounded Wolf," the harsh winter wasteland heightens the plight of Roko, who is fair game for other starving animals looking for food.

23. (Challenge) *Guidelines for student response:* Students may surmise that in "The Wounded Wolf," the animals are only following the natural law of survival of the fittest in a harsh, unforgiving environment. The story teaches that nature is unforgiving and at times cruel. Most students will probably say they would be be less forgiving of the characters' behavior if the characters were people and not animals. They may explain by saying that humans possess a knowledge of good and bad, unlike animals who behave instinctively.

"The All-American Slurp"
by Lensey Namioka
"The Stone" by Lloyd Alexander

Selection Test (p. 128)

Critical Reading/Vocabulary, Spelling, and Grammar

1. c   2. b   3. c   4. d   5. b   6. a   7. c   8. b
9. c   10. a   11. a   12. d   13. c   14. b   15. b
16. c   17. d   18. b   19. d   20. b

Questions are classified in these categories:
   Comprehension 1(A), 7(A), 8(A), 11(E)
   Interpretation 3(E), 9(A), 14(C)
   Literary Analysis 2(C), 5(A), 12(A)

Reading Strategy 4(A), 6(C), 10(C), 13(E)
Vocabulary 15(A), 18(A)
Spelling 16(A), 19(E)
Grammar 17(A), 20(A)
E = Easy, A = Average, C = Challenging

Essay Questions

21. (Easy) *Guidelines for student response:* Students who choose "The All-American Slurp" should infer that the narrator learns how to adapt to new surroundings. They should cite the ways she learns how to eat, dress, and socialize to support their inferences. Those who choose "The Stone" should explain that Maibon learns that he must accept that change is a necessary part of life. To show how he learns this lesson, they should cite several examples from the story that show how an unchanging life prevents growth and fruition, that is, crops don't grow, baby doesn't cut teeth, eggs don't hatch.

22. (Average) *Guideline for student response:* Students' essays should compare and contrast how each main character in the two stories deals with change. Problems of the narrator in "The All-American Slurp" include having difficulty mastering an unfamiliar language, learning social customs, dressing as others do. Problem solving involves adjustment and discrimination as to blending two distinct cultures. Problems of Maibon involve resistance to change—growing old. Problem solving involves listening to the response of others (Doli and Madrona), seeing firsthand that no fruition is possible without change, and accepting old age as inevitable.

23. (Challenging) *Guidelines for student response:* Students who write about "The All-American Slurp" might say that change is sometimes necessary. Those incapable of making changes cannot successfully adapt to the situations into which life leads them. They should cite as examples the problems the Lin family members have before they begin to adapt to their new country, and the rewards of learning to adapt. Students might also mention that the story implies that, while change is necessary, people should not be too willing to change things that are central to their lives; for example, the Lins

cherish their Chinese heritage and traditions. Those who choose "The Stone" might say that change, even growing old and eventually dying, is a positive aspect of life. To back up this idea, they might cite as an example the failure of crops, animals, and people to grow and thrive when there is no change.

Unit Test (p. 131)

Critical Reading/Vocabulary, Spelling, and Grammar

1. c   2. b   3. d   4. b   5. a   6. d   7. c   8. a
9. c   10. d   11. a   12. b   13. d   14. a   15. c
16. b   17. c   18. d   19. a   20. d   21. b
22. b   23. c   24. a   25. c   26. d   27. b
28. a   29. d   30. b

Questions are classified in these categories:
   Comprehension: 3(E), 5(C), 10(E), 15(A)
   Interpretation: 2(A), 6(E), 8(A), 11(A), 13(A), 17(C), 19(C)
   Literary Analysis: 4(A), 9(C), 12(E), 16(A)
   Reading Strategy: 1(A), 7(C), 14(E), 18(A)
   Vocabulary: 21(A), 24(E), 28(C)
   Spelling: 22(E), 26(A), 29(C)
   Grammar: 20(C), 23(E), 25(A), 27(A), 30(A)
   E = Easy, A = Average, C = Challenging

Essay Questions

31. (Easy) *Guidelines for student response:* Students may observe that Becky has a conflict with the Wheels-and-Brake Boys, who refuse to teach her to ride a bike or let her take part in their fun. Her mother helps her resolve this conflict by getting Becky a bicycle—one so impressive that the boys accept her. Students may also see a conflict between Becky and Granny-Liz, whose old-fashioned viewpoint has no room for "tomboys": girls who want to indulge in bike-riding or other activities Granny-Liz believes are for boys only. There is no resolution between Becky and Granny-Liz in the story. In "Eleven," students may say that Rachel has a conflict within herself because she is too shy to express her feelings. She also has a conflict with her teacher, who seems unable or unwilling to feel any sympathy for Rachel's embarrassment or pain. Although a time may come when Rachel is more able to cope with her feelings, no

resolution takes place within the story. In "The Wounded Wolf," Roko is in conflict with the law of nature which says animals that are too weak, old, or hurt to take care of themselves are likely to become prey of stronger animals, who also must eat. However, Roko's will to survive keeps him alive until another natural law—that members of a wolf pack look out for one another—saves him. In this story, wolves are shown to have an instinct for mutual support that is not always evident among people. In "Overdoing It," Gleb faces a conflict that exists only in his imagination when he thinks that his driver, Klim, is a villain who means to attack him. Gleb succeeds too well in making Klim believe that he is a dangerous man himself and winds up creating an equally nonexistent conflict in Klim's mind. This is the only story in which no real conflicts exist.

32. (Average) *Guidelines for student response:* Students may point out that the author of "Dragon, Dragon" mixes modern references (cars and spark plugs) with imaginary details such as a dragon and a wizard to get a funny mix of fairy tale and modern story. Also, while dragons are traditionally linked to killing and destruction, this dragon does things like stopping up chimneys and tearing the last chapters out of books, creating a humorous contrast. In addition, the climax of the story—having the dragon laugh so hysterically that it cannot defend itself—is a comical finishing touch. "The Lawyer and the Ghost" is similar to "Dragon, Dragon" in that it uses a surprising twist on readers' expectations to achieve a humorous effect. When ghosts appear in stories, readers expect scary outcomes. But it turns out that this ghost continues to haunt the lawyer's dreary rooms only because the ghost had never thought about visiting more pleasant places. When a potentially frightening figure like a ghost is shown to be slow-witted and not frightening at all, the result is a funny ending. "Overdoing It" uses a similar kind of humor. The timid Gleb, growing more and more afraid as he travels

through a dark and deserted landscape with a rough-looking peasant, creates a threatening image of an imminent attack; when Klim jumps off the sleigh and reveals that he is even more terrified than his passenger, the sudden twist is comic.

33. (Average) *Guidelines to student response:* Students may say that Becky in "The Wheels-and-Brake Boys" is a self-confident girl who wants to take part in the kinds of activities that are traditionally thought of as appropriate for boys only. Outspoken as she is, Becky is bound to get into arguments with the older women with whom she lives: her mother and Granny-Liz. While she is stubborn and self-confident, students may say that she does have some appreciation of her mother's situation, and they should also note how badly she misses her father, who might have been more sympathetic to her wishes. Rachel, in "Eleven," contrasts sharply with Becky. Where Becky says what is on her mind, Rachel has trouble expressing herself. Becky is aggressive and willing to do unconventional things, but Rachel is easily embarrassed and gets tongue-tied. Students may note, however, that Rachel seems more observant and sensitive than Becky and that she is capable of analyzing why she feels miserable to be what she is, an eleven-year-old girl who is trapped by her shyness.

34. (Average) *Guidelines for student response:* Students may say that the struggle in "Eleven" is mostly within Rachel herself, a struggle between her feelings and the shyness that prevents her from expressing them. Other characters add to Rachel's misery because of misunderstanding and not because they want to harm her. Similarly, in "The Wheels-and-Brake Boys," Becky battles against the attitudes of the Wheels-and-Brake Boys and their desire to keep their club exclusive, and against the beliefs of Granny-Liz, who reflects the values of a different generation. Roko's adversaries in "The Wounded Wolf" want Roko to die and might even kill him if they have the chance, but their goal is only to feed themselves; they do not wish Roko harm out of any other motive. In "The All-Ameri-

can Slurp," the difficulties faced by the narrator's family all stem from the misunderstanding and ignorance that can exist between people of different cultures when each group is unfamiliar with the culture of the other. In none of these stories, then, could the central conflicts be described as moral. In all cases it involves misunderstanding, ignorance, or, in the case of "The Wounded Wolf," conflicting needs.

35. (Challenging) *Guidelines for student response:* In "Overdoing It," students may note that the author goes into some detail about the gloomy wilderness into which Klim takes Gleb. This setting serves to give Gleb more motivation to feel afraid and suspicious of what Klim's intentions might be—and to give *Klim* motivation to become afraid of Gleb as the story goes on. The setting leads the reader, too, to wonder whether the story might take a grim turn, which makes the final twist even more amusing. In "The Wounded Wolf," the author also describes a harsh natural setting in detail. This setting, with its snow, wind, and rough terrain, is a suitable background for the kind of life-and-death struggle that is so common in nature. Dickens has given "The Lawyer and the Ghost" the kind of setting that is traditional for classic ghost stories: the dark and dingy rooms, the ancient furniture, and so forth. The appearance of a ghost, together with that setting, makes readers expect a typically chilling story. As with "Overdoing It," the setting helps to make the final comic twist more effective. In all three stories, settings contribute to create a mood, but in two of the stories, that mood helps the writer play a joke on the reader.

Alternative Unit Test (p. 135)

Critical Reading

1. b 2. e 3. a 4. c 5. a 6. d 7. b 8. c
9. e 10. d 11. b 12. a 13. a 14. b 15. e

Questions are classified in these categories:
 Comprehension: 4(A), 8(E)
 Interpretation: 2(C), 7(A), 13(E), 15(A)
 Literary Analysis: 1(E), 5(A), 9(C), 11(C), 14(A)

Reading Strategy: 3(A), 6(E), 10(C), 12(C)
E = Easy, A = Average, C = Challenging

Essay Questions

16. (Easy) *Guidelines for student response:* Students may say that Colm lives in a rural setting, presumably on a farm. He seems to be content with his own company, able to amuse himself tossing and skipping rocks in the lake. He is at ease with animals and appears to be particularly interested in wild creatures, such as the duck. He is impulsive and doesn't hesitate to wade into the water to search for the duck. Noreen, by contrast, seems to be a sad girl, who lives in a constant state of embarrassment due to the seedy store kept by her father. She does not have the self-confidence to cope with the taunts of her classmates, and lacks the will or the ability to make the most of a difficult domestic life. The fact that the only response she can make to the teasing of other girls is to cry shows that she has nothing like Colm's self-assurance. She sees things in a negative light, unlike Colm, who seems naturally cheerful. She shows no sign of Colm's spontaneity or boldness.

17. (Average) *Guidelines for student response:* Students should have no trouble identifying the problem or conflict faced by Noreen in Passage 1: she is very unhappy and unable to cope with her feelings of shame about her father's failure and the rundown nature of the fish store. She is always painfully aware that people (especially at school) see her as a pathetic and laughable figure, and her problem is likely to be finding a way to make this situation better. Passage 2 is less clear in establishing the main problem or conflict of the story, although students should recognize that it is likely to involve the wild duck. They should conclude this in part because of the story's title, and also because of Colm's reaction to seeing the bird—he is fascinated and willing to wade through the water and mud to catch a better glimpse of it. His problem, then, might be finding a way to satisfy his curiosity about the duck, who is timid and apt to fly off if he gets too close. Students might see Noreen's conflict as an internal one (her

Alternative Unit Test (p. 135)
(continued)

feelings and her inability to change them or deal with them), or with other people (her father, perhaps, or the taunting students at school). Colm's conflict may be with nature, in the form of the duck's natural timidity and the ruggedness of the area in which he wants to learn more about it.

18. (Challenging) *Guidelines to student response*: Students may say that the setting of Passage 1 is a particularly run-down urban one: a poorly-kept fish store in the middle of New York City. The author goes into some detail about the smells and unsightly appearance of the

store, and also the weak and irresponsible character of Noreen's father, who owns the store and is responsible for the state it is in. The setting of Passage 2 stands in sharp contrast: a lonely lake in a rural area, which is shown to be isolated and scenic. The setting of Passage 1 might serve to make Noreen's predicament even worse; someone as uncertain and unhappy as she is not likely to have the assertiveness necessary to overcome her lack of self-esteem. The setting of Passage 2 provides Colm with a challenging area in which to continue his search for the wild duck, and an environment that could bring him to fully appreciate nature and its rules.

Unit 7: Nonfiction

"The Shutout"
by Patricia C. McKissack and
Frederick McKissack, Jr.

Selection Test (p. 139)

Critical Reading/Vocabulary, Spelling, and Grammar

1. b 2. a 3. b 4. a 5. c 6. a 7. b 8. d
9. c 10. d 11. c 12. a 13. b 14. d 15. d
16. b 17. a 18. a 19. d 20. c

Questions are classified in these categories:
Comprehension 6(E), 9(C), 10(C), 13(A)
Interpretation 4(A), 7(C), 12(A), 14(E)
Literary Analysis 2(A), 3(E), 8(C)
Reading Strategy 1(E), 5(A), 11(C)
Vocabulary 15(A), 17(A), 19(A)
Spelling 16(E)
Grammar Skill 18(E), 20(A)
E = Easy, A = Average, C = Challenging

Essay Questions

21. (Easy) *Guidelines for student response:* Students' essays should include the following: During the Civil War, Union soldiers played baseball, often choosing African Americans to play on their teams; afterwards, while baseball was not popular in the South, free blacks played on integrated teams in large eastern cities and small midwestern towns; it

is believed that some of the players were emancipated slaves and runaways; in 1867 the National Association of Base Ball Players excluded African Americans from major-league teams; African Americans were shut out of the major leagues until after World War II.

22. (Average) *Guidelines for student response:* Students should mention that "The Shutout" is a short piece of nonfiction that includes facts, evidence, explanations, and insights. They should cite examples such as the following. Facts: In 1845, the New York Knickerbocker Club was organized; by 1860, there were about sixty teams in the National Association of Base Ball Players; in 1867 the Association voted to exclude African Americans. Evidence: Doubleday's diaries never mention Cooperstown, which is evidence that he did not "invent" baseball there; records and documents that show people were playing stick-and-ball games before 1839 are evidence that the game was "invented" earlier. Explanations: During the Civil War, African Americans were chosen to play on Union teams because of their skill as ball handlers; slave owners preferred individual sports to team sports because they

could enter their slaves in the competitions; African Americans formed the Negro Leagues because they were not permitted to play in the major leagues. Insights: The history of the Negro Leagues is not unlike the history of the major leagues.

23. (Challenging) *Guidelines for student response:* Students might begin by writing, "I believe the decision made by the National Association of Base Ball Players in 1867 to exclude African Americans from their baseball teams is wrong." Reasons they might offer are: Excluding African Americans from baseball is against the law because it violates their Constitutional rights; if the Association is given the power to exclude one group of people, it might decide to exclude others as well; the decision keeps many talented players out of the game.

"Letter to Scottie" by F. Scott Fitzgerald
"Olympic Diary" by Amanda Borden

Selection Test (p. 142)

Critical Reading/Vocabulary, Spelling, and Grammar

1. b 2. d 3. a 4. d 5. d 6. b 7. b 8. c
9. d 10. a 11. b 12. c 13. b 14. d
15. c 16. a 17. d 18. b 19. a 20. c

Questions are classified in these categories:
  Comprehension 1 (E), 2(A), 5(A), 6(E), 7(E), 8(A), 11(C)
  Interpretation 4(C), 9(E), 12(A), 14(A)
  Reading Strategy 13(C)
  Literary Analysis 3(A), 10(E)
  Vocabulary 16(E), 19(A)
  Spelling 15(A)
  Grammar 17(C), 18(E), 20(C)
  E = Easy, A = Average, C = Challenging

Essay Questions

21. (Easy) *Guidelines for student response:* Students should explain that in "Letter to Scottie," the author's purpose is to explain how to make the most of one's abilities and character. Steps to achieving this goal include "Worry about courage," "Don't worry about popular opinion," and "Think about scholarship." In "Olympic Diary,"

Amanda Borden's goal is to become a world-class athlete. Steps students might cite include being ready for a new challenge, training hard, and learning how to cope with disappointment.

22. (Average) *Guidelines for student response:* In "Letter to Scottie," examples of personal details include the White Cat, the camp bill, and Fitzgerald's threat to call Scottie Egg. Fitzgerald strikes an informal tone when he includes lists as well as teases his daughter. Colloquial language is exemplified by the use of nicknames, sentence fragments, and phrases like "crack you open" and "hang it on you." As revealed through the letter, Fitzgerald seems affectionate, intelligent, and sensitive. In "Olympic Diary," personal details include Borden's admiration for Mary Lou Retton and Michael Jordan, her reaction to her first trip away from home, her response to physical injuries and other setbacks, and her thrill at making the Olympic team and going to Atlanta to compete. Borden creates an informal tone by using short sentences and including frequent exclamations. Colloquial language is illustrated by expressions such as "Wow, did my life change!" and "I think we will do just great." Borden reveals a spirited, determined personality in her diary.

23. (Challenging) *Guidelines to student response:* Students should recognize that Fitzgerald implies that doing one's duty and being virtuous are the most important things in life. They might cite as evidence quotes such as "I feel very strongly about you doing [your] duty," "I never believe much in happiness," and "All I believe in in life is the rewards for virtue." Amanda Borden implies that the most important thing in her own life is to be a world-class athlete. She begins by writing about her involvement with sports and how she chose gymnastics. Then she goes on to describe her dedicated training, overcoming disappointments, elation after successful performances, and confidence in the future.

"My Papa, Mark Twain"
by Susy Clemens
"The Drive-In Movies" by Gary Soto
"Space Shuttle *Challenger*"
by William Harwood

Selection Test (p. 145)

Critical Reading/Vocabulary, Spelling, and Grammar

1. c 2. c 3. d 4. a 5. b 6. d 7. a
8. b 9. b 10. a 11. b 12. a 13. b 14. d
15. d 16. b 17. d 18. a 19. b 20. d

Questions are classified in these categories:
  Comprehension 2(E) 6(A) 11(E)
  Interpretation 3(A) 7(E) 12(A) 14(C) 15(A)
  Literary Analysis 4(A) 9(C)
  Reading Strategy 1(C) 5(E) 8(A) 10(A) 13(A)
  Vocabulary 16(A) 19(A)
  Spelling 17(E)
  Grammar 18(C) 20(A)

Essay Questions

21. (Easy) *Guidelines for student response:* Students' essays should include as key points that Twain was a humorist with a serious side; an impractical person, yet an inspired writer; an impatient but affectionate character; a largely self-educated man. Examples should include Susy Clemens's references to his works; the example of the burglar alarm; references to his short temper and the contrasting example of his affection toward family cats; Twain's playing hooky, yet emerging educated and accomplished.

22. (Average) *Guidelines for student response:* Students' essays should shows awareness that all three authors use personal observation and numerous details to construct their accounts. When writing about "My Papa, Mark Twain," students may indicate that the author makes a number of direct observations about her father. Students should note that Twain was a humorist with a serious side; an impractical person, yet an inspired writer; an impatient but affectionate character. When discussing "The Drive-In Movies," students should note examples of details about the author's work in the garden; his efforts to clean the family car; his perseverance in

the face of obstacles; his attitude toward the other members of the family. When writing about "Space Shuttle *Challenger,*" students should note details such as the author's information about the physical surroundings; the comments about the pressures and priorities that a good journalist must keep in mind; the author's evaluations of his own perceptions during the launch; and the author's comments on his own feelings when he realized a catastrophic disaster had occurred. Finally, students should draw inferences about characters and actions through an examination of these points and examples.

23. (Challenging) *Guidelines for student response:* Students' essays should show evidence that they have analyzed the wealth of detail in the selection and have drawn inferences about the author and other characters in "The Drive-In Movies." For example, they may use details such as the author's attention to the neighbor's dog to make the inference that the narrator is kind and sympathetic, and that he has a playful as well as a serious side. They might infer from the details given about the author's mother that she is exhausted, somewhat unpredictable, yet ultimately fair toward her children. Substantial essays will make associations between a number of such details and arrive at inferences about indirectly stated observations.

"Restoring the Circle"
by Joseph Bruchac
"How the Internet Works"
by Kerry Cochrane
"Turkeys" by Bailey White

Selection Test (p. 148)

Critical Reading/Vocabulary, Spelling, and Grammar

1. a 2. a 3. c 4. b 5. b 6. a 7. d 8. a
9. a 10. c 11. c 12. d 13. c 14. a 15. b
16. c 17. b 18. d 19. a 20. a

Questions are classified in these categories:
  Comprehension 3(A) 5(E) 9(C) 12(A)
  Interpretation 1(A) 7(A) 8(E) 10(E) 11(E) 14(A)

Literary Analysis 4 (C) 6 (C) 13 (E)
Reading Strategy 2 (A) 15 (A)
Vocabulary 17 (A) 19 (A)
Spelling 16 (E)
Grammar 18 (A) 20 (C)

Essay Questions

21. (Easy) *Guidelines for student response:* Students should note that the author describes literature written by authors who have little knowledge or understanding of Native American culture. This literature has created the following stereotypes: Native American men are "savage and dangerous," Native American women are "nothing more than beasts of burden," and "all Indians look and sound alike." To correct these stereotypes, the author informs readers that "none of America's so-called 'Indian wars' were ever begun by Indians"; that in many Native American cultures, "the women were the heads of families, the owners of the houses, and the ones who chose the chiefs"; and that "more than 400 different languages are spoken by the various Native American nations of North America." He also mentions the "complexity and variety of Native American cultures."

22. (Average) *Guidelines for student response:* Students should note that "Restoring the Circle" is a persuasive essay. Students may cite examples such as ". . .imaginative portrayals of Native American people and Native American cultures become painful stereotypes and distorted history." "How the Internet Works" is an informational essay. Students may note how the author explains the use of computer protocols. "Turkeys" is a narrative essay. Students should note that the author discusses a memorable event from her childhood; students should also note that the narration is similar to a story.

23. (Challenging) *Guidelines for student response:* For "Restoring the Circle," students might write that the essay's message has to do with the importance of maintaining cultural traditions. A main idea might be the importance of preserving Native American languages. An example might be that not allowing children to

speak their own Native languages undermined their sense of self-worth. For "How the Internet Works," students should note that the author points out that the Internet is easy to use when you understand its protocols. A main idea might be the comparison of the Internet to the postal system. An example might be that "once you have the IP address of a computer, you know where to send messages or other information." For "Turkeys," students might note that the message is that a childhood experience can make a lasting impression on a person's life. Main ideas might include the author's memory of waking up with the baby turkeys. A supporting explanation might be the author's memory of feeling the eggshells crackling and the baby turkeys snuggling against her.

Unit Test (p. 151)

Critical Reading/Vocabulary, Spelling, and Grammar

1. b   2. a   3. b.   4. d   5. c   6. a   7. d   8. c
9. b   10. a   11. c   12. d   13. a   14. c   15. c
16. b   17. c   18. b   19. c   20. a   21. b
22. d   23. a   24. b   25. a   26. d   27. b
28. c   29. a   30. b

Questions are classified in these categories:
Comprehension 3(E), 12(A), 15(A)
Interpretation 2(C), 6(A), 9(A), 13(E), 14(C) 16(A), 19(A)
Literary Analysis 1(A), 5(E), 8(A) 10(C), 18(A)
Reading Strategy 4(A), 7(E), 11(A), 17(C)
Vocabulary 21(C), 24(A), 28(E)
Spelling 22(E), 26(A), 30(C)
Grammar 20(A), 23(C), 25(E), 27(A), 29(A)
E = Easy, A = Average, C = Challenging

Essay Questions

31. (Easy) *Guidelines for student response:* Students should be aware that "My Papa, Mark Twain" is an affectionate portrait of Twain by his daughter. She shows him as attractive, intelligent, absent-minded, and not very bright mechanically. She praises his writing and discusses her personal favorite among his books, *The Prince and the Pauper.* Her goal is to give readers a picture of her father as she sees him,

wanting them to find him as appealing as she does. In "The Drive-In Movies," Gary Soto provides a vivid autobiographical sketch of an episode that happened during his childhood. Students should note the details that the writer offers about his mother, his brother Rick, and his sister Debra, as well as about the household chores the children perform. Soto's goal is to give readers an insight into a close-knit, affectionate family.

32. (Average) *Guidelines to student response:* Students might mention the fact that baseball had ancestors in many cultures, although the sport evolved in the United States. The tradition of racial inequity is brought out, and it is clear that this bias led to the exclusion of African Americans from professional baseball. These facts support the insight that, in baseball as in other aspects of American culture, systematic segregation and exclusion victimized African Americans. "Space Shuttle *Challenger*" gives the facts about the events leading up to the fatal *Challenger* launch from the viewpoint of a journalist covering the event. The facts presented, including the reactions and actions of the journalists, stress the insights that space exploration is hazardous, and that journalists have a duty to forget their personal reactions to tragedy and do their jobs so that the public is informed.

33. (Average) *Guidelines for student response:* Students may say that, in "Olympic Diary," Amanda Jordan reveals that she was not only a talented athlete but also very determined and self-confident. She persevered despite many setbacks: injuries, exclusion from the 1992 U.S. Olympic team, and others. Despite it all, she stayed focused on her goal until she achieved it. Her purpose was not to brag about herself but to give readers a sense of what an athlete must endure to reach world-class status. "The Drive-in Movies" is also about determination, on a smaller scale. The author demonstrates how important a Saturday night at the drive-in theater was to him by describ-

ing in detail the exhausting list of chores he did in order to put his mother in a good mood. He is revealed as a boy who is not only very determined, but willing to work very hard. After he falls asleep during the movie, he shows himself as able to learn from his mistakes, and vows not to work quite so hard on future Saturdays. The author of "Turkeys" reveals that, even at an early age, she had come to regard waking up in a sickbed and finding herself surrounded by baby turkeys as a normal event, and treating it calmly. She adapts the ornithologists' goals as her own and serves as a substitute mother to the turkey family, until they are ready to fly away and live in the wild. Her adaptability allows her to be part of an unforgettable and rewarding experience.

34. (Average) *Guidelines to student response:* Students should know that the "Letter to Scottie" shows a warm and caring relationship between F. Scott Fitzgerald and his daughter. There are references to previous correspondence, and clues that she wants her father's opinions on what she does. Also, the joking about the nicknames, "Pappy" and "Egg" shows that both Fitzgeralds can joke with each other freely. The author's concern that Scottie make the most of her life is shown by the advice he gives her. In "My Papa, Mark Twain," Susie gives evidence that she loves and admires her father (her description of him and her admiration of his writing, for example), but she is aware of some shortcomings and willing to write about them, such as his fondness for talking at length and lack of mechanical aptitude. The sense readers get of the relationship is that it is close and affectionate, but that Susie, like her father, looks at things clearly enough to recognize a flaw here and there, although she speaks of those, too, with fondness. Students should note that Joseph Bruchac, who is himself a distinguished Native American author, is intimately acquainted with a wide range of Native American cultural traditions. Bruchac cares deeply about his subject: he champions the safeguarding of these tradi-

tions, and he also upholds the importance of challenging detrimental stereotypes of Native Americans. Bruchac's familiarity with Native American literature is exemplified in his comments about Native American writers such as Michael Dorris, Linda Hogan, and N. Scott Momaday. Bruchac's essay and Susy Clemens's biography differ from Fitzgerald's letter in that they are intended for a wide audience rather than for a single individual reader.

35. (Challenging) *Guidelines for student response:* Students should recognize that "Space Shuttle *Challenger*" is an account by a journalist whose professional standards of accurate and prompt reporting involve a battle to control his personal feelings. At the moment of a disaster, such as the explosion of *Challenger,* the writer experiences strong emotions which he must stifle. It is only when he looks back on events that the true enormity of the disaster strikes home. In "How the Internet Works," the writer's careful, step-by-step explanation of her subject shows that she is deeply involved and very enthusiastic about the benefits of Internet technology. The author reveals her feelings about the Internet's potential in education, for example, when she refers to the "immense resources" available on line. In "Turkeys," the author's keen interest in the natural world is revealed by the vivid details she uses to describe the turkeys, the ornithologists' eccentric behavior, and the first flight of the birds in late summer. The author's pleasure in recalling her childhood experience is especially clear in the final paragraph, when she says she would like to think that all the wild turkeys that thrive today are descendants of the birds that she "saved from the vigilance of the ornithologists."

Alternative Unit Test (p. 155)

Critical Reading

1. c 2. a 3. e 4. b 5. e 6. d 7. b 8. c
9. a 10. d 11. a 12. b 13. d 14. a 15. c

Questions are classified in these categories:
Comprehension: 1 (A), 9 (E), 10 (E)
Interpretation: 6 (A), 7 (A), 8 (A), 13 (C), 14 (A), 15 (A)
Literary Analysis: 3 (E), 12 (A)
Reading Strategy: 2 (A), 4 (C), 5 (A), 11 (C)
E = Easy, A = Average, C = Challenging

Essay Questions

16. (Easy) *Guidelines for student response:* Students may say that Goodall and O'Keeffe both appreciate the natural world and are keen observers of that world. However, Goodall is interested in exploring the habitat of animals and in viewing animals. O'Keeffe's memory shows she is interested in the effects of light and of contrasts that occur in nature. Also, Goodall describes a memory from the age of twenty-six; O'Keeffe's memory is of being one year old.

17. (Average) *Guidelines for student response:* Students may say that Passage 1 is an autobiography because it is written in the first person and describes the scene from the author's point of view. The author shares her feelings as she gives the account. Passage 2 is a biography because another person describes a scene in O'Keeffe's life. The author gives her own impressions of the subject's experience. Both an autobiography and a biography tell events in a person's life. For example, in Passage 1 the author describes her first day at Chimpanzee Land. In Passage 2 the author describes the subject's earliest memory.

18. (Challenging) *Guidelines for student response:* Students may say that both Goodall and O'Keeffe appreciate nature. Goodall explores a wilderness in order to observe animals. As a baby, O'Keeffe's sees and feels the sun, keeping the memory despite her young age. Nature influences Goodall in that she tries to become an accepted member of the natural world in order to work among the animals. Nature influences O'Keeffe as an artist because her keen powers of observation and her appreciation for her surroundings are important attributes for an artist to have.

Unit 8: Drama

The Phantom Tollbooth, Act I
based on the book by Norton Juster,
by Susan Nanus

Selection Test (p. 159)

Critical Reading/Vocabulary, Spelling, and Grammar

1. d 2. b 3. a 4. d 5. c 6. c 7. a 8. a
9. c 10. b 11. c 12. b 13. b 14. d 15. a
16. c 17. d 18. b 19. a 20. c

Questions are classified in these categories:
Comprehension 2(E), 5(A), 14(A)
Interpretation 3(E), 4(C), 6(C), 9(A), 11(A)
Literary Analysis 8(E), 10(C), 12(A), 15(A)
Reading Strategy 1(E), 7(C), 13(A)
Vocabulary 16(A), 19 (E)
Spelling 17(A)
Grammar 18(A), 20(A)
E = Easy, A = Average, C = Challenging

Essay Questions

21. (Easy) *Guidelines for student response:*
Students' essays should focus on an individual character, such as Milo, Tock, the Humbug, or Azaz; or on related characters, such as the Lethargarians or the Ministers, and explore what Milo learns through positive or negative role modeling. For instance, Milo sees the danger of sloth from the Lethargarians, the importance of using time effectively from Tock, the senselessness of words run amok from long-winded Azaz. The deeper the exploration of character, the more successful students' essays will be.

22. (Average) *Guidelines for student response:*
Students' essays should indicate sensitivity to the author's viewpoint and should draw on at least two examples of characters and situations that exemplify the theme of knowledge as time used fruitfully. Strategies may include character/scene analysis, comparison and contrast, and in-depth analysis of authorial viewpoint drawing on multiple examples.

23. (Challenging) *Guidelines for student response:* Students' essays should show awareness of the relationship between the stage directions and content of the drama. For instance, they may note that the opening stage directions for Act I, Scene i emphasize time through the sound of winding and then the appearance of an alarm clock. Students should relate the stage directions that introduce Tock and describe the dog's body as identical with the face of the clock. Students' essays should also explore how stage directions help the audience to understand which emotions and attitudes are to be portrayed by the actors, such as the extreme laziness and exhaustion of the Lethargarians (yawns, slowness of movement) and the exaggerated self-importance of the Humbug (heel clicking, cane-swinging, etc.)

The Phantom Tollbooth, Act II
based on the book by Norton Juster,
by Susan Nanus

Selection Test (p. 162)

Critical Reading/Vocabulary, Spelling, and Grammar

1. d 2. c 3. c 4. b 5. d 6. b 7. c 8. a
9. d 10. b 11. d 12. c 13. b 14. c
15. d 16. a 17. a 18. d 19. c 20. b

Questions are classified in these categories:
Comprehension 2(E), 5(E), 12A
Interpretation 4(C), 8 (C), 9(A), 14(C)
Literary Analysis 1(A), 11(A), 13(A)
Reading Strategy 3(A), 6(E), 7(A), 10(C)
Vocabulary 15 (A), 18 (C), 19(A)
Spelling 17 (A)
Grammar 16 (E), 20 (E)
E = Easy, A = Average, C = Challenging

Essay Questions

21. (Easy) *Guidelines for student response:*
Characters who represent desirable qualities include the princesses Rhyme and Reason who represent such qualities as beauty, art, logic, gentleness, reasonable thinking. Characters who represent faults include the Everpresent Wordsnatcher (someone who interrupts and doesn't listen to what people say), Insincerity (one who lacks honest feeling and expression), the Terrible Trivium (someone who values only things that are meaningless and useless, rather than what

is really important), the Senses Taker (someone who tries to take all the humor out of life). Students should use hypothetical examples from real life to demonstrate the importance of the quality or fault.

22. (Average) *Guidelines for student response:* Students might choose ideas such as: learn from your mistakes (learned from the princess Reason), real education is knowing what to do with what you've learned (learned from the princess Rhyme), don't waste time (learned from Tock and the sum of Milo's experiences). Students should back up their ideas with logical arguments and sound reasoning.

23. (Challenge) *Guidelines for student response:* A main reason students should consider *The Phantom Tollbooth* a classic is that the lessons Milo learns about life and about time are appropriate for all people, however young or old, and at any time period. Students might also mention the cleverness and humor in the way the lessons are taught —through Milo's journeys to different lands and the experiences that Milo has with the different characters. Examples of the lessons that Milo learns should include: "...many things are possible just as long as you don't know they're impossible"; "...never feel badly about making mistakes as long as you take the trouble to learn from them"; "...it's not just learning that's important, but learning what to do with what you learn and learning why you learn..."; "...time is a valuable thing not to be wasted, and how long time really lasts depends on what you do with it."

Grandpa and the Statue
by Arthur Miller

Selection Test (p. 165)

Critical Reading/Vocabulary, Spelling, and Grammar

1. b 2. a 3. c 4. d 5. b 6. c 7. a 8. d
9. c 10. a 11. b 12. d 13. b 14. d 15. d
16. a 17. b 18. c 19. c 20. d

Questions are classified in these categories:
   Comprehension 1(E), 4(C), 7(A), 13(A)
   Interpretation 9(E), 11(C), 12(A), 14(A), 15(C)

Literary Analysis 2(E), 3(C), 10(A)
Reading Strategy 5(E), 6(A), 8(C),
Vocabulary 16(A), 18(E)
Spelling 20(A)
Grammar 17(C), 19(A)
E = Easy, A = Average, C = Challenging

Essay Questions

21. (Easy) *Guidelines for student response:* Students may agree with Grandpa Monaghan, or they may add that the words are particularly aimed at people who have had difficulties with poverty, homelessness, or oppression, citing the words, "tired," "poor," "huddled masses," "wretched refuse," "homeless," and "tempest-tost." They might also add that the words offer hope, as well as welcome, citing the words, "I lift my lamp beside the golden door," and explaining that the lamp and the golden door represent hope and opportunity.

22. (Average) *Guidelines for student response:* Students should grasp that Monaghan recognizes his grandfather's faults, including stinginess and a habit of trying to cover up his true feelings. Dialogue they might cite includes,"My grandfather was the stingiest man in Brooklyn," and "he reached into his pocket and kinda spied around over his eyeglasses to see if anybody was looking." They should also recognize that, in spite of his grandfather's faults, Young Monaghan has affectionate feelings toward him. In support, they might cite, "Reminds me of a lot of laughs," to show that Monaghan considers the memory of his grandfather's involvement with the statue to be pleasant; and "I got to be pretty attached to Grandpa." Throughout the essay, they should cite only dialogue spoken by Young Monaghan.

23. (Challenging) *Guidelines for student response:* Students should grasp that Child Monaghan is completely trusting and believing in his grandfather. He believes everything he says about the statue ("But Grampa, when is it going to fall down? All I do is wait and wait"), and believes that his grandfather's reason for not contributing to the base of the statue is lack of faith in the statue itself rather than just plain stinginess ("I guess you

Grandpa and the Statue by Arthur Miller
(continued)

were right, Grampa. Nobody seems to think it means anything). He is also full of youthful enthusiasm ("Gee, look at those two sea gulls. Wee!—look at them swoop! They caught a fish!") Young Monaghan, perhaps as a result of his war experiences, which have left him in a wheelchair, has become less enthusiastic, evidenced by his refusal to play checkers with August ("Not right now"), and somewhat bitter and sarcastic ("What do you want me to do, jump rope?") He has also come to see his grandfather's faults, although he still loves him ("My grandfather was the stingiest man in Brooklyn").

Unit Test (p. 168)

Critical Reading/ Vocabulary, Spelling, and Grammar

1. c 2. a 3. d 4. a 5. b 6. c 7. a 8. b
9. a 10. d 11. b 12. c 13. c 14. a 15. d
16. b 17. a 18. c 19. a 20. c 21. d
22. a 23. b 24. c 25. d 26. c 27. a
28. b 29. c 30. d

Questions are classified in these categories:
   Comprehension 3(E), 9(A), 14(C), 16(A),
   Interpretation 2(C), 5(A), 8(E), 11(A), 13(C),
      18(A), 19(E)
   Literary Analysis 1(A), 6(E), 10(C), 15(A)
   Reading Strategy 4(A), 7(E), 12(A), 17(A)
   Vocabulary 21(C), 24(A), 28(E)
   Spelling 22(E), 26(A), 30(A)
   Grammar 20(A), 23(C), 25(E), 27(A), 29(A)
   E = Easy, A = Average, C = Challenging

Essay Questions

31. (Easy) *Guidelines for student response:* Students should point out that Grandpa Monaghan has an Irish accent, indicating that he came to the United States from Ireland, and also that his speech is not polished, indicating that he has probably had little education. These facts help to explain Grandpa's unusual character traits; many immigrants knew poverty and were not comfortable spending their money. However, they also explain Grandpa's strong feelings about properly welcoming new arrivals to the country.

The Mathemagician tends to speak in a confusing fashion, rattling off long and bewildering streams of numbers and often sounding illogical. This shows that someone whose sole concern is numbers might easily lose touch with what we recognize as common sense and reality. Insincerity conveys the impression that he is a helpful, well-intended person, and does not reveal his true nastiness until he gets Milo and the others into trouble. In real life, people who are insincere are most dangerous and unpleasant when they convince others that they mean well and want to be friends.

32. (Average) *Guidelines for student response:* Students may observe that Milo, before he enters the strange world of the phantom tollbooth, seems like a real enough boy, and they may recognize his boredom and dissatisfaction as feelings with which they are familiar. While nothing that goes on for most of the play could be called realistic, the message can certainly apply to a lot of people: time is valuable and should be put to good use, and bringing a positive attitude to work and play is a good way to ensure that you make the most of your time and your energy.

33. (Average) *Guidelines for student response:* Students should see that *The Phantom Tollbooth* presents so many problems for stage presentation, especially in terms of special visual effects, that it would probably be quite difficult to perform on the stage. However, contemporary techniques in special effects for movies mean that this script could be filmed, and that the visual effects could contribute to an entertaining and effective film. *Grandpa and the Statue* does not present the kind of challenges that the other play does, but it, too, would not be easy to stage, at least in a realistic way. Scenes such as the warehouse or at the Statue itself could be a problem. But perhaps it could be done on an empty stage without realistic scenery. *Grandpa and the Statue* would also work as a film or as a play for voices only, to be broadcast on radio.

34. (Average) *Guidelines for student response:* Students may say that the important lesson for Milo in *The Phantom Tollbooth* is that he should consider time to be a valuable asset, not one to be wasted. Also, people often have more resources than they might think they do, and can even perform tasks that they had thought of as impossible, if they bring a positive frame of mind to them. In *Grandpa and the Statue,* Grandpa Monaghan learns about the message of welcome the Statue of Liberty was created to extend, a message that, even to him, is far more valuable than mere money. He learns that there are things in life that cannot be measured by mere dollars and cents.

35. (Challenging) *Guidelines for student response:* Students may say that the Castle-in-the-Air is *still* a symbol of impracticality in this play. It is also a prison, because people who totally disregard practical concerns are likely to find themselves "imprisoned"—unable to act effectively in the real world. In a society such as the Land of Ignorance, there can be neither common sense nor beauty, which is why Rhyme and Reason are prisoners there, and shut in the Castle-in-the-Air. The Pit is a confining dark hole, and represents the consequences of ignorance and of the dominance of "demons" of the kind that are mentioned here, such as Gross Exaggeration, "Horrible Hopping Hindsight," and Compromise. Where such things prevail, people can be rendered blind and powerless, and, in effect, cast into a pit.

(p. 172)

Critical Reading

1. a 2. c 3. d 4. c 5. c 6. e 7. b 8. e 9. a 10. d 11. a 12. b 13. d 14. e 15. b

Questions are classified in these categories:
Comprehension 6 (A)
Interpretation 3 (A), 5 (A), 14 (A)

Literary Analysis 1 (E), 2 (A), 4 (A), 9 (A), 10 (C), 11 (C), 12 (A)
Reading Strategy 7 (A), 8 (E), 13 (A), 15 (A)
E = Easy, A = Average, C = Challenging

Essay Questions

16. (Easy) *Guidelines for student response:* The families are alike in that the mother and children, or child, do household chores together. In both families there is a conflict because a child is not happy with the ways things are. In both it seems that a change may be coming; Melinda wants to leave home and visitors are coming to the McCools. The families are different in that in Passage 1 there is only Melinda and her mother. The Mc-Cools have five children and a mother and father.

17. (Average) *Guidelines for student response:* Students may say that Melinda would not find her fortune at the Mc-Cools. The household work seems to be harder, and there does not seem to be "something big" for her to do. In contrast, some students may say that Melinda might indeed find what she wants by visiting the McCools; she might find her fortune in some as yet unforeseen event involving the McCools.

18. (Challenging) *Guidelines for student response:* Owen complains because he is tired of carrying water in buckets up the hill, and he wishes his father would fulfill his promise of finding the spring on top of the mountain. Melinda complains because she is tired of staying home and doing the same thing every day. She wants to see more of the world. Students may say they are justified—Owen because his father has not done what he said he would do, and Melinda because her feeling is a natural one for a young person to have. Students may advise Owen to speak to his father and Melinda to go ahead and seek her fortune.

Unit 9: Poetry

"The Walrus and the Carpenter"
by Lewis Carroll
"The Geese" by Richard Peck
"Jimmy Jet and His TV Set"
by Shel Silverstein

Selection Test (p. 176)

Critical Reading, Vocabulary, Spelling, and Grammar

1. b   2. a   3. c   4. d   5. b   6. a   7. c   8. d
9. b   10. a   11. a   12. c   13. b   14. d   15. a
16. b   17. b   18. d   19. a   20. a

Questions are classified in these categories:
Comprehension 1(E), 4(A), 7(A), 8(E), 13(A)
Interpretation 5(E), 6(A), 9(E), 12(A), 14(C)
Literary Analysis 3(C), 11(E)
Reading Strategy 2(C), 10(A), 4(E)
Vocabulary 17(C) 20(A)
Spelling 19(E)
Grammar 16(E), 18(A)
E = Easy, A = Average, C = Challenging

Essay Questions

21. (Easy) *Guidelines for students response:* Students' essays should point out such nonsensical events as the sun shining during the night, the moon, walrus, and the oysters talking and behaving like humans, and oysters having feet and wearing shoes.

22. (Average) *Guidelines for students response:* Students who choose "The Walrus and the Carpenter" should recognize that the speaker has a good sense of humor and likes to tell stories. As examples, they should cite several humorous, nonsensical lines from the poem, such as, "Their shoes were clean and neat—/And this was odd, because, you know,/They hadn't any feet." Those who choose "February Twilight" should recognize that the speaker enjoys being alone with nature and appreciates nature's beauty. They should cite lines such as, "I stood and watched the evening star/As long as it watched me." Students who choose "Jimmy Jet and His TV Set" should recognize that the speaker doesn't think it's good for people to watch too much TV. They should cite lines such as, "Till he grew pale and lean," and "He watched till his eyes were frozen wide." Those who choose "The Geese" should recognize that the speaker is a person fondly remembers his or her father, and who had a deep understanding of his or her father's feelings. They might cite the passages, "He'd hear within his heart their call," "For he had lain awake till day,/Feeling his earthbound soul take flight," and "Recalling the lure of faroff things."

23. (Challenging) *Guidelines for student response:* Students should show that the speaker is expressing affectionate and sensitive feelings about his or her father. They might quote the passage, "My father was the first to hear / The passage of the geese each fall" to illustrate that the speaker remembers details about growing up with the father. They might quote, "He'd hear within his heart their call," "Feeling his earthbound soul take flight," and "Recalling the lure of faroff things" to illustrate that the speaker was aware of the father's deepest feelings. Students might also mention what the geese represented to the speaker's father—freedom of the spirit.

"The Sidewalk Racer"
by Lillian Morrison
Haiku by Matsuo Bashō
Limerick Anonymous

Selection Test (p. 179)

Critical Reading / Vocabulary, Spelling, Grammar

1. b   2. a   3. a   4. d   5. b   6. a   7. d   8. a
9. b   10. c   11. d   12. d   13. c   14. c   15. a
16. d   17. c   18. b   19. d   20. c

Questions are classified in these categories:

Comprehension 3(C), 5(A), 12(A), 13(A)
Interpretation 2(C), 4(A), 5(A), 9(A), 11(C), 14(E)
Literary Analysis 1(A), 6(E), 7(A), 10(C), 15(E)
Reading Strategy 8(E),
Vocabulary 17(A), 19(A)
Spelling 18(A)
Grammar 16(C), 20(A)
E = Easy, A = Average, C = Challenging

Essay Questions

21. (Easy) *Guidelines for student response:* For "The Sidewalk Racer" students should recognize sight as the main sense to which the poem appeals. Students should note the poem's shape. They should also cite the phrases "asphalt sea," and "I swerve, I curve, I sway." They should also mention that the words "whirring sound" appeal to the sense of sound. For the haiku by Bashō, students should recognize that sight and sound are the two main senses to which the poem appeals. They might cite words and phrases such as "silent," "frog jumps," and "splash!" as examples. For the limericks, students should recognize that the poets appeal mainly to the sense of sight, but also to the senses of sound (the dialogue between the fly and the flea) and the sense of touch (how the young man felt when he "fell in the spring").

22. (Average) *Guidelines for student response:* Students might compare and contrast the haiku and limerick forms of poetry. A haiku has three lines with five, seven, and five syllables. Haiku poems are often about nature and they are deeply expressive. Limericks have five lines and a special rhyming scheme. They are short, silly poems. These two forms are similar because each has strict requirements—the haiku for number of lines and syllables in each line, the limerick for number of lines and rhyming pattern. Otherwise, they are very different. Haiku is serious, while the limerick is a form of humorous nonsense verse. Language in haiku poems is spare and stark and does not draw attention to itself, but rather to the scene it describes. Language in limericks draws attention to itself through rhyme and double meaning, and adds to the poem's humor. The line "A fly and a flea in a flue," for example, is funnier because of the sound of the words than because of what they actually mean.

23. (Challenging) *Guidelines for student response:* Students should recognize that, while each poem may appeal directly to only one or two senses, each appeals indirectly to a number of senses, as well. "The Sidewalk Racer," in addition to the senses of sight and sound, may be said to appeal to the sense of touch (wind in the racer's face), for example. The haiku by Bashō, in addition to sight and sound, may be said to appeal to the sense of touch (feel of cold water in pond, feel of frog's skin when touched). "A flea and a fly in a flue" appeals directly to the sense of sight and sound (the dialogue between the flea and the fly, the sound of the humorous rhymes), and indirectly to the senses of smell and touch, depending on which details students choose to imagine inside the flue. "There was a young fellow named Hall" appeals directly to the sense of sight, and indirectly, to the senses of sound and touch, depending on which details of the poem students choose to imagine (e.g., the feeling of the water when the man falls into the spring, the smells of the spring or fall weather).

"Wind and water and stone"
by Octavio Paz
"February Twilight" by Sara Teasdale
"The Fairies' Lullaby"
by William Shakespeare
"Cynthia in the Snow"
by Gwendolyn Brooks
"Parade" by Rachel Field

Selection Test (p.182)

Critical Reading/Vocabulary, Spelling, and Grammar

1. b 2. a 3. c 4. b 5. c 6. a 7. b 8. c 9. a 10. b
11. d 12. a 13. a 14. c 15. c 16. d 17. b 18. a
19. b 20. a

Questions are classified in these categories:
   Comprehension 1(E), 7(C), 8(A), 12(A), 14(C)
   Interpretation 2(A), 3(C)
   Literary Focus 4(E), 6(A), 9(A), 11(C), 13(A)
   Reading Strategy 5(C), 10(E), 15(A)
   Vocabulary 19(A), 20(E)
   Spelling 17(A)
   Grammar Skill 16(C), 18(A)
   E = Easy, S = Average, C = Challenging

"Wind and water and stone" by Octavio Paz

"February Twilight" by Sara Teasdale

"The Fairies' Lullaby"
by William Shakespeare

"Cynthia in the Snow" by Gwendolyn Brooks

"Parade" by Rachel Field
(continued)

Essay Questions

21. (Easy) *Guidelines for student response:* Students should mention that "Parade" uses rhyme throughout the poem, while "Cynthia in the Snow" uses rhyme occasionally (SUSHES/hushes, flitter-twitters, shirts/hurts). Some might feel that the use of rhyme is particularly effective in "Cynthia in the Snow" because it is emphasizes the last two lines. Students should note that both poems use alliteration and onomatopoeia, citing examples such as "SUSHES," "hushes," "laughs a lovely whiteness," and "whitely whirs," for "Cynthia in the Snow," and "blare of brass," and "roar" for "Parade." For "The Fairies' Lullaby," students should note rhymes such as *seen* and *Queen, harm* and *charm, lullaby* and *nigh, here* and *near, hence* and *offense.* Examples of alliteration include the following phrases: *spotted snakes, sing in our sweet lullaby, lovely lady, beetles black.* An example of onomatopoeia is *Lulla, lulla, lullaby* which is repeated in each stanza.

22. (Average) *Guidelines for student response:* Students should cite phrases and lines such as ". . . wild beasts never heard before / Within town limits," "gilded cage," "riders dressed in red," and "Camels and elephants will pass / Beneath our elms, along our grass" that evoke a feeling of excitement. They should note that the second and third lines, and the last two lines of the poem emphasize that the circus brings exotic sights and sounds to a small, peaceful town. They should cite the uses of alliteration and onomatopoeia, explaining how these sound devices create a sense of excitement; for example, "blare of brass" and "clashing cymbals" evoke the stirring sound of circus music, while the word "roar" makes the reader "hear" the sound of a lion—right within the town limits.

23. (Challenging) *Guidelines for student response:* Students choosing "Parade" might use the first two lines of the poem as an example of how meaning can be lost or distorted by stopping or pausing when there is no punctuation. They should explain that the second line is a continuation of a sentence begun in the first line, and show that the meaning of the sentence calls for no pause between "comes" and "With." They might choose "Within town limits. Spick and span" as an example of a line that loses its meaning if the reader fails to stop at the period, treating the words as part of one sentence, rather than recognizing that the period marks the end of one thought and the beginning of another. Students choosing "Cynthia in the Snow" might cite "To be / Some otherwhere" as an example of how meaning can be lost or distorted by stopping or pausing when there is no punctuation. They might use the last two lines to demonstrate that the emphasis on the last line might be lost if the reader fails to stop after the period following "shirts," even though the last line is not technically a complete sentence.

"Simile: Willow and Ginkgo"
by Eve Merriam
"Fame Is a Bee" by Emily Dickinson
"April Rain Song" by Langston Hughes

Selection Test (p. 185)

Critical Reading/Vocabulary, Spelling, and Grammar

1. c 2. d 3. d 4. a 5. a 6. b 7. b 8. c
9. c 10. a 11. b 12. b 13. c 14. d 15. c
16. d 17. d 18. c 19. b 20. a

Questions are classified in these categories:
   Comprehension 4 (A), 14 (E)
   Interpretation 6 (A), 8 (A), 10 (E), 13 (C)
   Literary Analysis 2 (A), 3 (E), 5 (C), 9 (E), 12 (A)
   Reading Strategy 1 (C), 7 (A), 11 (A)
   Vocabulary 16 (E), 18 (A)
   Spelling 15 (A), 19 (C)
   Grammar 17 (A), 20 (E)
   E = Easy, A = Average, C = Challenging

Essay Questions

21. **(Easy)** *Guidelines for student response:* Students who choose "Simile: Willow and Ginkgo" may say they are familiar with the two trees and agree or disagree with the poet's comparison, citing lines such as "The willow is like a nymph with streaming hair," and "The ginkgo's like stubby rough wool." They should tell why they agree or disagree. Students who choose "Fame Is a Bee" may say that they have heard of famous people whose lives were negatively affected by fame, or who ceased to be famous. They might cite and paraphrase the line "It has a sting," or "Ah, too, it has a wing." They should explain how or why they think fame hurt the person. Students who choose "April Rain Song" may say that they, too, love the rain. They should give their reasons. They might cite and paraphrase lines such as, "Let the rain kiss you," or "Let the rain sing you a lullaby." Accept all answers that are well reasoned and logically presented.

22. **(Challenging)** *Guidelines for student response:* Students should show that they understand that the poet compares the willow to a person who lives an easy and even pampered life, ". . . like the king's favorite daughter;" while the ginkgo is compared to a person who lives a difficult life, but " . . . survives and even thrives," or succeeds, in spite of it. They should grasp that the speaker's reason for saying "My eyes feast upon the willow" is that the willow is more beautiful. They might cite passages such as "The willow is like an etching," "The willow is sleek as a velvet-nosed calf," or "The willow is like a nymph with streaming hair." They should note that the speaker says "But my heart goes to the ginkgo" because the speaker sympathizes more with the ginkgo. Lines to cite include, "Like a city child, it grows up in the street," and "Somehow it survives and even thrives."

23. **(Challenging)** *Guidelines for student response:* Students who choose "Simile: Willow and Ginkgo," should note that the poet makes extensive use of simile ("The ginkgo is like a crude sketch," "The willow is like a nymph . . ") They should explain that the similes that refer to the willow

compare the willow to something beautiful, graceful, or refined, while the similes that refer to the ginkgo compare the ginkgo to something crude, rustic, or rough. Students who choose "Fame Is a Bee" should notice that each line of the poem is a metaphor. They should explain that the first line makes a general comparison (fame and bee), then each subsequent line chooses a specific detail about a bee that can also apply to fame. They should explain the meaning of each metaphor: the "song" is the glamourous happy aspect of fame; the "sting" is the aspect of fame that can be hurtful; the "wing" implies that fame can fly away. Students who choose "April Rain Song" should cite examples of personification: "Let the rain kiss you," "Let the rain sing you a lullaby," and "The rain plays a little sleep-song on our roof at night." They might explain that the effect of the personification is to make the reader feel love for the rain, which one would not feel for an object or non-human force of nature.

Unit Test (p. 188)

Critical Reading/ Vocabulary, Spelling, and Grammar

1. a   2. c   3. a   4. b   5. d   6. a   7. d   8. b
9. b   10. c   11. a   12. d   13. c   14. a   15. b
16. c   17. d   18. c   19. a   20. b   21. d
22. c   23. b   24. a   25. c   26. c   27. d
28. a   29. b   30. d

Questions are classified in these categories:
   Comprehension 3 (A), 5 (A), 7 (A), 17 (C)
   Interpretation 4 (A), 6 (A), 8 (E), 12 (A),
      14 (C), 15 (A)
   Literary Focus 2 (A), 9 (E), 11 (C)
   Reading Strategy 1 (C), 10 (E), 13 (C),
      16 (E), 18 (A), 19 (C)
   Vocabulary 21 (A), 24 (A), 27 (E), 30 (E)
   Spelling 22 (C), 24 (A)
   Grammar Skill 20 (E), 23 (A), 26 (C), 28 (A),
      29 (A)
   E = Easy, A = Average, C = Challenging

Essay Questions

31. **(Easy)** *Guidelines for student response:* Students may say that "April Rain Song" displays an affectionate, peaceful mood that is in harmony with nature. The

speaker seems loving and giving. He or she wants those who read the poem to share in feelings of serenity and acceptance. The prevailing mood in the poem is upbeat, despite the rain. Students might think about how they would feel in the same setting and state whether their mood would be like that of the speaker. "Cynthia in the Snow" presents a much more cheerful reaction to a similar scene, on the part of a girl who finds the snow not only cheerful but playful. Students may want to compare their attitude toward being out on a snowy night, and explain why they would share Cynthia's feelings or not. "The Geese" presents a moody picture of a man who is fascinated by faraway places to which, it seems, he is not likely to go. Here, too, students may compare and contrast how they feel about distant lands—do they find them fascinating or do they consider them frightening?

32. (Average) *Guidelines for student response* Students should be aware of the absurdity of a great deal of "The Walrus and the Carpenter"—not merely the concept of a talking walrus and walking oysters, but the sun shining in the middle of the night, the strange choice of topics for conversation—"shoes and ships and sealing wax" and so forth, and the many nonsensical things that keep occurring; the sea is not boiling hot, and there is no need to talk about whether pigs have wings. They don't. The main humorous device in this poem is nonsense. In "Jimmy Jet and His TV Set," the story is also nonsensical, but instead of many silly statements, the poem presents a single ridiculous idea: a boy watches so much television that he turns into a set. The reaction of the people who then proceed to watch Jim is also funny. Unlike "The Walrus and the Carpenter," "Jimmy Jet and His TV Set" can be said to have a moral: "if you watch too much TV, you may turn into a TV." It's a silly moral, but more than Lewis Carroll offers. Limericks like these derive their humor from playing on words that sound the same—homophones, and from words

that have more than one meaning, such as "spring" and "fall." They are like puns, and are especially funny when said aloud.

33. (Average) *Guidelines for student response:* The speaker of "The Geese" describes his or her father in a sympathetic and understanding way, revealing sensitivity to the father's feelings and also the speaker's own compassion for a man who, it seems, yearns for the chance to see romantic and faraway places, but doesn't get to go. "The Sidewalk Racer" presents a speaker who is young and proud of what he or she can do on a skateboard. He or she also has a vivid imagination, using images of driving and sailing a boat to describe the excitement of racing along a sidewalk on a board. This speaker is younger but may be said to be as sensitive as the speaker of "The Geese." The speaker in "Simile: Willow and Gingko" is observant and displays keen sensitivity to nature. The speaker's unexpected comparisons reveal a thoughtful and imaginative personality, as well as an acquaintance with art, music, and folklore. At the end of the poem, the speaker displays compassion and sympathy for the gingko tree, which has to struggle to survive in its urban surroundings. Like the speaker in "The Geese," the speaker in "Simile: Willow and Gingko" seems sympathetic and understanding.

34. (Average) *Guidelines for student response:* Students may say that Shakespeare's use of alliteration and onomatopoeia add to the musical quality of "The Fairies' Lullaby." Examples of alliteration include "spotted snakes" and "beetles black," while onomatopoeia appears in the repeated "lulla, lulla, lullaby." The use of rhyme and the repetition of lines in a refrain also add to the musical effect. "Cynthia in the Snow" makes effective use of onomatopoetic words such as "sushes," "flitter-twitters," and "whirrs" to create a sound image for the reader that adds to the sense of a magical and delightful moment. "Fame Is a Bee" is a short poem that adds impact to its message through the punctuation it employs. The first line is a simple sentence, ending in a period, while the following two lines end in dashes, letting the reader know that there is more to come. The last line uses two

pauses, after "ah," and "too," before the final message, which ends the poem on a surprising, grim note. "Parade" suggests the sound of a parade, doing it partly by using a steady rhythm, like that of a marching band. It uses alliteration to put greater emphasis on the marching rhythm ("With blare of brass, with beating drums..."), and onomatopoeia ("clashing cymbals") to add to a vivid sound image of a parade.

35 (Challenging) *Guidelines for student response:* Students may say that the sensory language in "The Sidewalk Racer" is partly visual, creating the visual image of "skimming an asphalt sea." The use of the action words "swerve," "curve," and "sway" may also be said to create images of movement. Also, "whirring" is an onomatopoeia that conveys the sound a speeding skateboard makes. The images are designed to help the reader sense what the sidewalk racer experiences. "Cynthia in the Snow" also uses imagery to give the reader a sense of the speaker's experience. Here, too, onomatopoeia is used ("sushes," "flitter-twitters") to convey the quiet sounds of a snowstorm. The simile "white as milk or shirts" and the personification of the snow as it "laughs away from me. It laughs a lovely whiteness" supplies visual imagery as well as a sense of the speaker's joy at being out in the snow. "Simile: Willow and Ginkgo" presents a series of visual images created by a string of similes ("The willow is like an etching...." "The ginkgo is like a crude sketch") that help not only to give the readers images for both trees but to convey the speaker's feelings about them. Here, too, the reader may use the images created by sensory language (the ginkgo "thrust against a metal sky") to experience the speaker's sense of admiration and affection for this hardy, unassuming tree. "April Rain Song" also uses sensory language: sight ("The rain makes still pools on the sidewalk. / The rain makes running pools in the gutter."); sound ("The rain plays a little sleep-song on our roof at night"); and even touch ("Let the rain beat upon your head with silver liquid drops."). In addition, personification ("Let the rain kiss you") is employed. The total effect is

to create an appreciation on the reader's part for rain as a delightful and positive phenomenon. Unlike the previous poems, however, the imagery here is not used to convey an experience the speaker is having, but just an attitude on the speaker's part. In "The Fairies' Lullaby," Shakespeare appeals primarily to the reader's sense of sight with the references to creatures in nature. He also appeals to the reader's sense of hearing with the invocation to Philomel to sing the lullaby. The imagery in the poem enhances the poem's function as a lullaby, intended to ensure undisturbed sleep for the Fairy Queen. Students may add that the sounds and lilting rhythms of the poem, in addition to its images, make it an effective lullaby.

Alternative Unit Test (p. 192)

Critical Reading

1. c 2. e 3. b 4. a 5. e 6. d 7. c 8. a
9. d 10. b 11. a 12. e 13. b 14. c 15. d

Questions are classified in these categories:
   Comprehension 8(C), 14(A)
   Interpretation 4(A), 5(A), 7(C), 11(E), 13(A)
   Literary Analysis 1(A), 3(C), 9(E), 12(A), 15(A)
   Reading Strategy 2(E), 6(E), 10(A)
   E = Easy, A = Average, C = Challenging

Essay Questions

16. (Easy) *Guidelines for student response:* Students may say that the speaker in Passage 1 is more wrapped up in the music. She says that, while she plays, nothing is "real" except the music, the metronome, and the voice of her teacher. Her love for music is linked to her love for her music teacher and, while she plays, her thoughts are of the teacher, with whom she has a warm relationship. The music and her thoughts go together. In contrast, the speaker of Passage 2 seems to be following orders to practice the piano. He or she would much rather be playing ball outside. This speaker pays more attention to the sounds of the ball game outside than to practicing, which seems to be mechanical on the speaker's part. The title of the passage sums up the speaker's situa-

tion. Unlike the other speaker, he or she shows no interest in, or love for, the music he is being made to play. His thoughts have nothing to do with music, except for the mechanics of playing.

17. (Average) *Guidelines for student response:* Students should note that the speaker of Passage 1 has a deep natural feeling for music, so much so that she becomes totally involved in it while she plays, and that everything other than her music and her teacher becomes irrelevant. She loves her piano teacher, who has helped her to appreciate music and has introduced her to some non-musical delights as well, such as delicious Hungarian food. This speaker has a love not only for music but for the elegance and culture to which her teacher has introduced her. She is a person with strong artistic feelings who might well play as an adult, either professionally or as a hobby. In contrast, the speaker of Passage 2 shows no feeling for the music he or she is made to practice. While the speaker plays piano, his or her attention is fixed on the ball game outside, where he or she would rather be. The speaker's enthusiasm is reserved for the sounds of the ball field, and practice is considered a purely mechanical chore. While there is no direct complaint from this speaker, there is an implied feeling of unhappiness. "Climbing / the ladder of the minor scale" has the sound of a tiresome task being carried out. And the realization that the ball game is over while the speaker is still practicing comes as a disappointment. This speaker is not likely to continue playing the piano, once the choice is up to him or her.

18. (Challenging) *Guidelines for student response:* Students may say that Passage 1 is a lyric poem because the speaker reveals her feelings and thoughts throughout. She points out that she is wrapped up in her playing and her teacher's voice so that nothing else is "real." She expresses her love for her teacher, and her thoughts, as expressed in the passage, are centered on the teacher. The speaker describes how the teacher lives and tells of the precious times she and the teacher have spent together at the teacher's home. Passage 2, on the other hand, is more of a narrative poem. The speaker describes playing through an afternoon while "the others" are outside playing ball. The passage ends when the ball game does. At no point does the speaker describe what he or she is feeling, or thinking.

Unit 10: The Oral Tradition

"The Ant and the Dove"
by Leo Tolstoy
"He Lion, Bruh Bear, and Bruh Rabbit" by Virginia Hamilton
"Señor Coyote and the Tricked Trickster" by I. G. Edmonds

Selection Test (p. 196)

Critical Reading/Vocabulary, Spelling, and Grammar

1. b 2. d 3. c 4. a 5. b 6. b 7. d 8. a
9. a 10. c 11. b 12. d 13. c 14. d 15. d
16. d 17. b 18. c 19. d 20. c

Questions are classified in these categories:
  Comprehension 2(E), 7(A), 13(C)
  Interpretation 5(E), 9(C), 11(A)
  Literary Analysis 1(A), 6(A), 8(C), 12(E)
  Reading Strategy 3(A), 4(C), 10(A), 14(E)
  Vocabulary 15(E), 18(A), 19A

  Spelling 16(A)
  Grammar 17(C), 20(A)
  E = Easy, A = Average, C = Challenging

Essay Questions

21. (Easy) *Guidelines for student response:* Students should explain whether the purpose of the folk tale they chose is to entertain, teach, or to both teach and entertain, citing details in support. For example, students who chose "Señor Coyote and the Tricked Trickster" should point out that the tale both entertains and teaches. They might cite one of the humorous exchanges between Mouse and Coyote to demonstrate that the tale is entertaining, and they should indicate that it teaches a lesson about not demanding too much from someone who owes you a favor.

22. (Average) *Guidelines for student response:* Students should choose one of the works in the selection and explain why it is a good example of a folk tale. They should briefly explain what a folk tale is and point out how the work they chose illustrates the main characteristics of a folk tale, citing details from the text where appropriate. For example, students who chose "Señor Coyote and the Tricked Trickster" should point out that is a traditional African American tale that has been handed down from generation to generation. It entertains while teaching a lesson about common sense and modesty. They should cite some details from the work that they found entertaining and amusing.

23. (Challenging) *Guidelines for student response:* Students might point out the following similarities and differences as they compare and contrast "The Ant and the Lion" with "He Lion, Bruh Bear, and Bruh Rabbit" or with "Señor Coyote and the Tricked Trickster." Similarities: Both are works of folk literature in that they do not originate with a single author but rather have been handed down from generation to generation; both teach lessons about life. Differences: "He Lion" and "Señor Coyote" both teach and entertain, while the primary purpose of "The Ant and the Dove" is to teach; the lesson that "The Ant and the Dove" teaches is summed up at the end of the tale, while the lessons that the other two tales teach are indirectly stated.

"Why Monkeys Live in Trees"
by Julius Lester
"Arachne" by Olivia E. Coolidge
"A Crippled Boy" by My-Van Tran
"The Three Wishes"
by Ricardo E. Alegría

Selection Test (p. 199)

Critical Reading, Vocabulary, Spelling, and Grammar

1. d 2. c 3. a 4. c 5. b 6. c 7. d 8. b
9. a 10. d 11. c 12. b 13. c 14. a 15. d
16. c 17. b 18. a 19. c 20. b

Questions are classified in these categories:
Comprehension 1(E), 5(E), 10(A), 13(A)

Interpretation 3(C), 6(C), 9(E), 12(A), 15(A)
Literary Analysis 2(A), 8(C), 11(C)
Reading Strategy 4(E). 7(A), 14(A)
Vocabulary 16(A), 20(A)
Spelling 18(E)
Grammar 17(A), 19(E)
E = Easy, A = Average, C = Challenging

Essay Questions

21. (Easy) *Guidelines for student response:* Students' essays should point out that Hippopotamus and Leopard are boastful about their abilities and greedy to get King Gorilla's gold. They should also mention the trickery of the monkeys in winning the gold by pretending that only Monkey is eating the black pepper.

22. (Average) *Guidelines for student response:* Students who choose "Why Monkeys Live in Trees" might mention the greedy animals who deserve to lose the contest and the cheating monkeys who deserve to be found out and chased into the trees. Students who choose "Arachne" might say the title character's pride and disregard for others leads to her punishment of being transformed into a lowly spider. Students who choose "A Crippled Boy" might mention that Theo's skill in throwing pebbles and his loyalty to the King earn him a place in the palace, while the talkative mandarins need to learn respect for their ruler. Students who choose "The Three Wishes" may say that the couple's realization that the wishes and the wealth they can bring are destructive to their lives earn them a better reward— a son.

23. (Challenge) *Guidelines for student response:* Students who choose "Why Monkeys Live in Trees" may point out that the pot of gold offered in the contests brings out the worst in the animals—greed, trickery and pride. Similarly, students who pick "The Three Wishes" will point out the destructive power of riches in the lives of the couple, who realize their mistake in time to correct it. Students who choose "The Crippled Boy" can contrast the loyalty of Theo with the self-centeredness of the mandarins who learn a lesson in humility. Finally, students who pick "Arachne" may point out that Arachne may have saved herself if she had showed respect for the superior powers of Athene, a god.

Unit Test (p. 202)

Critical Reading/Vocabulary, Spelling, and Grammar

1. a 2. c 3. c 4. c 5. d 6. d 7. b 8. c 9. a
10. b 11. a 12. b 13. d 14. b 15. d 16. c
17. b 18. d 19. b 20. c 21. b 22. a 23. c
24. d 25. d 26. a 27. d 28. b 29. b 30. c

Questions are classified in these categories:
- Comprehension 1(A), 4(A), 7(E), 10(A), 11(E), 12(A), 14(A), 17(C)
- Interpretation 3(A), 5(E), 8(A), 9(C), 13(A), 18(A), 19(C)
- Literary Analysis 2(E), 6(C) 15(A),
- Reading Strategy 16(A)
- Vocabulary 20(C), 22(A), 27(A), 30(A),
- Spelling 25(E)
- Grammar 21(C), 23(A), 24(E), 26(A), 28(E), 29(A)

E = Easy, A = Average, C = Challenging

Essay Questions

31. (Easy) *Guidelines for student response:* Students should clearly tell what is explained in the tale and show how the storyteller makes the explanation emerge logically in the story. For example, in "Why Monkeys Live in Trees," the other animals are so angry at Monkey's deceit that they chase him and his fellow monkeys right up to the treetops, where they live to this day. In "Arachne" Athene is furious Arachne for mocking her and turns her into the world's first spider. (The word *arachne*, in fact, means "spider" in ancient Greek.) Arachne is a skilled weaver, and, as a spider, she continues to weave beautiful webs.

32. (Average) *Guidelines for student response:* In Señor Coyote and the Tricked Trickster" Coyote, Mouse, and Snake all display great cleverness. Coyote attempts to trick Mouse into freeing him without a guarantee of safety, but Mouse is too intelligent to let himself be deceived. Coyote does suceed, however, in tricking Snake. Mouse attempts to trick Coyote at the end of the story by arguing that, since Mouse has a short life, Coyote should continue to serve Mouse, but Mouse fails in this effort—largely due to Snake's clever intervention. Students may contrast Mouse, Coyote, and Snake in terms of physical size, effectiveness of their tricks and scheming, and self-image: for example, Coyote is more conceited than any of the other characters, and thus more gullible. Students' choices about which character they admire the most will vary.

33. (Average) *Guidelines for student response:* Students should express an understanding of how folk tales can accomplish both purposes: For example, the portrayal of the animal characters in "He Lion, Bruh Bear, and Bruh Rabbit" is full of humor, building on stereotypes for each animal's behavior. The story's humor also depends on Lion's entertaining description of the young hunter from an animal's point of view. The serious message of the tale—that we should not be conceited or "blow our own horn" too loudly—comes to the surface toward the end, when Lion is forced to act more humbly.

34. (Average) *Guidelines for student response:* Students should focus on the combination of realism and fantasy in two tales of their choice. For example, in "Arachne" the story treats Arachne's history and achievements realistically for the most part until the arrival of Athene, when the plot involves supernatural, fantastic events and a miraculous transformation. By contrast, the setting, plot, and characters in "A Crippled Boy" are predominantly realistic—with the exception of Theo's larger-than-life ability to throw pebbles at targets with phenomenal accuracy. In "The Three Wishes," the setting is described realistically, and the characters' motivations are understandable. The tale's fantastic dimension involves the supernatural granting of the wishes, as well as details such as the donkey ears.

35. (Challenge) *Guidelines for student response:* Students' essays should support their answers with details about character and plot in their chosen story. For example, in "The Ant and the Dove" the values of kindness and thoughtfulness are stressed as important to life and survival itself. A random act of kindness has great consequences for the dove when the ant repays the by biting the hunter. Tol-

stoy, the storyteller, is telling people to be kind and helpful to one another, for one never knows when a kindness will be returned.

Alternative Unit Test (p. 206)

Critical Reading

1. d 2. b 3. a 4. d 5. b 6. e 7. c 8. a
9. b 10. a 11. b 12. e 13. c 14. d 15. c

Questions are classified in these categories:
  Comprehension 5 (E), 10 (E), 14 (A)
  Interpretation 1 (E), 7 (A), 13 (A), 15 (C)
  Literary Analysis 2 (A), 3 (C), 4 (C), 6 (A)
  Reading Strategies 8 (A), 9 (A), 11 (A), 12 (C)
  E = Easy, A = Average, C = Challenging

Essay Questions

16. (Easy) *Guidelines for student response:* Students might note that in Passage 1, Small Bear "could not but admire the graceful, intelligent moose family and the gentle, patient way they communicated as they searched for food." In Passage 2, students might cite that Moves Walking "saw the roots, plants, and insects that the bears ate, many of which his people had thought inedible. He learned the roots and plants they ate when they were ill." They might also mention that in Passage 1, Small Bear shares his wisdom about the moose family with White Wolf, who becomes a better leader because of Small Bear's insights. In Passage 2, "When Moves Walking went back to his people, he had a vision for the direction they should go [to find food], and he had the wisdom that the bears had taught him." The lessons learned from the animals are important because a large group of people cannot live together for the common good without kindness and patience, and people cannot survive without food.

17. (Average) *Guidelines for student response:* Passage 1 refers to and describes White Wolf, once a chief of the tribe ("White Wolf was good and kind at heart but given to fits of bad temper and loud yelling for even the slightest wrong"). The passage explains how she became a better leader through the wisdom that Small Bear learned from the moose family ("White

Wolf realized the moose story was directed at her. She apologized to the council for her past rudeness"). The passage implies that consideration and politeness were valued by the tribe (After the council meeting "she was polite and considerate and always set a good example for her people"). Passage 2 refers to a difficult time for the people, when they could not find enough food to eat and had to break up into small bands ("...food was getting hard to find, so our people split into smaller bands, each band going in a different direction"). The passage relates how Moves Walking helped his band survive ("Moves Walking saw the roots, plants, and insects that the bears ate, many of which his people had thought inedible. He learned the roots and plants they ate when they were ill"). The passage implies that wisdom was highly valued by the people ("...he had a vision for the direction they should go, and he had the wisdom that the bears had taught him").

18. (Challenging) *Guidelines for student response:* Students should note that both Small Bear and Moves Walking are representations of the wise person who has gained "medicine power," or the power to teach, lead, and influence his people. It is obvious that Small Bear and Moves Walking are not fully developed characters. In the two passages, we learn only of their position in their tribes and the tasks they perform; we learn little of their personalities, feelings, and thoughts. Students might suggest that, in order to further individualize these characters, the storyteller would have to provide details such as actual conversations, thoughts, actions, and relationships of the characters. Students should grasp that such individualization of character would probably detract from each story's purpose—to relate the history, reflect the values of a group of people, and to teach an important lesson. It is easier to teach a lesson using characters that can be easily identified as either simply good or bad rather than by using characters who are complex mixtures of both good and bad attributes.